D0463887

THE QUARK MODEL

Frontiers in Physics

DAVID PINES, Editor

S. L. Adler and R. F. Dashen
CURRENT ALGEBRAS: AND APPLICATIONS TO PARTICLE PHYSICS

P. W. Anderson **CONCEPTS IN SOLIDS:** *Lectures on the Theory of Solids*

N. Bloembergen **NONLINEAR OPTICS:** *A Lecture Note and Reprint Volume*

N. Bloembergen **NUCLEAR MAGNETIC RELAXATION:** *A Reprint Volume*

R. Brout **PHASE TRANSITIONS**

G. F. Chew **S-MATRIX THEORY OF STRONG INTERACTIONS:** *A Lecture Note and Reprint Volume*

P. Choquard **THE ANHARMONIC CRYSTAL**

P. G. de Gennes and Philip A. Pincus (Trans.)
SUPERCONDUCTIVITY OF METALS AND ALLOYS

R. P. Feynman **QUANTUM ELECTRODYNAMICS:** *A Lecture Note and Reprint Volume*

R. P. Feynman **THE THEORY OF FUNDAMENTAL PROCESSES:** *A Lecture Note Volume*

H. L. Frisch and J. L. Lebowitz
THE EQUILIBRIUM THEORY OF CLASSICAL FLUIDS: *A Lecture Note and Reprint Volume*

H. Frauenfelder **THE MOSSBAUER EFFECT:** *A Review—With a Collection of Reprints*

S. C. Frautschi **REGGE POLES AND S-MATRIX THEORY**

M. Gell-Mann and Y. Ne'eman
THE EIGHTFOLD WAY: *A Review—With a Collection of Reprints*

W. A. Harrison **PSEUDOPOTENTIALS IN THE THEORY OF METALS**

R. Hofstadter **ELECTRON SCATTERING AND NUCLEAR AND NUCLEON STRUCTURE:** *A Collection of Reprints with an Introduction*

M. Jacob and G. F. Chew
STRONG-INTERACTION PHYSICS: *A Lecture Note Volume*

L. P. Kadanoff and G. Baym
QUANTUM STATISTICAL MECHANICS: *Green's Function Methods in Equilibrium and Nonequilibrium Problems*

I. M. Khalatnikov and Pierre C. Hohenberg (Trans.)
AN INTRODUCTION TO THE THEORY OF SUPERFLUIDITY

J. J. J. Kokkedee **THE QUARK MODEL**

A. M. Lane **NUCLEAR THEORY:** *Pairing Force Correlations to Collective Motion*

T. Loucks **AUGMENTED PLANE WAVE METHOD:** *A Lecture Note and Reprint Volume*

A. B. Migdal **THE QUASIPARTICLE METHOD IN NUCLEAR THEORY**

P. Nozières **THEORY OF INTERACTING FERMI SYSTEMS**

R. Omnès and M. Froissart
MANDELSTAM THEORY AND REGGE POLES: *An Introduction for Experimentalists*

G. E. Pake **PARAMAGNETIC RESONANCE:** *An Introductory Monograph*

D. Pines **THE MANY-BODY PROBLEM:** *A Lecture Note and Reprint Volume*

J. R. Schrieffer **THEORY OF SUPERCONDUCTIVITY**

E. J. Squires **COMPLEX ANGULAR MOMENTA AND PARTICLE PHYSICS:** *A Lecture Note and Reprint Volume*

L. Van Hove, N. M. Hugenholtz, and L. P. Howland
PROBLEMS IN QUANTUM THEORY OF MANY-PARTICLE SYSTEMS: *A Lecture Note and Reprint Volume*

THE QUARK MODEL

J. J. J. KOKKEDEE
University of Nijmegen, The Netherlands

W. A. Benjamin, Inc.
New York *Amsterdam*
1969

THE QUARK MODEL

Library of Congress Catalog Card Number 69–14391
Manufactured in the United States of America
12345K2109

The manuscript was put into production on August 27, 1968;
this volume was published on March 15, 1969

W. A. BENJAMIN, INC.
New York, New York 10016

EDITOR'S FOREWORD

The problem of communicating in a coherent fashion the recent developments in the most exciting and active fields of physics seems particularly pressing today. The enormous growth in the number of physicists has tended to make the familiar channels of communication considerably less effective. It has become increasingly difficult for experts in a given field to keep up with the current literature; the novice can only be confused. What is needed is both a consistent account of a field and the presentation of a definite "point of view" concerning it. Formal monographs cannot meet such a need in a rapidly developing field, and, perhaps more important, the review article seems to have fallen into disfavor. Indeed, it would seem that the people most actively engaged in developing a given field are the people least likely to write at length about it.

"Frontiers in Physics" has been conceived in an effort to improve the situation in several ways. First, to take advantage of the fact that the leading physicists today frequently give a series of lectures, a graduate seminar, or a graduate course in their special fields of interest. Such lectures serve to summarize the present status of a rapidly developing field and may well constitute the only coherent account available at the time. Often, notes on lectures exist (prepared by the lecturer himself, by graduate students, or by postdoctoral fellows) and have been distributed in mimeographed form on a limited basis. One of the principal purposes of the "Frontiers in Physics" series is to make such notes available to a wider audience of physicists.

It should be emphasized that lecture notes are necessarily rough and informal, both in style and content, and those in the series will prove no exception. This is as it should be. The point of the series is to offer new, rapid, more informal, and, it is hoped, more effective ways for physicists to teach one another. The point is lost if only elegant notes qualify.

A second way to improve communication in very active fields of physics is by the publication of collections of reprints of recent articles. Such collections are themselves useful to people working in the field. The value of the reprints would, however, seem much enhanced if the collection would be accompanied by an introduction of moderate length, which would serve to tie the collection together and, necessarily, constitute a brief survey of the present status of the field. Again, it is appropriate that such an introduction be informal, in keeping with the active character of the field.

A third possibility for the series might be called an informal monograph, to connote the fact that it represents an intermediate step between lecture notes and formal monographs. It would offer the author an opportunity to present his views of a field that has developed to the point at which a summation might prove extraordinarily fruitful, but for which a formal monograph might not be feasible or desirable.

Fourth, there are the contemporary classics—papers or lectures which constitute a particularly valuable approach to the teaching and learning of physics today. Here one thinks of fields that lie at the heart of much of present-day research, but whose essentials are by now well understood. such as quantum electrodynamics or magnetic resonance. In such fields some of the best pedagogical material is not readily available, either because it consists of papers long out of print or lectures that have never been published.

"Frontiers in Physics" is designed to be flexible in editorial format. Authors are encouraged to use as many of the foregoing approaches as seem desirable for the project at hand. The publishing format for the series is in keeping with its intentions. In most cases, both paperbound and clothbound editions of each book are available.

Finally, suggestions from interested readers as to format, contributors, and contributions will be most welcome.

David Pines

Urbana, Illinois
August 1964

Preface

The brilliant success of SU(3) symmetry in particle physics led, in 1964, to the Gell-Mann–Zweig hypothesis that the strongly interacting particles (hadrons) are built from a triplet of fundamental objects, quarks, and a corresponding triplet of antiquarks. These hypothetical entities (which borrow their name from Joyce's *Finnegans Wake*) have the queer property of being fractionally charged; that is, their charges are not integral multiples of the electron charge.

Although it is not yet known whether quarks exist as individual particles, it is undeniable that the quark idea is not only one of the most fascinating concepts in modern particle physics, but has proved to be a very fruitful working hypothesis. A great variety of observations concerning strong, electromagnetic, and weak interactions can be understood if we suppose that quarks are the basic constituents of hadronic matter. Moreover, the simplest dynamical assumption one can make, namely, that of *additivity,* in which some hadronic property is described as the sum of the corresponding quark properties, has been amazingly successful in providing simple relations between different facts. In this way the model not only reproduces the results of SU(3) and SU(6) symmetry, but leads to many experimentally correct predictions that do not follow directly from either symmetry. This fact is most strikingly demonstrated by its application to high-energy scattering.

Of course, the whole quark idea is ill-founded. So far quarks have escaped detection. This fact could simply mean that they are extremely massive and therefore difficult to produce, but it could also be an indication that quarks cannot exist as individual particles but, like phonons inside a crystal, can have meaning only inside the hadrons. In either case, nevertheless, the dynamical system of such quarks binding together to give the observed hadrons that has the properties demanded by the applications, is very difficult to understand in terms of conventional concepts. The quark model should, therefore, at least for the moment, not be taken for more than what it is, namely, the tentative and simplistic expression of an as yet obscure dynamics underlying the hadronic world. As such, however, the model is of great heuristic value.

This volume is based on a series of lectures, given at the European Organization for Nuclear Research (CERN) in Geneva during the fall of 1967, which were intended mainly for experimental high-energy physicists. Although we attempt to discuss all important applications of the quark model, this book should not be considered as an exhaustive, up-to-date review of the subject. In the first four chapters the quark notion is introduced. The applications fall roughly into three categories: hadron spectroscopy (Chapters 5–9), decay processes (Chapters 10–13), and high-energy scattering (Chapters 14–18). No attempt has been made to give a complete list of references. It should perhaps be mentioned that we have said nothing here about current algebra, although to a certain extent this successful approach to particle physics could be considered as another application of the quark hypothesis in the sense that a field-theoretical quark model naturally implies the basic current commutation relations (the opposite is not true) that give rise, for instance, to the famous Adler–Weisberger relation for the ratio of the vector and axial vector coupling constants of nuclear β decay.

A small selection of reprints of original papers on quarks and composite models is included in the volume. Many details that could not be included in the lecture notes can be found here. I am aware that in selecting these reprints it is almost impossible to avoid criticism. There is, therefore, no point in trying to justify the choice reflected in this book. Let me only remark that for technical reasons, several important papers unfortunately could not be included. Among these are Zweig's paper, which exists only in the form of a preprint of about 80 pages, and a few relevant articles from the Dubna group that appeared only in the Russian literature.

I am greatly indebted to many people: to Professor Léon Van Hove for numerous conversations on almost all topics discussed in this book, and for a critical reading of the manuscript; to Professor J. J. de Swart and Dr. R. Van Royen for many valuable comments and for carefully reading the chapters on spectroscopy and decay processes, respectively; and finally to Dr. A. Bialas, Dr. R. Hagedorn, Professor J. Prentki, Dr. D. G. Sutherland, and Dr. K. Zalewski for many useful discussions. The main part of this work was done when I was a research associate in the Theoretical Study Division of CERN in Geneva.

J. J. J. KOKKEDEE

INSTITUTE FOR THEORETICAL PHYSICS
UNIVERSITY OF NIJMEGEN
THE NETHERLANDS, MAY 1968

Contents

Chapter 1

SU(2)

Quarks were introduced in particle physics in the beginning of 1964 by Gell-Mann[1] and Zweig.[2] The idea evolved from considerations of unitary symmetry. To follow the arguments of Gell-Mann and Zweig it is useful to summarize briefly the simple case, long recognized, of charge independence or isospin symmetry.

Charge independence for nonstrange hadrons (which include all strongly interacting stable and unstable particles) corresponds loosely to the hypothesis that their interaction energy is invariant with respect to any unitary transformation between the states of the nucleon doublet (P, N), where P = proton and N = neutron; that is, their interactions are invariant with respect to the SU(2) group of isospin transformations. We can consider P and N as the basic isospin states; however, more generally, we denote the basic states by $\xi_1 = p$ and $\xi_2 = n$, which have the same isospin transformation properties as P and N but need not be identical to them. Like P and N, they form a two-dimensional covariant isospinor

$$\xi = \begin{pmatrix} \xi_1 \\ \xi_2 \end{pmatrix} \tag{1-1}$$

which, under the transformations U of the SU(2) group, transforms as

$$\xi \to \xi' = U\xi \tag{1-2}$$

in which U is a 2×2 unitary matrix satisfying $\det U = 1$. Any isospin rotation can be completely characterized by its effect on ξ as described by Eq. (1-2). The doublet (ξ_1, ξ_2) with isospin $I = \frac{1}{2}$ forms the basis for the fundamental representation of the isospin group SU(2).

Besides the covariant spinors we define contravariant spinors

$$\eta = (\eta^1, \eta^2) \tag{1-3}$$

which, under the U transformations, transform in such a way that $\eta\xi = \eta^a \xi_a$ is invariant. (Summation of repeated indices is understood throughout.) Just as ξ describes the isospin transformation properties of the basic states or "particles" p and n, η describe the transformation properties of the doublet of "antiparticles" $\bar{p}$ and $\bar{n}$.

Higher isospin multiplets can be constructed by forming direct products of the spinors ξ or η or both. For example, consider a system composed of a particle and an antiparticle. We obtain four states that can be written

$$M^i_k = \eta^i \xi_k \qquad (i, k = 1, 2) \tag{1-4}$$

The tensor M^i_k has mixed properties under isospin rotations; that is, it does not correspond to an irreducible representation of SU(2). However, by judiciously taking linear combinations of the above states we can construct two sets of orthonormal states such that, under the action of SU(2), the states within each set transform among each other and as such form the basis of an irreducible representation, that is, a *multiplet.* Evidently one of these sets consists of the invariant or isoscalar $\eta^i \xi_i$; the remaining states form a triplet. The two sets in question are

$$\frac{1}{\sqrt{2}}(\eta^1 \xi_1 + \eta^2 \xi_2) = \frac{1}{\sqrt{2}}(\bar{p}p + \bar{n}n) \qquad \text{singlet} \qquad I = 0 \tag{1-5a}$$

$$\left.\begin{aligned} &\eta^1 \xi_2 = \bar{p}n \\ &\eta^2 \xi_1 = p\bar{n} \\ &\frac{1}{\sqrt{2}}(\eta^1 \xi_1 - \eta^2 \xi_2) = \frac{1}{\sqrt{2}}(\bar{p}p - \bar{n}n) \end{aligned}\right\} \qquad \text{triplet} \qquad I = 1 \tag{1-5b}$$

showing that the direct product of the two isospin doublets breaks down into an isospin singlet and an isospin triplet. We can write this symbolically as

$$2 \times \bar{2} = 1 + 3 \tag{1-6}$$

With n and p carrying zero strangeness we can represent the triplet of pions by the triplet (1-5b). This fact can mean two things. Either the fundamental objects $p, n, \bar{p}, \bar{n}$ are mathematical objects; thus identification of the pion triplet with Eq. (1-5b) means only that the pion has the same isospin transformation properties as the combinations given by Eq. (1-5b). Or the objects $p, n, \bar{p}, \bar{n}$ are physical particles; hence the pion must be regarded as the bound state of these particles. For instance, identifying p and n with P and N, respectively, leads to the Fermi-Yang model.[3] In the quark model p and n are the nonstrange members of the quark triplet.

Similarly the η meson can be represented in this model by the singlet (1-5a). In this way we can construct all nonstrange hadrons from our building blocks p, n, and their antiparticles. The assumption of invariance of the mechanics of the system under isospin transformations ensures that these hadrons fall into isospin multiplets, each of which is characterized by the value of the isospin I. If the symmetry is perfect, each multiplet is degenerate in mass. Electromagnetic forces, which break isospin symmetry, cause small mass splittings within the multiplets. Once one member of a given multiplet is found, all the other members of the multiplet must also exist.

It is evident that with this procedure we will never be able to construct the strange particles. For that purpose we must have at least one more fundamental object with nonzero strangeness. This requirement leads to SU(3).

Chapter 2

SU(3)

2-1. THE FUNDAMENTAL TRIPLET

The only difference between SU(2) and SU(3) is that in SU(3) our basic state is a three-component spinor

$$\xi = \begin{pmatrix} \xi_1 \\ \xi_2 \\ \xi_3 \end{pmatrix} \equiv \begin{pmatrix} p \\ n \\ \lambda \end{pmatrix} \tag{2-1}$$

We have simply added a third component to Eq. (1-1). Under the transformations of SU(3) this spinor transforms as

$$\xi \to \xi' = U\xi \tag{2-2}$$

in which U is now a 3×3 unitary matrix with det $U = 1$. As in Chapter 1 we also introduce the generalization of the contravariant spinor

$$\eta = (\eta^1\, \eta^2\, \eta^3) \equiv (\bar{p}\bar{n}\bar{\lambda}) \tag{2-3}$$

describing the antiparticles. It transforms such that $\eta\xi$ is invariant. The triplets (p, n, λ) and $(\bar{p}, \bar{n}, \bar{\lambda})$ form the bases for the two fundamental representations of SU(3). We denote them by {3} and {3}, respectively. [With SU(2) it is not necessary to distinguish between the bases 2 and $\bar{2}$ because the states of one transform as a specific linear combination of the others. This is not true for SU(3).] The particles p, n, and λ are called quarks and the antiparticles $\bar{p}$, $\bar{n}$, $\bar{\lambda}$ antiquarks, the names used by Gell-Mann.[1] Whether quarks really exist in nature or are purely formal objects is an open question to which we return later.

The p and n quarks form an isodoublet ($I = ½$) of strangeness $S = 0$; the λ quark is an isoscalar ($I = 0$) to which we assign strangeness $S = -1$. Since, as we shall see later, three quarks are necessary to construct a baryon and a quark-antiquark pair is necessary to construct a meson, we have to assign to each of the quarks baryon number $B = 1/3$. Hence the hypercharge Y, defined by

$$Y = S + B \tag{2-4}$$

is $+1/3$ for p and n, and $-2/3$ for λ. The Gell-Mann–Nishijima relation

$$Q = I_z + \tfrac{1}{2}Y \tag{2-5}$$

in which Q is the charge, then gives for the charges e_q of the quarks p, n, λ the fractional values $\frac{2}{3}e, -\frac{1}{3}e, -\frac{1}{3}e$, respectively. Here e is the charge of the proton. We have collected the quantum numbers of the quarks in Table 1.

Table 1. Quantum Numbers of the Quarks.

	B	I	I_z	Y	S	e_q/e
p	$\frac{1}{3}$	$\frac{1}{2}$	$\frac{1}{2}$	$\frac{1}{3}$	0	$\frac{2}{3}$
n	$\frac{1}{3}$	$\frac{1}{2}$	$-\frac{1}{2}$	$\frac{1}{3}$	0	$-\frac{1}{3}$
λ	$\frac{1}{3}$	0	0	$-\frac{2}{3}$	-1	$-\frac{1}{3}$

For the antiquarks the quantum numbers I_z, S, B, Y, and e_q are the opposites of those of the corresponding quarks. We can represent the basic triplets of SU(3) graphically as in Figure 1.

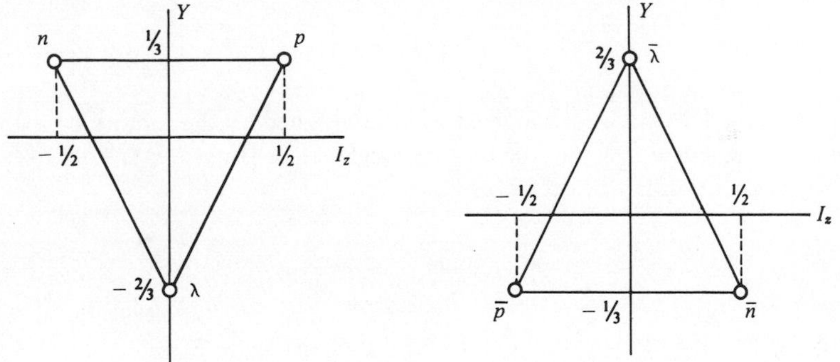

FIGURE 1. The triplets of quarks and antiquarks.

2-2. HIGHER MULTIPLETS

In the same manner as that briefly demonstrated in Chapter 1 for SU(2) we can obtain higher representations of SU(3) by forming direct products of the basic spinors ξ and η. First, consider the states for a quark–antiquark pair

$$M^i_k = \eta^i \xi_k \qquad (i, k = 1, 2, 3) \tag{2-6}$$

There are nine of them that have mixed properties under SU(3) transformations; that is, they do not form the basis for an irreducible representation. To construct irreducible representations we take suitable linear combinations of the above states just as we did in Chapter 1. The combination

$$\frac{1}{\sqrt{3}}\eta^i \xi_i = \frac{1}{\sqrt{3}}(\bar{p}p + \bar{n}n + \bar{\lambda}\lambda) \tag{2-7}$$

is invariant under any U transformation and, as such, forms the basis for a one-dimensional representation. The factor $1/\sqrt{3}$ is a normalization factor. We have obtained a unitary singlet. It can be directly verified that the remaining eight states transform among each other and span the basis for the eight-dimensional representation. We call it an *octet.* Hence we have found that the direct product of a triplet and an antitriplet decompose into a singlet and an octet. We write symbolically

$$\{3\} \times \{\bar{3}\} = \{1\} + \{8\} \tag{2-8}$$

The two central states of the octet, those with $I_z = 0$, are linear combinations of $\bar{p}p$, $\bar{n}n$, and $\bar{\lambda}\lambda$. One of them is chosen by demanding that it forms an isotriplet with $\bar{p}n$ and $\bar{n}p$. Hence it is

$$x = \frac{1}{\sqrt{2}}(\bar{p}p - \bar{n}n) \tag{2-9}$$

The remaining state y is an isosinglet and is determined by the requirement that it should be orthogonal to x and the unitary singlet state [Eq. (2-7)]. This gives, with the proper normalization factor,

$$y = (\bar{p}p + \bar{n}n - 2\bar{\lambda}\lambda)\frac{1}{\sqrt{6}} \tag{2-10}$$

Thus we have the array of octet states as shown in Figure 2.

Next we consider the product of two quark triplets. The basic states are

$$\xi_i \xi_k \qquad (i, k = 1, 2, 3) \tag{2-11}$$

Again these nine states have mixed SU(3) transformation properties. By observing their behavior under exchange of two quark indices, we see immediately that we can form six symmetric states

$$pp \qquad nn \qquad \lambda\lambda$$

$$\frac{1}{\sqrt{2}}(pn + np) \qquad \frac{1}{\sqrt{2}}(p\lambda + \lambda p) \qquad \frac{1}{\sqrt{2}}(n\lambda + \lambda n) \tag{2-12}$$

and three antisymmetric states

$$\frac{1}{\sqrt{2}}(pn - np)$$
$$\frac{1}{\sqrt{2}}(p\lambda - \lambda p) \tag{2-13}$$
$$\frac{1}{\sqrt{2}}(n\lambda - \lambda n)$$

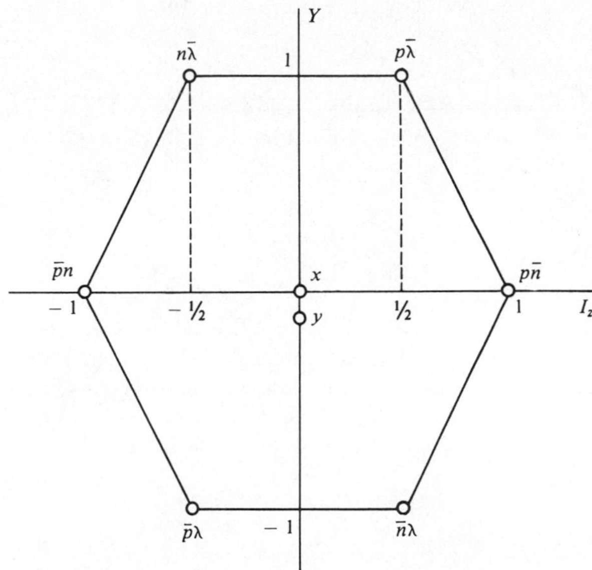

FIGURE 2. Octet of quark–antiquark states.

The two sets of states transform independently; that is, they form bases for irreducible representations of SU(3). The former set is a sextet {6}, the latter an antitriplet, $\{\bar{3}\}$, as is clear by noting that the state $1/\sqrt{2}\,(pn-np)$ is an isoscalar with hypercharge ⅔; that is, it transforms as $\bar{\lambda}$ (see Figure 1). Hence

$$\{3\} \times \{3\} = \{\bar{3}\} + \{6\} \tag{2-14}$$

Finally, in a three-quark configuration we have the basic states

$$\xi_i \xi_j \xi_k \qquad (i, j, k = 1, 2, 3) \tag{2-15}$$

This case is more complicated; however, using first Eq. (2-14) and then Eq. (2-8) we can write

$$\begin{aligned}\{3\} \times \{3\} \times \{3\} &= [\{\bar{3}\} \times \{3\}] + [\{6\} \times \{3\}] \\ &= \{1\} + \{8\} + [\{6\} \times \{3\}]\end{aligned} \tag{2-16}$$

It is not difficult to check,[4] using Eq. (2-12), that in the product $\{6\} \times \{3\}$ there are 10 fully symmetric states, transforming among each other, which form a decuplet $\{10\}$. The remaining eight states form an octet. We thus have

$$\{3\} \times \{3\} \times \{3\} = \{1\} + \{8\} + \{8\} + \{10\} \tag{2-17}$$

Here the decuplet states are fully symmetric in the quark labels i, j, k; the octet states have mixed permutation symmetry and the singlet is antisymmetric. [Note that $\{\bar{3}\}$ in Eq. (2-14) contains the antisymmetric states, Eq. (2-13).]

2-3. UNITARY SPIN

It is convenient to introduce in analogy to the isospin operator an operator F whose eigenvalues characterize the SU(3) multiplets. We call it *unitary spin* or *F spin.* It suffices to know that this operator is defined in such a way that the eigenvalues of F^2 for the various multiplets are as shown in Table 2.[5, 6]

Table 2. Eigenvalues of F^2.

F^2	Multiplet
0	$\{1\}$
8	$\{3\}, \{\bar{3}\}$
20	$\{6\}$
18	$\{8\}$
36	$\{10\}$

For a system composed of two particles with F spins F_1 and F_2 the total F spin is $F = F_1 + F_2$. For later purposes we need the value of $F_1 . F_2$. It is given by

$$F_1 . F_2 = \tfrac{1}{2}[F^2 - F_1^2 - F_2^2] \tag{2-18}$$

and can be calculated by using Table 2. For instance, for a $\bar{q}q$ octet state $F_1 . F_2 = 1$; for a $\bar{q}q$ singlet state $F_1 . F_2 = -8$ [q = quark, $\bar{q}$ = antiquark].

Chapter 3

SU(6)

Until now we have not discussed the possible mechanical spins of our hypothetical particles, the quarks. If, however, we wish to use the quarks as the building blocks of the hadrons in much the same way as nucleons make up the nuclei, as we do in the nonrelativistic quark model described in later chapters, we have to assume that quarks carry mechanical spin. We assume that quarks are fermions and have spin $\sigma = \frac{1}{2}$. This assumption appears to be most natural in view of the fact that the lowest mesonic states have spin 0 or 1, the lowest baryonic states have spin $^1/_2$ or $^3/_2$. In a nonrelativistic description we then have six quark states that we take as the components of a six-dimensional covariant spinor

$$\xi = \begin{pmatrix} \xi_1 \\ \xi_2 \\ \xi_3 \\ \xi_4 \\ \xi_5 \\ \xi_6 \end{pmatrix} \equiv \begin{pmatrix} p\uparrow \\ n\uparrow \\ \lambda\uparrow \\ p\downarrow \\ n\downarrow \\ \lambda\downarrow \end{pmatrix} \tag{3-1}$$

Here "↑" means spin up and "↓" spin down. The linear transformations U belonging to the group SU(6) act on this basic spinor and form linear combinations of the states ξ_A exactly similar to SU(2) and SU(3) discussed in the preceding chapters. The corresponding contravariant spinor η^A is defined such that $\eta^A \xi_A$ is a scalar under the action of U. The sets $p\uparrow, \cdots, \lambda\downarrow$ and $\bar{p}\downarrow, \cdots, \bar{\lambda}\uparrow$ constitute the basic multiplets [6] and [$\bar{6}$] of SU(6). (Henceforth brackets [] will denote SU(6) multiplets and braces { } SU(3) multiplets.)

Higher multiplets arise by forming direct products of basic spinors. There are 36 quark–antiquark states

$$\eta^A \xi_B \qquad (A, B = 1, \cdots, 6)$$

which are easily seen to break down into two multiplets, that is, bases for irreducible representations of SU(6), namely, the singlet $\eta^A \xi_A$ and the 35-plet,

$$[6] \times [\bar{6}] = [1] + [35] \tag{3-2}$$

which is the SU(6) generalization of Eq. (2-8). Of course the singlet has total mechanical spin equal to zero. The 35-plet consists of eight states with total spin zero (antiparallel quark spins) forming an SU(3) octet, 24 states with total spin one (parallel quark spins) that also form an SU(3) octet with each octet state having three spin states, and finally three states of total spin one, forming an SU(3) singlet. This can be easily demonstrated[5b] by writing

$$[6] = [\{3\}, \tfrac{1}{2}] \qquad [\bar{6}] = [\{\bar{3}\}, \tfrac{1}{2}]$$

in which the SU(3) content and the spin value ½ of the fundamental sextets are explicitly shown. We now use Eqs. (2-8) and (3-2) together with the rules for combining angular momentum to obtain

$$[6] \times [\bar{6}] = [1] + [35] = [\{1\}, 0] + [\{1\}, 1] + [\{8\}, 0] + [\{8\}, 1]$$

When we count the number of states on the left and right of the second equation, thereby distinguishing between spin states of different s_z (s being the total spin), we obtain as the only possibility

$$[1] = [\{1\}, 0]$$

$$[35] = [\{1\}, 1] + [\{8\}, 0] + [\{8\}, 1] \tag{3-3}$$

which corresponds to the above statement.

The SU(6) generalization of Eq. (2-17) is

$$[6] \times [6] \times [6] = [20] + [56] + [70] + [70] \tag{3-4}$$

To arrive at this formula we start from the result

$$[6] \times [6] = [15] + [21]$$

which expresses the fact that, from the 36 products $\xi_A \, \xi_B$, we can construct one set of 15 antisymmetric and one set of 21 symmetric combinations with each set forming a multiplet. Hence

$$[6] \times [6] \times [6] = [21] \times [6] + [15] \times [6] \tag{3-5}$$

The 126 states contained in [21] × [6] are of the type $(\xi_A \xi_B)_{(s)} \xi_C$, in which the subscript (s) indicates that this product is symmetric in the variables A and B. This set can be split into two irreducible sets, namely, one containing 56 states that are symmetric in all three variables and one with 70 states having mixed symmetry. Thus

$$[21] \times [6] = [56] + [70] \tag{3-6}$$

Similarly

$$[15] \times [6] = [20] + [70] \tag{3-7}$$

in which the states contained in [20] are fully antisymmetric. Combining these results leads to Eq. (3-4).

The SU(3) content of the multiplets on the right of this equation can be found by the method leading to Eq. (3-3). Using Eq. (2-14) gives

$$[6] \times [6] = [21] + [15] = [\{\bar{3}\}, 0] + [\{\bar{3}\}, 1] + [\{6\}, 0] + [\{6\}, 1]$$

Looking at the dimensions we conclude

$$[21] = [\{\bar{3}\}, 0] + [\{6\}, 1]$$

$$[15] = [\{\bar{3}\}, 1] + [\{6\}, 0]$$

From this fact, making use of the formula $\{3\} \times \{6\} = \{8\} + \{10\}$, we obtain

$$[21] \times [6] = [56] + [70] = [\{8\}, \tfrac{1}{2}] + [\{10\}, \tfrac{1}{2}] + [\{8\}, \tfrac{3}{2}] + [\{10\}, \tfrac{3}{2}] + [\{1\}, \tfrac{1}{2}] + [\{8\}, \tfrac{1}{2}]$$

showing that

$$[56] = [\{8\}, \tfrac{1}{2}] + [\{10\}, \tfrac{3}{2}] \tag{3-8a}$$

$$[70] = [\{1\}, \tfrac{1}{2}] + [\{8\}, \tfrac{1}{2}] + [\{8\}, \tfrac{3}{2}] + [\{10\}, \tfrac{1}{2}] \tag{3-8b}$$

Similarly we find

$$[20] = [\{1\}, \tfrac{3}{2}] + [\{8\}, \tfrac{1}{2}] \tag{3-9}$$

For our purpose the most interesting multiplet on the right of Eq. (3-4) is [56] since it accommodates the low-lying baryon states. From Eq. (3-8a) we see that [56] comprises a SU(3) octet of spin ½ and a decuplet of spin $^3\!/_2$. As stated above, in terms of the three quarks the states belonging to [56] are fully symmetric in the variables *A. B,* and *C.* Note that the decuplet states [Eq. (3-8a)] are symmetric separately in the SU(3) variables *i, j,* and *k* [see Eq. (2-15)] and in the spin variables. This is not true for the octet.

Chapter 4

Quarks and Quark Models

4-1. GENERAL REMARKS

We now try to give the mathematical ideas described in the foregoing chapter a physical content and discuss their relevance with respect to the physics of hadrons. In the quark model quarks are not viewed as mere mathematical objects but as capable of somehow being realized in nature. We do not yet know how. Thus quarks are considered the fundamental building blocks of hadronic matter,* and each hadron is supposed to be a bound state of quarks or antiquarks or both due to some strongly attractive force whose nature is unknown. SU(3) invariance means that the three quarks making up the triplet representation of SU(3) have the same mass, and that the forces between them do not change under SU(3) transformations. This fact ensures the existence of SU(3) multiplets consisting of $nqm\bar{q}$ states $(n, m = 0, 1, 2, \ldots)$, according to the formulas given in the foregoing chapters. With perfect symmetry the states within each multiplet are degenerate in energy. If the symmetry is broken, the degeneracy is lifted. Hence from the quark picture we arrive in a natural way at the classification of mesons, baryons, and their resonances into certain SU(3) multiplets. In the simplest scheme, in which the mesons are $q\bar{q}$ states and the baryons qqq states, only singlets, octets, and decuplets are allowed [see Eqs. (2-8) and (2-17)]. Experimental verification of this ordering of hadrons into SU(3) multiplets has been one of the most striking discoveries in particle physics in recent years.[7] The observed multiplets are only approximately degenerate, thus showing that SU(3) is only an approximate symmetry.

We can go one step further and include mechanical spin, which is treated nonrelativistically (see below). The assumption that interactions between quarks are also independent of their spin directions gives rise automatically to the classification of hadrons into SU(6) multiplets,[5b, 8] each of which, as we have seen, generally includes several SU(3) multiplets. Each of the latter comprises a set of states with identical total spin. Again it appears that SU(6) multiplets are realized in nature, thus implying that SU(3) multiplets of different spins are not completely independent, but the big mass differences within the observed SU(6) multiplets show that the latter are a reflection of a symmetry that is only very approximate.

* It has been speculated that in analogy to hadronic quarks, the basic constituents of hadronic matter, there could exist leptonic quarks building the leptonic world [see T. Massam and A. Zichichi, *Nuovo Cimento* **43**, 227 (1966)].

Orbital angular momentum can be readily incorporated in the picture. (We see all this explicitly in later chapters.) It is evident that the existence of higher multiplets, although naturally explained by the quark model, by no means proves the existence of quarks as physical particles.

4-2. THE SEARCH FOR QUARKS

Do quarks exist? We do not know! Until now quarks have not been found in nature although for several years experimentalists have vigorously hunted for them.[9, 10a] Note that because of charge conservation at least one nonintegrally charged particle is supposed to be stable. The search for quarks takes place along the following lines.

One is the geophysical–chemical approach, which assumes that for some reason stable quarks or, more generally, nonintegrally charged particles, are present with small concentrations in meteorites, planets, and particularly in the earth's crust.[11] They could be the remnants of a production process that took place during the cosmological "big bang" or the collision products from high-energy cosmic rays interacting with the atmosphere of the earth since its formation. When negatively charged these quarks will be bound to nuclei in Bohr orbits and result in fractionally charged atoms that can produce peculiar chemical or physical properties of small fractions of the earth's crust. A chemical analysis of sea water[12] has yielded an upper limit for the quark concentration per nucleon $C_q \lesssim 10^{-24}$–10^{-27}. Theoretical estimates are very unreliable and highly model-dependent.[11, 13] Experiments of the Millikan type, but modified because of the low concentration, are in progress.[14] The idea here is to perform the Millikan experiment on larger bodies–grains of matter–that are magnetized and held in position by suitable magnetic fields. In another experiment,[15] with negative result, researchers looked for evidence of quark atoms (i.e., hydrogenic atoms formed of one positive quark and one electron) in the solar photosphere by examining solar spectra.

Another approach is direct detection of quarks in cosmic rays[16] and in accelerator experiments.[17] These experiments lead to upper limits for quark fluxes or production cross sections, which in turn can lead to lower limits on the quark mass m_q; this is assuming one can estimate a production cross section. In accelerator experiments one looks for quarks in reactions of the type

$$P + P \to P + P + q + \bar{q} + \text{(possibly) mesons} \qquad (4\text{-}1)$$

The energy of present machines does not permit production of quarks with a mass much above 3 GeV. Recent experiments have set an upper limit for the cross section $\sigma(q\bar{q})$ of reaction [Eq. (4-1)] at proton laboratory momenta of about 30

GeV/c of 10^{-35} to 10^{-37} cm^2. Estimates[13, 18] of this cross section on the basis of the statistical model for production show a strong dependence on the quark mass m_q. According to Hagedorn[18]

$$\sigma(q\bar{q}) = C\left(\frac{m_q}{T_0}\right)^3 e^{-2m_q/T_0} \tag{4-2}$$

where $T_0 \simeq 0.16$ GeV and $C \simeq 250$ mb. This formula holds far above the threshold for production, and gives a result independent of the total energy. Note that $\sigma(q\bar{q})$ decreases by 10^{-6} if m_q increases by one nucleon mass. For $m_q = 3$ GeV, Eq. (4-2) gives $\sigma(q\bar{q}) \simeq 10^{-37}$ cm^2, which is of the order of the experimentally found lower limit. This fact suggests a lower limit for the quark mass of about 3–4 GeV.

There may be several reasons for the apparent lack of success in the search for quarks.

(1) Quarks may be very massive. If m_q is high, for example, 10 GeV, the production cross section according to Eq. (4-2) becomes far too low to produce a sizable flux of particles.

(2) Up to now researchers have looked almost exclusively for quarks with fractional charge $|1/3|$ or $|2/3|$. (See, however, Reference 19.) It has been remarked[20] that the existence of bound quark systems (such as qq, $qqqq$, with nonintegral charge and mass less than m_q) into which quarks could strongly decay is not excluded. If this is so, the stable system would not necessarily have charge $|1/3|$ or $|2/3|$, but could have fractional charge more than $|2/3|$.

(3) It may be that quarks do not exist as free particles but, owing to some selection principle, occur only in certain bound combinations having integral charge and baryon number. A few speculations pointing in that direction have been made by Schiff[21] (see Section 7-2).

(4) Perhaps quarks are some kind of quasiparticles that, like phonons inside a crystal lattice, have meaning only as dynamic entities inside the hadrons. It is well known that many properties of a vibrating crystal can be adequately described in terms of noninteracting, independent phonons that evidently cannot exist outside the crystal.

The latter two alternatives allow us to think of quarks as rather light objects with masses of the order of a few hundred MeV [compare Eq. (4-6)].

4-3. BASIC ASSUMPTIONS

As stated before, in the quark model the observed hadrons are interpreted as bound states of quarks or antiquarks or both. If quarks are heavy objects, these bound states are characterized by extremely high binding energies, high enough almost to compensate for the high rest masses of the composing quarks. Despite these high binding energies it is assumed in many of the applications of the quark model that the motion of the quarks inside the hadrons is nonrelativistic (*nonrelativistic quark model*). It has been shown[22, 23] that this assumption is not unreasonable; however, its validity may depend on the nature of the force field binding the quarks. To illustrate this situation we consider the simple case of a quark with mass m_q moving in a deep square-well potential U with depth $-U_0$ and width b, caused by the other quarks of the bound system. We consider two cases: U as the fourth component of a vector potential such as the Coulomb potential; U as a scalar potential. The Dirac equations for the quark corresponding to the two cases are, respectively,

$$[m_q + \boldsymbol{\gamma}\cdot\mathbf{p}]\psi_q = (E + U_0)\gamma_0\psi_q \tag{4-3}$$

and

$$[(m_q - U_0) + \boldsymbol{\gamma}\cdot\mathbf{p}]\psi_q = E\gamma_0\psi_q \tag{4-4}$$

The quark behaves in the force field approximately as a free particle with typical momentum given by b^{-1} and an effective mass m_q^* shifted from the free value m_q by an amount determined by the force field. The condition for nonrelativistic motion is approximately*

$$b^{-1} \ll m_q^* \tag{4-5}$$

With the vector field [Eq. (4-3)]

$$m_q^* = m_q$$

The presence of the potential does not affect the quark mass but changes only the energy scale. With $m_q \gtrsim 4$ GeV, condition (4-5) can be easily satisfied. Indeed, with b of the order of 1 f, the left-hand side of condition (4-5) becomes $b^{-1} \simeq$ 0.2 GeV. However, if U is a scalar field, we have [Eq. (4-4)]

$$m_q^* = m_q - U_0$$

Since the depth of the well should be such as to produce the observed mass of the bound system, we find that in this case

$$m_q^* \simeq \frac{m_M}{2} \simeq \frac{m_B}{3} \simeq 400 \text{ MeV} \tag{4-6}$$

in which m_M and m_B are the average masses of the 35-plet and 56-plet, respectively. This condition makes it more difficult to satisfy Eq. (4-5). We must choose b quite large. Nevertheless, as we see later, the electromagnetic properties of hadrons appear to suggest a mainly scalar binding potential. One should remark

* We use units such that $\hbar = c = 1$.

here that, for potentials having a narrow gorge, such as the Yukawa potential, it is more difficult to achieve nonrelativistic motion because, owing to the gorge, the particle is actually constrained to a region smaller than that given by the range b of the potential and therefore has an average momentum larger than b^{-1}.[24]

A second basic assumption that underlies all applications of the quark model is the additivity assumption, by means of which some property of a hadron is described as a sum of contributions from the constituent quarks or antiquarks (*independent quark model*). For instance, amplitudes for hadron decay and high-energy scattering processes are calculated as sums of contributions of the type depicted in Figure 3. (It must be stressed that one cannot really speak about *the* quark model. There are various quark models just as there are various nuclear models. The nonrelativistic quark model used to describe low-energy properties of hadrons and the quark model for high-energy scattering are two different things.)

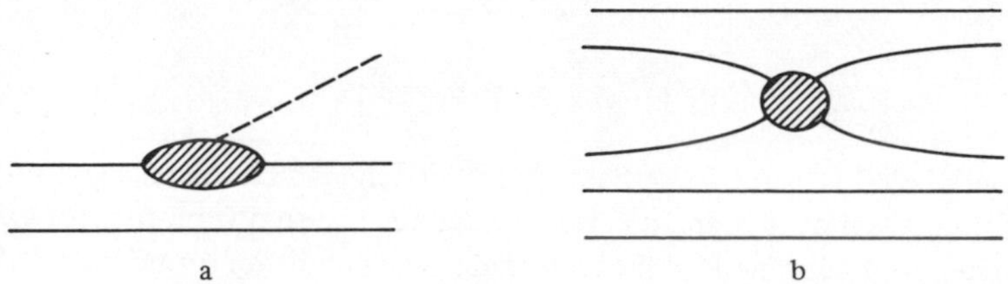

FIGURE 3. Meson decay and meson-baryon scattering in the quark model. The lines represent quarks or antiquarks; the dotted line can be a photon, a lepton pair, a pion, and so forth.

For the decay processes $A \to B + X$, A and B being hadrons and X representing the emitted system (the dotted line in Figure 3a), additivity explicitly reads

$$\langle B + X | T | A \rangle = \langle B | \sum_{ij} T_{ij}(X) | A \rangle \qquad (4\text{-}7)$$

in which the operator $T_{ij}(X)$ describes the single quark transition $q_i \to q_j + X$. The spin and unitary spin wave functions of A and B in terms of the quarks are constructed according to SU(6) symmetry (see the next chapters).

As we note later, the additivity assumption works surprisingly well. This success is in marked contrast to the failure of all attempts, especially in high-energy scattering, to find an *a priori* justification for it. For the time being, at least, we must consider it as a "rule of the game," to use the phraseology of Lipkin.

Equally nontrivial is the usual assumption that hadrons can be described in terms of a fixed number of quarks and a fixed number of antiquarks, that is, that baryons, for instance, can be considered as pure three-quark states without multiquark admixtures such as $qqq\,\bar{q}q$ (meson clouds).

We finally wish to point out that in many cases the quark model, as described above, and certain higher symmetry schemes give rise to the same predictions without the explicit use of this symmetry in the quark model calculations. The origin of this "symmetry without symmetry" has been examined in detail by Lipkin.[25] He points out that in decay processes, for instance, this situation arises if the transformation properties of the operator $T_{ij}(X)$ in the additivity assumption [Eq. (4-7)], which are determined by the requirement that it be a one-body operator transforming only single-quark (antiquark) states into other single-quark (antiquark) states, happen to be the same as those used in conventional symmetry description. (For an extensive discussion of a number of cases see Reference 25.)

4-4. OTHER COMPOSITE MODELS

We conclude this chapter by remarking on other possible composite models. The quark model is a very economical scheme in that only one triplet (and, of course, one antitriplet) of fundamental objects is needed to build the observed hadrons. For this scheme, however, we must accept particles with fractional charge and baryon number. Many people have tried to avoid these nonintegral quantum numbers. This approach is possible only by increasing the number of fundamental triplets. For instance, in the Bacry–Nuyts–Van Hove model[26] two triplets are introduced; in the Han–Nambu[26] model there are three. We do not discuss these models further here, but mention only that an interesting point in favor of integrally charged triplets recently has been made by Cabibbo *et al.*[27a] These authors set out to calculate radiative corrections to the β decays of hadrons in a composite model and find that one of the conditions to obtain finite results to order e^2 is to assign charges 0 or $\pm e$ to the fundamental triplet particles. This conclusion should be contrasted with an earlier one of Okubo,[27b] who, by investigating sum rules obtainable from current commutation relations argues in favor of the fractionally charged quark model rather than the integrally charged ones.

Chapter 5

Low-Lying Meson States

5-1. QUARK COMPOSITION

In the quark model the mesons are considered to be bound states of a quark–antiquark pair $q\bar{q}$. The attractive force between q and $\bar{q}$ could, for instance, arise from the exchange of vector mesons (see Chapter 7). In general the $q\bar{q}$ system can have nonzero orbital angular momentum L. In the $q\bar{q}$ model the only SU(3) multiplets that are allowed for the mesons are, according to Eq. (2-8), the singlet and the octet. It is satisfactory that until now no mesonic resonances have been established that cannot be accommodated in the singlet and octet representations; so at present there is no need for higher representations corresponding to quark systems of the type $q\bar{q}q\bar{q}$, and so on.[10] Of course the possibility is not definitely excluded that the observed nonets of higher spin mesons, such as the 2^+ mesons, are $q\bar{q}q\bar{q}$ states instead of L-excited $q\bar{q}$ systems, as we assume here. It should also be stressed that nothing except simplicity is against these many-quark configurations. In an SU(6) invariant theory the $q\bar{q}$ model permits only the SU(6) representations [1] and [35] for the mesonic states [see Eq. (3-2)]. Notice that, for the mesons, a particle and its antiparticle are always in the same SU(3) multiplet.

Since quark and antiquark have opposite intrinsic parity, the parity P of the $q\bar{q}$ state is given by

$$P = (-1)^{L+1} \tag{5-1}$$

The charge conjugation quantum number C for the neutral states is

$$C = (-1)^{L+s} \tag{5-2}$$

where s is the total intrinsic spin, which is zero or one according to whether the quark spins are antiparallel or parallel. The spin of the hadron is given by $\mathbf{J} = \mathbf{L} + \mathbf{s}$.

The above equations show that in the $q\bar{q}$ model only certain combinations of J, P, and C are allowed (see also Section 9-1); $J^{PC} = 0^{--}$, $(\text{odd})^{-+}$, $(\text{even})^{+-}$ are excluded. The model's great success is that all mesonic states established today satisfy Eqs. (5-1) and (5-2).

The lowest $\bar{q}q$ states are the S states corresponding to $L = 0$. Depending on the value of s, there are two sets of nine S states (two nonets) having the following quantum numbers

$$\begin{array}{llll} \text{(a)} & s=0 & P=-1 & C=+1 \\ \text{(b)} & s=1 & P=-1 & C=-1 \end{array} \tag{5-3}$$

each of which falls into an SU(3) singlet and an SU(3) octet. The singlet with $s = 0$ is the SU(6) multiplet [1], the remaining states make up [35]. Sets (a) and (b) may be identified with the two nonets of observed pseudoscalar and vector mesons, respectively. Compare, for instance, the quantum numbers of the octet of antiquark–quark states displayed by Figure 2 and those of the octets of pseudoscalar and vector mesons shown in Figure 4.

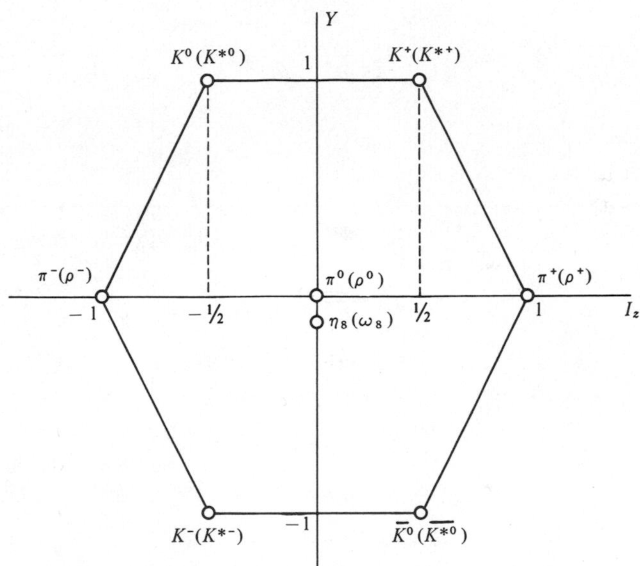

FIGURE 4. Octet of pseudoscalar (vector) mesons.

In Table 3 we have the quark content of the $L = 0$ mesons together with other characteristics. [(When not quoted otherwise experimental data concerning particles are taken from the tables by Rosenfeld *et al.*[28] We have taken η' (or X°) to be the ninth pseudoscalar meson. This is not strictly necessary. Another candidate is the $E(1420)$. (See also the end of Section 8-1).] The ω_8 and η_8 are pure unitary octet combinations, ϕ_1 and η_1' pure singlets. Since these states have the same quantum numbers $I = Y = 0$, they can mix in broken SU(3) when belonging to the same nonet, and the observed particles ω, ϕ, η, and η' are coherent superpositions of them. Explicitly,

$$\begin{aligned} \phi, \eta &= \psi_8 \cos\vartheta - \psi_1 \sin\vartheta \\ \omega, \eta' &= \psi_8 \sin\vartheta + \psi_1 \cos\vartheta \end{aligned} \tag{5-4}$$

Table 3. The Pseudoscalar and Vector Mesons.

SU(3) Multiplet	Particle	Quark content	Mass MeV	J^P	I	S
	ρ^+ π^+	$p\bar{n}$	774 139.6	1^- 0^-	1	0
	ρ^0 π^0	$\frac{1}{\sqrt{2}}(p\bar{p} - n\bar{n})$	780 135.0	1^- 0^-	1	0
	ρ^- π^-	$\bar{p}n$	774 139.6	1^- 0^-	1	0
	K^{*0} K^0	$n\bar{\lambda}$	890 497.7	1^- 0^-	$\frac{1}{2}$	1
{8}	K^{*+} K^+	$p\bar{\lambda}$	890 493.8	1^- 0^-	$\frac{1}{2}$	1
	$\overline{K}^{*0}$ $\overline{K}^0$	$\bar{n}\lambda$	890 497.7	1^- 0^-	$\frac{1}{2}$	−1
	K^{*-} K^-	$\bar{p}\lambda$	890 493.8	1^- 0^-	$\frac{1}{2}$	−1
	ω_8 η_8	$\frac{1}{\sqrt{6}}(\bar{p}p + \bar{n}n - 2\bar{\lambda}\lambda)$		1^- 0^-	0	0
{1}	ϕ_1 η_1'	$\frac{1}{\sqrt{3}}(\bar{p}p + \bar{n}n + \bar{\lambda}\lambda)$		1^- 0^-	0	0
	ω	$\frac{1}{\sqrt{2}}(p\bar{p} + n\bar{n})$	783.3	1^-		
Mixture of	ϕ	$-\lambda\bar{\lambda}$	1018.6	1^-		
{1} and {8}	$\eta'(X^\circ)$	$-\eta_8 \sin 11^\circ + \eta_1' \cos 11^\circ$	958.3	0^-	0	0
	η	$\eta_8 \cos 11^\circ + \eta_1' \sin 11^\circ$	548.6	0^-		

in which ψ_8 and ψ_1 denote the pure octet and singlet states, respectively. We see later that for vector mesons the mixing angle ϑ has the value $\vartheta_V \simeq 40°$. This value is very close to the "ideal" value given by arctan (½ $\sqrt{2}$) for which

$$\phi = -\lambda\bar{\lambda}$$
$$\omega = \frac{1}{\sqrt{2}}(p\bar{p} + n\bar{n}) \tag{5-5}$$

Unless stated otherwise, we always use Eq. (5-5) to represent ϕ and ω. For pseudoscalar mesons the mixing angle is $\vartheta_P \simeq -11°$. We return to the question of mixing when we discuss the masses of the particles.

5-2. WAVE FUNCTIONS

The wave function for the $\bar{q}q$ state A with $L = 0$ can be written as the product

$$\Psi(A) = f(A, \{\mathbf{r}_i\})\,\phi(A) \tag{5-6}$$

in which f and ϕ represent the space part and the spin-unitary spin part, respectively, and the variable $\{\mathbf{r}_i\}$ stands for the set of position vectors describing the quarks inside hadron A. Both f and ϕ are supposed to be normalized to unity. The wave function ϕ is easy to construct. For the pseudoscalar mesons the spins of quark and antiquark are antiparallel so that the spin wave function is a singlet; that is, in obvious notation

$$\frac{1}{\sqrt{2}}[|\uparrow\downarrow\rangle - |\downarrow\uparrow\rangle] \tag{5-7}$$

in which we have included a normalization factor. Reading off the unitary spin part (the term "unitary spin wave function" refers to the obvious SU(3) generalization of "isotopic spin wave function") from Table 3, we have, for instance,

$$\phi(\pi^+) = \frac{1}{\sqrt{2}}[|\bar{n}\uparrow p\downarrow\rangle - |\bar{n}\downarrow p\uparrow\rangle]$$
$$\phi(\pi^0) = \tfrac{1}{2}[|\bar{p}\uparrow p\downarrow\rangle - |\bar{p}\downarrow p\uparrow\rangle - |\bar{n}\uparrow n\downarrow\rangle + |\bar{n}\downarrow n\uparrow\rangle] \tag{5-8}$$

With vector mesons in which quark spins are parallel we have for the spin wave functions

$$\begin{array}{ll} |\uparrow\uparrow\rangle & s_z = +1 \\ \frac{1}{\sqrt{2}}[|\uparrow\downarrow\rangle + |\downarrow\uparrow\rangle] & s_z = 0 \\ |\downarrow\downarrow\rangle & s_z = -1 \end{array} \tag{5-9}$$

with the help of which we can again write $\phi(A)$. Examples are

$$\begin{aligned}
\phi(\rho^+, s_z = +1) &= |\bar{n}\uparrow p\uparrow\rangle \\
\phi(\rho^+, s_z = 0) &= \frac{1}{\sqrt{2}}[|\bar{n}\uparrow p\downarrow\rangle + |\bar{n}\downarrow p\uparrow\rangle] \\
\phi(\omega, s_z = +1) &= \frac{1}{\sqrt{2}}[|\bar{p}\uparrow p\uparrow\rangle + |\bar{n}\uparrow n\uparrow\rangle] \\
\phi(\omega, s_z = 0) &= \tfrac{1}{2}[|\bar{p}\uparrow p\downarrow\rangle + |\bar{p}\downarrow p\uparrow\rangle + |\bar{n}\uparrow n\downarrow\rangle + |\bar{n}\downarrow n\uparrow\rangle]
\end{aligned} \tag{5-10}$$

Because we are completely ignorant of the dynamics of the motion of quarks inside a hadron, we are not able to calculate the space wave functions $f(A,\{\mathbf{r}_i\})$. In some applications of the model, for instance, in deriving relations between high energy total cross sections, knowledge of this wave function is not necessary. In many applications, however, integrals of the type*

$$\begin{aligned}
F_i^{AA'}(\mathbf{q}) &= \int d\tau f^*(A, \{\mathbf{r}_i\}) f(A', \{\mathbf{r}_i\}) e^{-i\mathbf{q}\cdot\mathbf{r}_i} \\
d\tau &= \prod_j d\mathbf{r}_j \, \delta\left(\frac{1}{N}\sum \mathbf{r}_j\right)
\end{aligned} \tag{5-11}$$

appear, with the momentum transfer $|\mathbf{q}|$ in the range $0 \lesssim |\mathbf{q}| \lesssim 1$ GeV/c. If $A \equiv A'$, we have, of course, $F_i^{AA'}(0) = 1$. The approximation often made for want of something better (again a rule of the game!) is to put

$$F_i^{AA'}(\mathbf{q}) = F_i^{AA'}(0) = 1 \tag{5-12}$$

also for $A \neq A'$ but in the same SU(6) multiplet. The latter approximation of putting $F_i^{AA'}(0) = 1$ may not be too bad. It means that one neglects symmetry breaking effects in $f(A, \{\mathbf{r}_i\})$. If SU(6) were a perfect symmetry $F_i^{AA'}(0)$ would, of course, be exactly unity; if A and A' belong to the same SU(3) multiplet, SU(3) symmetry is sufficient. The first part of Eq. (5-12) amounts to the assumption that quarks have spatial dimensions of the order of those of the hadrons with their centers of mass close enough together in space for the form factors $F_i^{AA'}(\mathbf{q})$ to be nearly flat in the above range of $|\mathbf{q}|$ values. We defer a more detailed discussion of these points to later chapters.

* See Appendix.

Chapter 6

Low-Lying Baryon States

6-1. DECUPLET STATES

The baryon states are supposed to be three-quark bound states qqq having total angular momentum L. Approximate invariance under SU(3) leads in this scheme to an ordering of the baryons into singlets, octets, and decuplets [see Eq. (2-17)]. Until recently there was no evidence of baryon resonances that did not fit into one of these multiplets. However, at the moment the situation is less clear. If the newly discovered bumps in the K^+P total cross section are confirmed to be resonances, the simple qqq scheme is untenable because it cannot accommodate resonances with positive strangeness and we need more complex configurations, such as $qqq\bar{q}q$ (see also Chapter 9).

The lowest-lying baryon states are three-quark states with $L = 0$. There are 10 states in which the quark spins add up to the value $s = 3/2$. They form the well known SU(3) decuplet of baryon resonances with $J^P = 3/2^+$. In Table 4 we have compiled these resonances and listed their quark content. Just as in the case of pseudoscalar and vector mesons, their wave functions can be written in the product form of Eq. (5-6). The spin-unitary spin parts of these decuplet wave functions can be constructed as follows. We have seen (Chapter 2) that the unitary spin parts of the decuplet states occurring in Eq. (2-17) are fully symmetric under permutations of the three quarks. On the other hand, since the quark spins have to combine in such a way as to give total spin $3/2$, their spin wave functions are also symmetric. This implies that $\phi(A)$ is symmetric. Now let us assume that the quarks, as ordinary spin $-$ ½ particles, obey Fermi statistics. This requires the complete wave function $\Psi(A)$ to be antisymmetric under the interchange of any two quarks; hence the space part $f(A, \{\mathbf{r}_i\})$ has to be antisymmetric. We comment later (Chapter 7) on the peculiarity of having a ground state ($L = 0$) spatial wave function that is antisymmetric. According to Eqs. (3-4), (3-8), and (3-9) the $s = 3/2$ decuplet can belong only to the SU(6) multiplet [56].

It is easy to construct the wave functions $\phi(A)$ for the decuplet, noting that the spin wave functions are

$$
\begin{aligned}
&|\uparrow\uparrow\uparrow\rangle && s_z = \tfrac{3}{2} \\
&\frac{1}{\sqrt{3}}\,[|\uparrow\uparrow\downarrow\rangle + |\uparrow\downarrow\uparrow\rangle + |\downarrow\uparrow\uparrow\rangle] && s_z = \tfrac{1}{2} \\
&\frac{1}{\sqrt{3}}\,[|\uparrow\downarrow\downarrow\rangle + |\downarrow\downarrow\uparrow\rangle + |\downarrow\uparrow\downarrow\rangle] && s_z = -\tfrac{1}{2} \\
&|\downarrow\downarrow\downarrow\rangle && s_z = -\tfrac{3}{2}
\end{aligned}
\tag{6-1}
$$

Table 4. Low-lying baryon states[a]

particle	Quark content	Mass (MeV)	SU(3) multiplet	J^P	I	S
Δ^{++}	ppp	1236	{10}	$\frac{3}{2}^+$	$\frac{3}{2}$	0
Δ^+	ppn	1236	{10}	$\frac{3}{2}^+$	$\frac{3}{2}$	0
P		938.3	{8}	$\frac{1}{2}^+$	$\frac{1}{2}$	
Δ^0	pnn	1236	{10}	$\frac{3}{2}^+$	$\frac{3}{2}$	0
N		939.6	{8}	$\frac{1}{2}^+$	$\frac{1}{2}$	
Δ^-	nnn	1236	{10}	$\frac{3}{2}^+$	$\frac{3}{2}$	0
Y^{*+}	$pp\lambda$	1382	{10}	$\frac{3}{2}^+$	1	−1
Σ^+		1189.5	{8}	$\frac{1}{2}^+$		
Y^{*0}	$pn\lambda$	1382	{10}	$\frac{3}{2}^+$	1	−1
Σ^0		1192.6	{8}	$\frac{1}{2}^+$	1	
Λ		1115.6	{8}	$\frac{1}{2}^+$	0	
Y^{*-}	$nn\lambda$	1382	{10}	$\frac{3}{2}^+$	1	−1
Σ^-		1197.4	{8}	$\frac{1}{2}^+$		
Ξ^{*0}	$p\lambda\lambda$	1529	{10}	$\frac{3}{2}^+$	$\frac{1}{2}$	−2
Ξ^0		1314.7	{8}	$\frac{1}{2}^+$		
Ξ^{*-}	$n\lambda\lambda$	1529	{10}	$\frac{3}{2}^+$	$\frac{1}{2}$	−2
Ξ^-		1321.2	{8}	$\frac{1}{2}^+$		
Ω^-	$\lambda\lambda\lambda$	1674	{10}	$\frac{3}{2}^+$	0	−3

[a] For the decuplet particles we have given for each isospin multiplet the mass value for the particle with highest I_z. Antibaryon states are obtained by replacing each quark by its antiquark.

For example, using Table 4,

$$\phi(\Delta^+, s_z = \tfrac{3}{2}) = \frac{1}{\sqrt{3}}\,[|p\uparrow p\uparrow n\uparrow\rangle + |p\uparrow n\uparrow p\uparrow\rangle + |n\uparrow p\uparrow p\uparrow\rangle]$$

$$\begin{aligned}\phi(\Delta^+, s_z = \tfrac{1}{2}) = \tfrac{1}{3}[&|p\uparrow p\uparrow n\downarrow\rangle + |p\uparrow n\downarrow p\uparrow\rangle + |n\downarrow p\uparrow p\uparrow\rangle \\ &+ |p\uparrow p\downarrow n\uparrow\rangle + |p\downarrow p\uparrow n\uparrow\rangle + |p\uparrow n\uparrow p\downarrow\rangle \\ &+ |p\downarrow n\uparrow p\uparrow\rangle + |n\uparrow p\downarrow p\uparrow\rangle + |n\uparrow p\uparrow p\downarrow\rangle]\end{aligned} \tag{6-2}$$

6-2. OCTET STATES

The octet of $J^P = \frac{1}{2}^+$ baryons consists of $L = 0$ three-quark states in which the total quark spin is ½. The quark content of the baryons is listed in Table 4. Their wave functions are given by Eq. (5-6). It is natural to assume that this octet completes the above-mentioned SU(6) multiplet [56] containing the $\frac{3}{2}^+$ decuplet states. This assumption seems to be experimentally correct and is supported in particular by the strikingly successful prediction of the ratio of the proton and neutron magnetic moments ensuing from this classification (see Chapter 11). The fact that the $3q$ states in $[56, L = 0]$ are apparently much lower in mass than those in $[20, L = 0]$ and $[70, L = 0]$, there being at present no experimental evidence for the latter two, has to be explained in the quark model as a special feature of the binding forces between the quarks (Chapter 7).

With the above assumption the space wave functions of octet and decuplet would be identical if SU(6) were a perfect symmetry. In the actual situation in which SU(6) is only an approximate symmetry, this need not be the case. We assume, however, that these wave functions have at least the permutation symmetry properties dictated by SU(6), which means that we assume that, not unlike the decuplet particles, the baryons have antisymmetric space wave functions. Moreover, in many applications we further assume that the latter approximately satisfy the condition $F_i^{AA'}(0) = 1$ [see Eqs. (5-11) and (5-12)].

To obtain the spin-unitary spin wave functions ϕ for the baryons, we may proceed as follows. Let us take as an example the proton with spin up ($s_z = \frac{1}{2}$) and remember that ϕ has to be wholly symmetric; its spin and unitary spin wave functions separately have mixed symmetry. How can we combine three spins ½ into total spin ½? One way to do this is to put two quarks in a spin singlet state and add a third quark with spin up. The spin singlet state is given by

$$\frac{1}{\sqrt{2}}(\uparrow\downarrow - \downarrow\uparrow)$$

To obtain a fully symmetric combination, the two quarks have to be in an antisymmetric unitary state. The only possibility in the case of the proton is the combination

$$\frac{1}{\sqrt{2}}(pn - np)$$

Adding the third quark (the p quark) with spin up, we obtain

$$\tfrac{1}{2}(p\uparrow n\downarrow - p\downarrow n\uparrow - n\uparrow p\downarrow + n\downarrow p\uparrow)p\uparrow$$

The factor within parentheses is fully symmetric for the exchange of two states, but the whole expression is not. Symmetrizing and normalizing readily leads to

$$\phi(P, s_z = \tfrac{1}{2}) = \frac{1}{\sqrt{18}} [2|p{\uparrow}n{\downarrow}p{\uparrow}\rangle + 2|p{\uparrow}p{\uparrow}n{\downarrow}\rangle + 2|n{\downarrow}p{\uparrow}p{\uparrow}\rangle$$
$$-|p{\uparrow}p{\downarrow}n{\uparrow}\rangle - |p{\uparrow}n{\uparrow}p{\downarrow}\rangle - |p{\downarrow}n{\uparrow}p{\uparrow}\rangle - |n{\uparrow}p{\downarrow}p{\uparrow}\rangle$$
$$- |n{\uparrow}p{\uparrow}p{\downarrow}\rangle - |p{\downarrow}p{\uparrow}n{\uparrow}\rangle] \tag{6-3}$$

Of course, we could have started in a different way, namely by putting two quarks in a spin triplet state and combining this with the spin of the third quark. The final result is the same.

For the neutron, we similarly find

$$\phi(N, s_z = \tfrac{1}{2}) = \frac{1}{\sqrt{18}} [-2|n{\uparrow}p{\downarrow}n{\uparrow}\rangle - 2|n{\uparrow}n{\uparrow}p{\downarrow}\rangle - 2|p{\downarrow}n{\uparrow}n{\uparrow}\rangle$$
$$+ |p{\uparrow}n{\downarrow}n{\uparrow}\rangle + |n{\uparrow}p{\uparrow}n{\downarrow}\rangle + |n{\downarrow}p{\uparrow}n{\uparrow}\rangle + |n{\uparrow}n{\downarrow}p{\uparrow}\rangle$$
$$+ |p{\uparrow}n{\uparrow}n{\downarrow}\rangle + |n{\downarrow}n{\uparrow}p{\uparrow}\rangle] \tag{6-4}$$

Other examples written out in full can be found in a paper by Thirring.[29]

For later purposes we give the permutation symmetry properties of three-quark wave functions[6] in Table 5, assuming that the quarks satisfy Fermi statistics [$\Psi(A)$ is antisymmetric].

Table 5. Symmetry Properties of Three-Quark Wave Functions[a]

Total quark spin	Multiplet	Unitary spin wave function	Spin wave function	Space wave function
	{10}	*s*	*s*	*a*
$\frac{3}{2}$	{8}	*m*	*s*	*m*
	{1}	*a*	*s*	*s*
	{10}	*s*	*m*	*m*
$\frac{1}{2}$	{8}	*m*	*m*	*s*, *m*, or *a*
	{1}	*a*	*m*	*m*

[a] *s, m, a,* stand for symmetric, mixed, and antisymmetric respectively.

Chapter 7

Dynamical Questions

7-1. FORCES BETWEEN QUARKS

The dynamical mechanisms underlying the observed quark bound states are completely obscure. Nor do we know the true nature of the forces that glue quarks together, nor the dynamical equations that govern the motion of quarks inside a hadron. With conventional ideas taken from nuclear physics, the quark bound states having the peculiar properties (such as additivity and nonrelativistic motion) demanded by the applications are hard to understand.

Let us suppose that the binding forces between quarks and/or antiquarks are of two-body type. Following Dalitz[6, 10] we assume, as a working basis, the following hierarchy of forces listed according to decreasing symmetry.

(1) Superstrong forces $V(q_i\, q_j)$ and $V(\bar{q}_i q_j)$ of unknown nature, providing the enormous binding energies needed to almost compensate the large quark masses. The mass spectrum of the low-lying hadronic states suggests that these forces are independent of the spin σ and unitary spin F of the quarks. If only this binding force is present all mesonic states of given orbital angular momentum L are degenerate in mass. The same is true for the baryonic states of given L and given permutation symmetry of the space wave function.

(2) Strong forces V' with σ and F dependence, but still SU(6) symmetric, causing splitting between SU(6) multiplets. Each SU(6) multiplet by itself remains degenerate.

(3) Central forces with σ or F dependence of the form (see the end of Chapter 2)

$$V_\sigma = A\boldsymbol{\sigma}_i \cdot \boldsymbol{\sigma}_j \qquad V_F = BF_i \cdot F_j \tag{7-1}$$

They are SU(3) symmetric but lift the degeneracy between the various SU(3) multiplets within an SU(6) multiplet.

(4) Spin-orbit forces of the form

$$V_{so} = C\mathbf{s} \cdot \mathbf{L} \tag{7-2}$$

consistent with SU(3).

(5) Other noncentral SU(3) conserving, SU(6) violating forces of tensor character.

(In general each of the above forces will depend on the interquark distances.)

(6) Medium-strong SU(3) breaking forces, causing mass differences between

the various isospin multiplets within an SU(3) multiplet. The simplest and probably dominating SU(3)-breaking mechanism is the one that can be represented by a mass difference between the λ quark and the p, n quarks (see the next chapter).

(7) Electromagnetic forces, generating mass splittings within an isospin multiplet.

On the basis of this list of forces we can try to analyze the various hadron multiplets, their relative positions, and the way they break down into lower multiplets, and see whether the force constants can be chosen in such a way that a consistent picture emerges. We look into this question in some detail in the next chapters, restricting ourselves here to pointing at some difficulties connected with a too simplistic interpretation of the quark model.

7-2. DIFFICULTIES WITH SIMPLE DYNAMICAL MODELS

An obviously puzzling question is the following one. Why are the forces between quarks seemingly such that only bound states of the type $\bar{q}q$ and qqq (and eventually $q\bar{q}q\bar{q}$, $qqq\bar{q}q$, . . .) occur, at least in the mass range below about 4 GeV? Why do we observe a $3q$ state, but not a $4q$ state, that is, why does attraction in an N-quark state saturate at $N = 3$? Would we not expect a $4q$ state to be even more strongly bound, and hence lighter in mass, than a $3q$ state? And, why does a system of six quarks form a deuteron and not a collapsed aggregate? There are no convincing answers to these kinds of questions. Morpurgo[30] has remarked that we should be careful in treating the saturation problem in the framework of the nonrelativistic quark model. Consider, for instance, a $4q$ configuration. We know that three of the quarks can form a bound state, say the proton. The fourth quark then "sees" an object much lighter in mass than the quark mass. Hence even if the quark motion within the $3q$ configuration is nonrelativistic, this need not be true for the relative motion of the latter and the fourth quark. It therefore would be inconsistent to deal nonrelativistically with the binding problem of four or more quarks. In this connection one should not forget that the compatibility of nonrelativistic motion and strong binding is not very well understood even in $3q$ configurations (compare Section 4-3). A detailed study of the different types of saturation that can occur in triplet models has been made by Greenberg and Zwanziger.[31]

Let us leave the saturation problem for what it is and restrict ourselves to the simplest configurations. As noted above, nothing is known about the nature of the dominant forces binding quarks inside baryons and quarks and antiquarks inside mesons. If we are naive and assume that these forces arise from the exchange of a single neutral vector meson that couples equally with each quark, we run into trouble, because we find attraction for $\bar{q}q$ but repulsion for qq. Exchange of all possible $L = 0$ vector and pseudoscalar mesons does not improve the situation, in the sense that central forces generated in this way produce attraction for $\bar{q}q$ in [35], attraction for qq in [20] and [70], but repulsion for qq in [56].[29] Hence, with central forces of this type, we cannot explain the experimental fact that the low-lying baryons are in [56, $L = 0$] rather than in [20, $L = 0$] or [70, $L = 0$]. A correct dynamical model should be able to explain why the latter two multiplets are apparently much higher in mass than [56, $L = 0$], or, in other words, why the forces in the qqq system do give rise to an $L = 0$ ground state with antisymmetric space wave function, assuming the quarks obey Fermi statistics. To be sure, it is possible to construct an $L = 0$ wave function that is totally antisymmetric, as shown by the following example given by Dalitz[6, 10]

$$f(\mathbf{r}_1, \mathbf{r}_2, \mathbf{r}_3) = (r_1^2 - r_2^2)(r_2^2 - r_3^2)(r_3^2 - r_1^2)\,\phi(\mathbf{r}_1, \mathbf{r}_2, \mathbf{r}_3) \tag{7-3}$$

in which ϕ is totally symmetric. This wave function corresponds to the quarks being in relative p and f states. Since it has nodal planes, however, the kinetic energy is high so that one does not expect it to represent the ground state at least if the system is bound by two-body nonexchange attractive forces. In fact, a general theorem[6, 31] states that the ground state wave function of a system interacting through such forces can have no nodes. This difficulty does not exist if the two-body qq potential has dominantly space-exchange character.[6] Such a potential is attractive if the internal orbital angular momentum is odd, and in that case it can give rise to an $L = 0$ ground state for the qqq system with antisymmetric space wave function (remember that L is the *total* orbital angular momentum). However, there seems to be no natural mechanism to generate such a potential. An alternative, by which one also escapes this dilemma, is to assume that in the $3q$ system three-body attractive forces are operative.[32] This has been proposed, for instance, by Kuo and Radicati,[32] who demonstrate that it is possible to account for a low-lying [56] by assuming the existence of strongly attractive three-body exchange forces and two-body repulsive forces between the quarks. The latter are necessary to shift [20] upwards with respect to [56]. How such forces could be generated in a natural way is again not clear. Note that in this model the formation of qq bound states is automatically excluded, but the apparent absence of low mass N-quark states with $N > 3$ remains unexplained.

We have mentioned that in the $L = 0$ wave function [Eq. (7-3)] the quarks are in relative p and f states. It is possible, however, to construct an antisymmetric wave function having $L = 1$ and positive parity with the quarks only in relative p states.[10, 29] We expect such states to lie lower in energy than the $L = 0$ states, in contradiction with experimental evidence. So again, why are the baryons in [56] with $L = 0$?

It should be remarked in connection with these and similar questions that the binding forces need not necessarily be central. One cannot exclude the possibility of having strong, noncentral qq forces, for example, tensor forces, present, a situation not unfamiliar in nuclear physics. However, such forces violate SU(6) symmetry. Consequently, if they, rather than the SU(6) invariant forces (1) and (2), were the dominant binding forces, SU(6) symmetry would not be of any deep significance and its successes for the low-mass hadronic states would be more or less accidental.[6] The situation would be similar to the one in nuclear physics in connection with the SU(4) symmetry in Wigner's supermultiplet theory for light nuclei. Even though the nucleon-nucleon potentials for singlet and triplet states violate this symmetry because of the presence of tensor forces, the low-lying levels of such nuclei approximately satisfy the predictions of SU(4), the reason being that the corresponding wave functions happen to have the property of being nearly identical in the relevant potential region.

Be that as it may, no convincing model for the quark bound states exist at present, and it seems most likely that quark forces cannot be simply modelled after those binding the nucleons inside nuclei.

Schiff[21] has made an attempt to understand the peculiar behavior of quarks inside hadrons in terms of a selection principle that would restrict the baryon number and charge for any cluster of mutually interacting quarks and/or antiquarks that lie within a certain interaction range R of each other to integer values. We expect $R \simeq 10^{-13}$ cm, but appreciably higher values are not excluded.[21] It is clear that such a selection principle would present a solution to the above-mentioned saturation problem and would also explain why quarks have not been seen as individual particles.

Schiff proposes two models for this selection principle. The first one is a phenomenological model in terms of many-particle forces between quarks. No arguments are offered as to how these forces are generated. The potential energy of a system of n quarks and m antiquarks is written as

$$V_{nm} = m_q \sum_{s=0}^{n} \sum_{t=0}^{m} a(s,t) \frac{n!}{(n-s)!\,s!} \frac{m!}{(m-t)!\,t!} \tag{7-4}$$

in which $a_{00} = 0$ and $a_{10} = a_{01} = 1$, and the remaining coefficients a_{st} are nonzero only if the corresponding particles are within interaction range of each other. The above selection rule is obtained by choosing a_{st} in such a way that the $3q$, $3\bar{q}$, and $q\bar{q}$ states have zero energy, that is, have a mass that is negligible compared to the supposedly large free quark mass m_q, whereas all other states have large positive energy. Assuming that only one-, two-, and three-body potentials are nonzero, the following conditions are imposed on the coefficients:

$$\begin{aligned} -2 < a(2,0) < -\tfrac{4}{3} \qquad & a(1,1) = -2 \\ a(3,0) = -3[1 + a(2,0)] \qquad & a(2,1) > 1 - a(2,0) \end{aligned} \tag{7-5}$$

that is, all two-body forces have to be attractive, all three-body forces repulsive. Compare this conclusion with the above remarks.

The second model is more exotic and is based on Dirac's idea that the quantization of electric charge derives from the existence of a point magnetic pole. Assuming that this pole has finite size, of the order of R, a modification of Dirac's approach leads to the result that the total charge of all particles within a distance R of each other is quantized, whereas the individual charges need not be. In other words, only bound quark clusters of integer baryon number are allowed. Note that no assumptions are made here with regard to the masses of the quarks or the forces between them. We can assume them to be such that, within each cluster, the quarks move almost freely and nonrelativistically.

7-3. CAN QUARKS OBEY FERMI STATISTICS?

A further difficulty connected with antisymmetric space wave functions has been pointed out by Mitra and Majumdar.[33] They remark that such functions give rise to zeros in the baryon form factors. This is easy to see.[34] Nonrelativistically this form factor, in the case of point quarks, is

$$F(q^2) = \int d^3 r \rho(r) e^{i\mathbf{q}\cdot\mathbf{r}} \tag{7-6}$$

in which $\rho(r)$, the normalized charge distribution, can, for a completely symmetric or antisymmetric $L = 0$ space wave function $f(\mathbf{r}_1, \mathbf{r}_2, \mathbf{r}_3)$, be written as

$$\rho(r) = \int d^3 r_2 |f(\mathbf{r}, \mathbf{r}_2, -(\mathbf{r} + \mathbf{r}_2)|^2 \tag{7-7}$$

In Eqs. (7-6) and (7-7) we chose the coordinates of the three quarks in the center-of-mass system in which $\mathbf{r}_1 + \mathbf{r}_2 + \mathbf{r}_3 = 0$. For $L = 0$ the functions ρ and F depend only on the magnitudes of $\mathbf{r}$ and $\mathbf{q}$. If f is antisymmetric, the charge density at the origin is zero because the integrand in Eq. (7-7) vanishes identically. Hence

$$\rho(0) \equiv \frac{1}{2\pi^2} \int_0^\infty dq\, q^2 F(q^2) = 0 \tag{7-8}$$

from which we conclude that $F(q^2)$ should have a zero. [This argument holds only if $\rho(r)$ is continuous at $r = 0$.[34]] The actual position of the zero is not determined by this argument.

Using an antisymmetric wave function of the Eq. (7-3) type with

$$\phi = \exp[-\beta^2(r_1^2 + r_2^2 + r_3^2)] \tag{7-9}$$

Mitra and Majumdar find the position of the zero at $q^2 \simeq 17.3\,\beta^2$. With the above wave function the rms radius r_q associated with the three-quark distribution is of the order of β^{-1}. Identifying this with the rms radius of 0.81 f of the proton charge distribution, the zero occurs at about $q^2 = 25\,f^{-2}$. Since the experimental data[35] do not show any sign of a zero up to $q^2 = 600\,f^{-2}$, the use of an antisymmetric wave function seems to be ruled out by this argument. However, we have to be careful. First, the wave function [Eq. (7-9)] may be too simple. In fact, as shown by Kreps and de Swart,[34] more complicated antisymmetric wave functions can be constructed yielding form factors with zeros at much higher values of q^2, near the end of the experimental region. But, at such high values of q^2, a nonrelativistic calculation of the form factor does not, of course, make much sense, and the whole argument is in the air. Second, one has to remember that the above conclusion was made on the assumption that quarks are point particles without structure and that the spatial distribution of electromagnetic properties of baryons comes about from the spatial extension of the $3q$ wave function. If quarks, however, have structure, that is, charge and magnetic moment distributions with a size of the order of the nucleons themselves (compare the discussion at the end of Section 5-2), r_q need no longer be identified with the rms radius of the proton charge distribution and in fact can be quite small, thereby pushing the zero to large q^2 values. For instance, taking $r_q \simeq \beta^{-1} = 0.1\,f$ will produce the zero at $q^2 \simeq 1700\,f^{-2}$, far outside the present experimental region.

Summing up we can say that the form-factor data so far do not necessarily exclude the possibility of an antisymmetric space wave function, but if a zero is never found in the nucleon form factors there may be a serious difficulty. In that case one has to abandon Fermi statistics for the quarks and assume parastatistics, as has been proposed by Greenberg,[36] or, what amounts to the same, the existence of three triplets of quarks distinguished by a new label α_i ($i = 1, 2, 3$), as in the Han–Nambu model (Chapter 4). The wave function for the lowest baryon states then takes the form

$$\Psi(A) = \epsilon_{\alpha_1\alpha_2\alpha_3}\, f(A, \{\mathbf{r}_i\})\, \phi(A) \tag{7-10}$$

in which $\epsilon_{\alpha_1\alpha_2\alpha_3}$ is the completely antisymmetric tensor with $\epsilon_{123} = 1$. It is clear that this allows f to be completely symmetric if ϕ is symmetric, as is the case for [56]. The question concerning the permutation symmetry of the baryon space wave function, although by itself an important one, is not very relevant for most practical applications in which this function appears in an expression of the form of Eq. (5-11), which is approximated by unity or treated as a free parameter anyway. Note that the new degree of freedom available in the three-triplet model gives rise to extra excitations, as a consequence of which it allows the construction of SU(3) multiplets of three-body states, such as $\{\overline{10}\}$, which cannot be obtained from three ordinary quarks. We return to the symmetric model in Section 9-5.

7-4. STUDIES OF THE QUARK–ANTIQUARK SYSTEM

To close this chapter on questions related to quark dynamics, we briefly mention a few attempts to study the strongly bound quark–antiquark system as a solution of a dynamical equation, as, for instance, the Bethe–Salpeter equation.[10, 37] Pagnamenta[37] uses the fully relativistic Bethe–Salpeter equation with a kernel corresponding to the exchange of a light scalar boson (mass μ) between q and $\bar{q}$ in the ladder approximation. The spins of the quarks are neglected. The question is whether it is possible to obtain bound states at integral values of the orbital angular momentum and whether it is possible to reproduce the associated Regge trajectories. There are two parameters in the problem, m_q and the coupling constant λ. Setting $\mu = 500$ MeV and $m_q = 20\,\mu$, λ is determined such that an S-wave bound state of meson mass is obtained. With this value of λ it is asked whether there exist excited states of higher orbital angular momentum. It is found that their masses are of the order of m_q or above, that is, the Regge trajectory comes out much too flat. Lowering m_q does not improve the situation; for a quark mass as low as 1 GeV and a ground state at 500 MeV one does not even find excited bound states. It seems that the observed linear trajectories require potentials of a shape much different from the Yukawa potential, namely, more flat and open in the region of the lower excitations. [Compare also Reference 10.]

Chapter 8

Mass Differences Within SU(3) Multiplets

8-1. MESONS

We continue the discussion of the low mass ($L = 0$) hadronic states by considering the mass differences within the corresponding SU(3) multiplets. We begin with the pseudoscalar and vector mesons.

With only the forces of types (1) and (2) present, in the notation of Chapter 7, the mesons belonging to the same SU(6) multiplet are degenerate in mass. The considerable differences observed between the central masses of the pseudoscalar octet and the vector octet must be due to the presence of SU(6)-breaking spin-dependent forces of types (3) and (5). As is well known, the masses of the isospin multiplets within each SU(3) multiplet also show differences due to SU(3)-breaking interactions. The simplest and most natural hypothesis we can make in the quark model is that these mass splittings are only due to a mass difference Δ between the λ quark and the p and n quarks, that is,

$$m_p = m_n = m \qquad m_\lambda = m + \Delta \tag{8-1}$$

and $m_q = m_{\bar{q}}$. Electromagnetic effects are neglected. In the nonrelativistic quark model one then writes for the mass m_A of particle A within SU(3) multiplet $\{\alpha\}$

$$m_A = \langle \Psi(A) | \sum_i m_{q_i} - U(\{\alpha\}) | \Psi(A) \rangle \tag{8-2}$$

in which the sum runs over the quarks composing hadron A and U denotes the $q\bar{q}$ potential, which, under the above hypothesis, does not depend on the quark labels and the label A. $U(\{\alpha\})$ may include all possible SU(3)-invariant contributions, as well as a supposedly small kinetic energy term. The function Ψ denotes the wave function as given by Eq. (5-6).

Let us apply this formula to the vector mesons V. Using Table 3 we find

$$\begin{aligned} m_\rho &= 2m - B(V,\{8\}) &&\equiv m_8 \\ m_{K^*} &= 2m + \Delta - B(V,\{8\}) &&\equiv m_8 + \Delta \\ m_{\omega_8} &= 2m + \tfrac{4}{3}\Delta - B(V,\{8\}) &&\equiv m_8 + \tfrac{4}{3}\Delta \\ m_{\phi_1} &= 2m + \tfrac{2}{3}\Delta - B(V,\{1\}) &&\equiv m_1 + \tfrac{2}{3}\Delta \\ \delta m_{\omega_8\phi_1} &= -\frac{2\sqrt{2}}{3}\,\Delta F \end{aligned} \tag{8-3}$$

with

$$B(V, \{\alpha\}) = \langle \Psi(V) | U(\{\alpha\}) | \Psi(V) \rangle \tag{8-4}$$

Here $F = F(0)$ is the overlap integral, defined by Eq. (5-11), between the ϕ_1 and ω_8 space wave functions; m_1 and m_8 are the unitary-pure singlet and octet masses.

The first two relations give

$$m_{K^*} - m_\rho = \Delta \tag{8-5}$$

which, using the mass values given in Table 3, leads to $\Delta = 113$ MeV. We see that ω_8 and ϕ_1 are not eigenstates of the energy; the SU(3)-breaking mechanism causes a transition between these states described by $\delta m_{\omega_8 \phi_1}$($\omega$–$\phi$mixing). To obtain the physical ω and ϕ we write them in the form of Eq. (5-4) and diagonalize the mass matrix

$$\begin{pmatrix} m_{\omega_8} & \delta m_{\omega_8 \phi_1} \\ \delta m_{\omega_8 \phi_1} & m_{\phi_1} \end{pmatrix} = \begin{pmatrix} m_8 + \frac{4}{3}\Delta & -\frac{2\sqrt{2}}{3}\Delta F \\ -\frac{2\sqrt{2}}{3}\Delta F & m_1 + \frac{2}{3}\Delta \end{pmatrix} \tag{8-6}$$

with the rotation matrix

$$R(\vartheta) = \begin{pmatrix} \cos\vartheta_V & \sin\vartheta_V \\ -\sin\vartheta_V & \cos\vartheta_V \end{pmatrix} \tag{8-7}$$

This leads to the following equations for the eigenvalues m_ϕ and m_ω and the mixing angle ϑ_V:

$$m_\omega + m_\phi = m_1 + m_8 + 2\Delta \tag{8-8}$$

$$m_\omega m_\phi = m_1 m_8 + \tfrac{2}{3}\Delta(2m_1 + m_8) + \tfrac{8}{9}\Delta^2(1 - F^2) \tag{8-9}$$

$$\tan 2\vartheta_V = \frac{(4\sqrt{2}/3)\, F\Delta}{m_8 - m_1 + (2/3)\,\Delta} \tag{8-10}$$

We see from these equations that the quark model predicts the mixing angle including the sign as opposed to the phenomenological analysis based on the Gell-Mann–Okubo mass formula in which only the absolute value can be obtained.[7]

Using the observed mass values given in Table 3, we have, from Eqs. (8-3) and (8-8),

$$m_1 = 799 \text{ MeV} \qquad m_8 = 777 \text{ MeV} \tag{8-11}$$

This near equality of m_1 and m_8 is precisely what we would expect if within the 35-plet the dominant SU(6)-breaking forces are the spin–spin forces V_σ [see Eq. (7-1)]. Indeed, in that case we have for the vector mesons $U(\{1\}) \simeq U(\{8\})$, and from Eqs. (8-3) and (8-4),

$$m_1 \simeq m_8 \tag{8-12}$$

We then also expect $F \simeq 1$. This checks with the above equations; however, the value for F that we obtain from Eq. (8-9) is very sensitive to the input values for the masses. The values of Table 3 give $F^2 > 1$, which is impossible; taking m_ρ = 769 MeV gives $F^2 = 1$. Therefore, within the experimental uncertainty in the value of m_ρ, the vector meson nonet is consistent with $F \simeq 1$. Inserting this value and relation (8-12) into formula (8-10) leads to $\vartheta_V = \arctan [(\frac{1}{2})\sqrt{2}] = 35°$, which is the value for which the $I = Y = 0$ eigenstates of the energy are given by Eq. (5-5) with masses $m_8 + 2\Delta$ and m_8. We have the mass relations

$$\begin{aligned} m_\rho &= m_\omega \\ m_\omega + m_\phi &= 2m_{K^*} \end{aligned} \tag{8-13}$$

which are satisfied to within a few percent. The small discrepancy indicates that relation (8-12) cannot be an exact equality due to the presence of other SU(6) violating forces. Also, the mixing angle is not precisely given by $\vartheta_V = \arctan [(\frac{1}{2})\sqrt{2}]$. From Eqs. (8-13) we get a second estimate for Δ,

$$\Delta = \tfrac{1}{2}(m_\phi - m_\omega) = 118 \text{ MeV} \tag{8-14}$$

very close to the above-mentioned value.

Going to the conventional use of the (mass)^2 operator for mesons instead of the linear mass operator results in

$$\begin{aligned} \delta &= m_{K^*}^2 - m_\rho^2 = 1.90 \times 10^5 \text{ (MeV)}^2 \\ \delta &= \tfrac{1}{2}(m_\phi^2 - m_\omega^2) = 2.14 \times 10^5 \text{ (MeV)}^2 \end{aligned} \tag{8-15}$$

For the vector mesons it makes little difference which operator we choose, but this is not so for the pseudoscalar mesons. From expressions analogous to Eqs. (8-3) we would find with linear masses

$$\Delta = m_K - m_\pi = 358 \text{ MeV} \tag{8-16}$$

in disagreement with the values obtained above for the vector mesons. However, using (mass)^2 gives

$$\delta = m_K^2 - m_\pi^2 = 2.27 \times 10^5 \text{ (MeV)}^2 \tag{8-17}$$

in accordance with Eqs. (8-15). The *a priori* reasons for preferring the use of $(\text{mass})^2$ here are not very clear.[6] The usual argument is that for bosons the mass always appears in the form $(\text{mass})^2$ in the energy operator, whereas for fermions it appears linearly.

For the pseudoscalar meson nonet, relation (8-12) is strongly violated and $\vartheta_P \neq \arctan[(\frac{1}{2})\sqrt{2}]$. This we can see by writing relations similar to Eqs. (8-8)–(8-10), but with $(\text{mass})^2$ instead of linear masses:

$$\begin{aligned} m_\eta^2 + m_{\eta'}^2 &= m_1^2 + m_8^2 + 2\delta \\ m_\eta^2 m_{\eta'}^2 &= m_1^2 m_8^2 + \tfrac{2}{3}\delta(2m_1^2 + m_8^2) + \tfrac{8}{9}\delta^2(1 - F^2) \\ \tan 2\vartheta_P &= \frac{(4\sqrt{2}/3)\,F\delta}{m_8^2 - m_1^2 + (2/3)\,\delta} \\ m_\pi^2 &= m_8^2 \end{aligned} \tag{8-18}$$

F is now the overlap integral $F(0)$ between the space wave functions of η_8 and η_1'. Inserting the observed masses for m_η, $m_{\eta'}$, and m_π and solving these equations we find

$$\begin{aligned} m_1 &= 863 \text{ MeV} \qquad & m_8 &= 135 \text{ MeV} \\ F &= 0.52 & \vartheta_P &= -11^\circ \end{aligned} \tag{8-19}$$

Compare these results with those for the vector mesons. The large difference between the values of m_8 for the two nonets points to the presence of strong SU(6)-breaking, spin-dependent forces, at least within the 35-plet. We may have roughly the picture shown in Figure 5. (See also Chapter 9.)

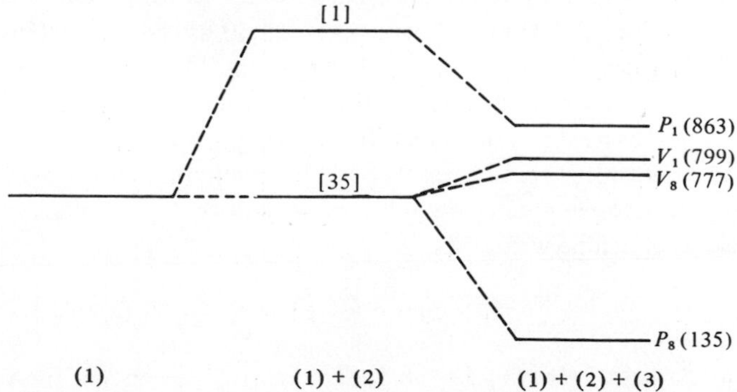

FIGURE 5. Mass splittings among the 36 mesonic states with L = 0 due to forces of types (1), (2), and (3). The figure is not according to scale.

In the above analysis we have identified the ninth pseudoscalar meson in the nonet with η'. Recently a tenth pseudoscalar meson has been discovered, namely the $E(1420)$, which probably has $I = 0$. Considering this meson instead of η' as the ninth member of the pseudoscalar nonet changes Eq. (8-19) into

$$\begin{aligned} m_1 &= 1360 \text{ MeV} \qquad & m_8 &= 135 \text{ MeV} \\ F &= 0.88 & \vartheta_P &= -6^\circ \end{aligned} \tag{8-20}$$

The actual situation may be more complicated in the sense that, in principle, mixing can occur between the three states η, η', and E.

8-2. BARYONS

We now turn to the baryons. In the case of the $\frac{3}{2}^+$ decuplet the simple SU(3)-breaking mechanism [Eq. (8-1)] immediately gives the equal spacing rule for the masses (see Table 4)

$$m_{\Omega^-} - m_{\Xi^*} = m_{\Xi^*} - m_{Y^*} = m_{Y^*} - m_\Delta = \Delta \tag{8-21}$$

From the empirical masses we find

$$\Delta = 147 \text{ MeV} \tag{8-22}$$

still in reasonable accordance with the value $\Delta \simeq 120$ MeV obtained from the vector meson masses.

For the baryon octet, the breaking mechanism [Eq. (8-1)] seems to be too simple. Formula (8-2) leads, in this case, to

$$\begin{aligned} m_\Lambda &= m_\Sigma = m_P + \Delta \\ m_\Xi &= m_P + 2\Delta \end{aligned} \tag{8-23}$$

The first relation does not reflect the actual situation in which $m_\Sigma - m_\Lambda = 77$ MeV. Moreover, Eqs. (8-23) predict values for Δ that are not consistent with the ones obtained earlier: $\Delta = m_\Lambda - m_P = 177$ MeV and $\Delta = (\frac{1}{2})(m_\Xi - m_P) = 189$ MeV. These discrepancies must be attributed to symmetry-breaking effects in the quark potentials, as has been discussed, for instance, by Zweig[2] and Federman *et al.*[38] The latter authors extend formula (8-2) by assuming that the symmetry-breaking forces between quarks are only of one- and two-body types so that the mass of baryon A can be written as

$$m_A = \langle \Psi(A) | \sum_i m_{q_i} - U(\{\alpha\}) + \sum_{i \neq j} D_{ij} | \Psi(A) \rangle \tag{8-24}$$

with the quark masses given by Eq. (8-1). The matrix elements of the two-body symmetry-breaking interactions D_{ij} depend, in general, on the spin and isospin of the two-quark system i-j, but are otherwise assumed to be the same for all $L = 0$

baryons. The number of these matrix elements is further restricted because the spin-unitary spin wave function of the $L = 0$ baryons is fully symmetric. This requires two isospin ½ quarks to be either in an isospin-triplet, spin-triplet or in an isospin-singlet, spin-singlet state, while two λ quarks are always in a spin-triplet state. Ansatz (8-24) leads to the following mass relations:

$$\begin{aligned} m_{\Omega^-} - m_{\Delta} &= 3(m_{\Xi^*} - m_{Y^*}) \\ m_{\Xi} - m_{\Sigma} &= m_{\Xi^*} - m_{Y^*} \\ m_{\Sigma} - m_{\Lambda} + \tfrac{2}{3}(m_N - m_{\Xi}) &= \tfrac{2}{3}(m_{\Delta} - m_{\Xi^*}) \end{aligned} \tag{8-25}$$

which are in excellent agreement with the experimental masses compiled in Table 4.

We can do the same for the mesons[39]; in this case, however, there are no relations without additional dynamical assumptions about the matrix elements of D_{ij}. If we assume that

$$\begin{aligned} \langle qq'|D_{ij}|qq'\rangle &= a \qquad \text{for any } qq' \text{ pair in an } s = 1 \text{ state} \\ \langle \bar{q}q'|D_{ij}|\bar{q}q'\rangle &= a' \qquad \text{for any } \bar{q}q' \text{ pair in an } s = 1 \text{ state} \end{aligned} \tag{8-26}$$

that is, the symmetry is only broken by the scalar ($s = 0$) part of the interaction, we obtain (among other things) the remarkable and successful relation involving mesons and baryon resonances with linear masses

$$m_{\phi} - m_{K^*} = m_{\Delta} - m_{Y^*}$$

which cannot be obtained from any symmetry. The first of conditions (8-26), when applied to baryons, is a sufficient, but not necessary, condition to obtain from Eq. (8-24) the equal-spacing rule for the decuplet and the Gell-Mann–Okubo mass formula[7] for the octet

$$\tfrac{1}{2}(m_N + m_{\Xi}) = \tfrac{1}{4}(m_{\Sigma} + 3m_{\Lambda}).$$

Finally we note that electromagnetic mass differences have been treated in the quark model along similar lines.[28, 40] For instance, the assumption that the electromagnetic mass shift of a hadron equals the sum of the electromagnetic mass shifts of the constituting quarks and the expectation values of the added electromagnetic two-body forces between the quarks leads to the famous, successful Coleman–Glashow relation[7]

$$m_P - m_N = m_{\Sigma^+} - m_{\Sigma^-} + m_{\Xi^-} - m_{\Xi^0}$$

without any assumption about strong interaction symmetries or about the transformation properties of the photon.

Chapter 9

L-Excited States

9-1. MESON RESONANCES

In the last three or four years an amazing number of mesonic and baryonic resonances has been established in the mass region from 1 to about 3 GeV. This number is still steadily rising and, witness the skill of the experimentalists, will undoubtedly continue to do so for quite a while. It is logical within the framework of the quark model to try to interpret these higher resonant states as rotational and possibly vibrational excitations of the $q\bar{q}$ and qqq systems, a simple guess that has proved to be surprisingly successful in providing a classification scheme for the observed states. This spectroscopic aspect of the quark model has been vigorously investigated by Dalitz,[6,10] and almost all we have to say here is based upon his work. This chapter should not be considered as an up-to-date analysis including all confirmed or unconfirmed resonances, but only as an illustration of the main points of the model. Because of the unstable experimental situation many detailed statements of the model are probably not guaranteed against the passage of time.

We start with the mesons. The higher L states in the $q\bar{q}$ model consist, for each L, of four nonets of parity $(-1)^{L+1}$, namely three for $s = 1$ having $C = (-1)^{L+1}$ and $J = L + 1, L, L - 1$, and one for $s = 0$ having $C = (-1)^L$ and $J = L$, in which J is the total angular momentum. For $L = 0$ there are, of course, only two nonets. Using the symbol ${}^{2s+1}L_J$ we denote these nonets by ${}^3L_{L+1}$, ${}^3L_L$, ${}^3L_{L-1}$, and ${}^1L_L$, respectively. Each of them consists of an SU(3) singlet and octet. With only the forces of type (1) (Chapter 7) present, the $36(2L + 1)$ states contained in the four nonets are degenerate in mass. For the mesons the forces of type (2) can be written in the form

$$V'(q_1\bar{q}_2) = D[(\tfrac{1}{4} - \boldsymbol{\sigma}_1 \cdot \boldsymbol{\sigma}_2)(1 - F_1 \cdot F_2)] \tag{9-1}$$

in which the function D may depend on the distance r between the quarks. Noting that $\boldsymbol{\sigma}_1 . \boldsymbol{\sigma}_2 = ¼$ for $s = 1$ and $-¾$ for $s = 0$, and using Eq. (2-18), we see that the second factor in Eq. (9-1) is nine for the SU(6) singlet and zero for the 35-plet. If only the forces V, V', V_σ, V_F, and V_{so} (see Chapter 7) are present, we have the following mass formula for the central masses of the various SU(3) multiplets:

$$\begin{aligned} m^2 = m_0^2 &+ d[\{\tfrac{1}{2} - s(s+1) + \sigma_1(\sigma_1+1) + \sigma_2(\sigma_2+1)\}\{2 - F^2 + F_1^2 + F_2^2\}] \\ &+ a[s(s+1) - \sigma_1(\sigma_1+1) - \sigma_2(\sigma_2+1)] \\ &+ b(F^2 - F_1^2 - F_2^2) + c[J(J+1) - L(L+1) - s(s+1)] \end{aligned} \tag{9-2}$$

with F^2, F_1^2, and F_2^2 given in Table 2. The parameters *a, b, c,* and *d* are determined by the functions *A, B, C,* and *D,* respectively. In Figure 6 we have shown a possible breaking pattern according to this formula. It corresponds to *a, c,* and *d* positive, and *b* negative.

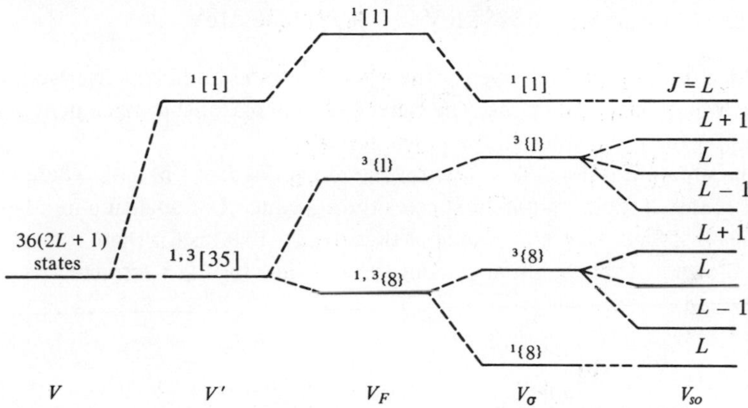

FIGURE 6. Possible pattern for mass splittings among the $q\bar{q}$ states for general L, corresponding to a, c, d > 0, and b < 0. $[\alpha]$ = SU(6) multiplet, $\{\alpha\}$ = SU(3) multiplet. The superscript is the value of 2s + 1. SU(3) breaking is not shown. The forces indicated are supposed to cause the splitting in the corresponding column.

For the $L = 0$ mesons the observed pattern is consistent with the above scheme (compare Figure 6 with Figure 5). Here $^1[1]$, $^3\{1\}$, and $^3\{8\}$ are close together in mass, whereas $^1\{8\}$ is pushed down considerably. The mass values given in Figure 5 require *b* negative and small, *a* positive and $\gg |b|$, $18d - 2a$ positive and small. In other words, the observed mass values suggest an empirical *S*-wave $q\bar{q}$ force $U(q\bar{q})$ that, to good approximation, can be written in the form

$$U(q_1\bar{q}_2) = V_0 + \delta V_{P8}(\tfrac{1}{4} - \boldsymbol{\sigma}_1 \cdot \boldsymbol{\sigma}_2)(8 + F_1 \cdot F_2)$$

The second term on the right of this formula is nonzero only for the pseudoscalar octet; the first term can be interpreted in our scheme as being composed of forces of type (1) to (3) adding up in such a way that V_0 is almost σ- and *F*-independent.

Of the $L = 1$ states, at present only the nonet $^3P_2$ with $JPC = 2{+}{+}$ is fairly well established. It is generally believed to accommodate the resonances $A_2(1315)$, $K^*(1410)$, $f(1250)$, and $f'(1500)$, but, especially with respect to the A_2, there is some uncertainty about the assignment $JP = 2+$.[41] Also, the remarkable splitting of this particle observed in the CERN missing-mass spectrometer experiment[42] adds to the confusion. With the above mass values we find, by the methods of Chapter 8, assuming the symmetry-breaking mechanism [Eq. (8-1)] and using $(\text{mass})^2$,

$$\begin{aligned} \delta &= 3 \times 10^5\,(\text{MeV})^2 \qquad \vartheta \simeq 28^\circ \qquad F \simeq 1 \\ m_8 &= 1315\,\text{MeV} \qquad m_1 = 1230\,\text{MeV} \end{aligned} \tag{9-3}$$

in which ϑ is the mixing angle for the $I = Y = 0$ states and F the overlap integral of their space wave functions. The value of δ is in reasonable agreement with those found for the $L = 0$ states in the previous chapter.

The situation is much less clear for the remaining $L = 1$ nonets. There are candidates for all of them, but in most cases the assignment of quantum numbers is by no means settled. Dalitz[10] speculates that the $I = 1$ states for these nonets are the ones shown in Table 6, but at present the evidence for the δ resonance is rather flimsy.

Table 6. $I = 1$ states of the $L = 1$ nonets.

	${}^3P_0$	${}^3P_1$	${}^1P_1$	${}^3P_2$
JPC	$0++$	$1++$	$1+-$	$2++$
$I = 1$ states	$\delta(962)$	$A_1(1080)$	$B(1200)$	$A_2(1315)$
$\langle \mathbf{L}\cdot\mathbf{s} \rangle$	-2	-1	0	1

We see that these four $I = 1$ states form a sequence with approximately equal spacing in mass. Using $(\text{mass})^2$ gives

$$m_{A_2}^2 - m_B^2 : m_B^2 - m_{A_1}^2 : m_{A_1}^2 - m_\delta^2 = 1:1.1:1$$

A possible explanation for this is to assume that, at least in the octets, the splitting is dominated by the spin-orbit force with the coefficient c in Eq. (9-2) positive. As shown by the last line in Table 6, such a force gives rise to an equal spacing rule for the $L = 1$ masses with the highest mass value being that for the state with highest J. If this interpretation is correct, then octet spin–spin forces, causing a further splitting between the ${}^1P$ and ${}^3P$ states, have to be rather weak, that is, $|a| \ll c$. The same should be true for possible tensor forces [type (5)].[10] However, we know that the former forces are very strong in the $L = 0$ case in which they account for the ${}^1\{8\} - {}^3\{8\}$ mass difference. Dalitz[10] remarks that such a situation is possible if the range of the spin–spin force is small compared to that of the main force V. Furthermore, we conclude from result (9-3), which states that for $L = 1$ the masses of the $J = L + 1$ states are approximately the same in octet and singlet, that also $|b| \ll c$. In sum, there are indications that in the P-wave $q\bar{q}$ interactions forces of type (3) and (5) cannot play an important role.

Possible candidates for the $I = ½$, $Y = \pm 1$ states in the ${}^3P_1$ and ${}^1P_1$ nonets are the $K^*(1250)$ and $K^*(1360)$[43] [see also remark (3) in Section 9-2]. Not enough information about the isoscalar members of the nonets ${}^3P_0$, ${}^3P_1$, and ${}^1P_1$ is available to calculate the singlet masses m_1 and the mixing angles.

Table 7. $I = 1$, $Y = 0$ mesonic states.

Name	Mass (MeV)	L
π	135	0
ρ	774	
δ	962	1
A_1	1080	
B	1200	
A_2	1315	
R_1	1630	2
R_2	1700	
R_3	1750	
R_4	1830	
S	1930	3
T	2195	4
U	2380	5

A number of $I = 1$, $Y = 0$ mesonic resonances has been found recently in the CERN missing-mass spectrometer experiment.[44] We have presented them in Table 7 together with the $I = 1$ S- and P-states discussed before. Evidence for some of these states has also been reported from other experiments; however, at the moment the situation is too confusing to try to tie various observations together and make meaningful statements about spin and parity assignments. It is natural to interpret these levels as rotational excitations of the $q\bar{q}$ system with the L values as given in the table. Following Goldhaber[45] we may call the group of states corresponding to a given L an "L cluster." From Table 7 we see that the observed L clusters are clearly separated from each other. Of the higher L clusters, only the R cluster presently appears to be separated into four levels corresponding to the four nonets associated with a given L; however, the R_4 is not statistically convincing. If we identify R_1, R_2, R_3, and R_4 with, respectively, the $I = 1$ states of the nonets ${}^3D_1$, ${}^3D_2$, ${}^1D_2$, and ${}^3D_3$ having the quantum numbers $JPC = 1--$, $2--$, $2-+$, and $3--$,* and assume that, just as for the $L = 1$ nonets, the splitting between them is mainly due to the spin-orbit force, we expect, on the basis of Eq. (9-2) for the relative (mass)^2 separations,

$$m_{R_4}^2 - m_{R_3}^2 : m_{R_3}^2 - m_{R_2}^2 : m_{R_2}^2 - m_{R_1}^2 = 2:1:2 \tag{9-4}$$

Experimentally the differences on the left are in the ratio $1.7 \pm 0.3 : 1 : 2.2 \pm 0.3$,[44] in good agreement with formula (9-4). The magnitude of the spin-orbit splitting, that is, of the parameter c, seems to decrease with increasing L. The (mass)^2 difference between the $I = 1$ states for $J = L \pm 1$ are for $L = 1,2$, and 3 : 7.6×10^5 (MeV)^2, 6.9×10^5 (MeV)^2, and $\lesssim 2 \times 10^5$ (MeV)^2, respectively, in which the last value is obtained from the upper limit of the width of the S system (see below). The corresponding values of c are 13×10^4 (MeV)^2, 7×10^4 (MeV)^2, and $\lesssim 1.4 \times 10^4$ (MeV)^2. This is what we expect if the spin-orbit force has a range that is small compared to that of V.[10] If that is the case, corresponding splittings within the higher L clusters become even smaller. The resolution of present experiments has not been high enough to separate the $I = 1$ states within these systems.

The R, S, T, and U resonances established in the missing mass experiment are characterized by surprisingly small widths; an upper limit for the width is 38 MeV.[44] This seems to be consistent with the above interpretation of these states in terms of the $\bar{q}q$ model. The high values of the angular momentum cause strong centrifugal barriers which may suppress their decays.[10, 46] This is expected to work most effectively for the ${}^3L_{L+1}$ nonet in an L cluster that, in nearly all cases, must decay via higher angular momentum states than the other three nonets. We refer to Goldhaber[45] for a detailed discussion of the decay schemes of the L clusters.

9-2. REMARKS

Before turning to the baryons, we have a few remarks.

(1) Another way of classifying the hadronic states, which is much in fashion nowadays, is with Regge trajectories, in which, for a set of particles with the same internal quantum numbers, we plot J versus (mass)^2. It turns out that, for instance, the mesonic states of Table 6 fall on approximately linear trajectories.[46]

* If it appears that the $\pi\pi$ enhancement at 1650 MeV (the g meson) is associated with R_1 and has $J^P = 3^-$ [which appears to be slightly favored above 1^- although confirmation is lacking; see D. J. Crennell *et al.*, Phys. Rev. Letters **18**, 323 (1967)], this identification cannot be correct. See also T. F. Johnston *et al.*, *Phys. Rev. Letters* **20**, 1414 (1968).

Trajectories corresponding to even and odd J, and hence to even and odd parity, seem to coincide (exchange degeneracy), which is what we expect in the $\bar{q}q$ model, because exchange forces that would correspond to qq exchange, are not expected to play a significant role. In the quark model such Regge trajectories can be interpreted as representing sequences of rotational levels. Dalitz[10] points out that, noting that the energy of a $\bar{q}q$ bound state can be as high as $2m_q$, the $\bar{q}q$ model suggests that the trajectories should move up to very large J values, of the order of $4m_q^2/\alpha' \simeq 10^2$, in which α', the slope of the trajectory at $m^2 = 0$, is of the order of 1 GeV^{-2}. (See the end of this Chapter.)

(2) So far we have only talked about rotational excitations of the $\bar{q}q$ system; however, we should also consider the possibility of internal radial oscillations. We then obtain for each L additional sets of nonets in excited vibrational states. A possible candidate for such a nonet is the $E(1420)$ meson, which most probably has $JPC = 0 - +$ and hence represents a tenth pseudoscalar meson. Since there is no room for this meson in the ordinary pseudoscalar nonet, the only possibility is to assign it to an excited ${}^1S_0$ state (see also the end of Section 8-1).

(3) Mixing can, in principle, occur between nonets ${}^3(J-1)_J$ and ${}^3(J+1)_J$, and between nonets ${}^1L_L$ and ${}^3L_L$. In the former case, the mixing effects are presumably small because of the large mass difference between the two nonets. In the second case, they may be appreciable and be caused, for instance, by spin-orbit forces. Here only the $I = ½$, $Y = \pm 1$ states of the two nonets can mix, charge parity and G-parity conservation forbidding the mixing among the isoscalar and isovector states. In particular, for the $L = 1$ mesons, we expect mixing between the K^* resonances belonging to the nonets ${}^3P_1$ and ${}^1P_1$. The two physical particles each may be a mixture of the ${}^3P_1$ and ${}^1P_1$ states. It has been suggested recently by Goldhaber[47] that this mixing phenomenon might be, in fact, what we observe in the variation in structure in the $K\pi\pi$ mass enhancement between 1100 and 1400 MeV as a function of the incident laboratory momentum.

9-3. NEGATIVE PARITY BARYON RESONANCES

In the case of the baryonic resonances the situation is, we discover, more complicated than in that of the mesons. We mention only a few important points, referring to Dalitz[6,10] for details. In this section we discuss the negative parity resonances, many of which are known in the mass region 1400–2300 MeV. They can all be accommodated into SU(3) singlets, octets, and decuplets; higher multiplets are not necessary, but are of course not ruled out. For the lowest mass states (the 1400–1800 MeV region apart from SU(3) breaking) we need a $J^P = \frac{1}{2}^-$ and $\frac{3}{2}^-$ singlet, two $\frac{3}{2}^-$ octets, two $\frac{1}{2}^-$ octets, a $\frac{1}{2}^-$ and $\frac{3}{2}^-$ decuplet, and a $\frac{5}{2}^-$ octet. It is natural to assume these states to be the $L = 1$ excited states of the qqq system. With $L = 1$ the $\frac{5}{2}^-$ octet requires $s = \frac{3}{2}$, which, according to Table 5, corresponds to a spin-unitary spin wave function of mixed permutation symmetry. From the results of Chapter 3 it follows that only SU(6) multiplet [70] is possible, the [56] and the [20] having symmetric and antisymmetric spin-unitary spin wave functions, respectively. By inspection of Table 5 we see that, apart from the $^4\{8\}$, the SU(3) multiplets $^2\{10\}$, $^2\{8\}$, and $^2\{1\}$ can have mixed spin-unitary spin wave functions. For a given value of L_z these four sets comprise 70 states that, when only the forces of type (1) and (2) are present, are degenerate in mass and constitute multiplet [70] of SU(6) [compare also Eq. (3-8b)]. With Fermi statistics for the quarks the corresponding space wave function also has mixed permutation symmetry. The forces V_σ, V_F, V_{so}, and eventually other noncentral forces V_{nc} split the 210 states corresponding to L = 1 into nine SU(3) multiplets, which are just the ones mentioned above. (Figure 7.) This is a nice result. As far as the classification is concerned, the *qqq* model with L excitation appears to work for the lowest negative parity resonances in the sense that it generates the above-mentioned multiplet structure in a natural way.

What about the relative locations of these multiplets? A possible breaking pattern showing for each multiplet the most prominent candidates available today is displayed in Figure 7. Henceforth we adopt the following symbols for the baryon resonances (S = strangeness): N (mass), for the $I = \frac{1}{2}, S = 0$ resonances; Δ (mass), for the $I = \frac{3}{2}, S = 0$ resonances; Λ (mass), for the $I = 0, S = -1$ resonances; Σ (mass), for the $I = 1, S = -1$ resonances; Ξ (mass), for the $I = \frac{1}{2}, S = -2$ resonances. The $S = -1$ resonances are often denoted by Y_1^*(mass) in the literature (see Table 4), the $S = 0$ resonances by N_1^* (mass). The $S = 0$ states in Figure 7 are obtained from pion-nucleon phase shift analyses and are taken from the recent paper by Donnachie *et al.*[48] (see also Reference 10b). Not all of these

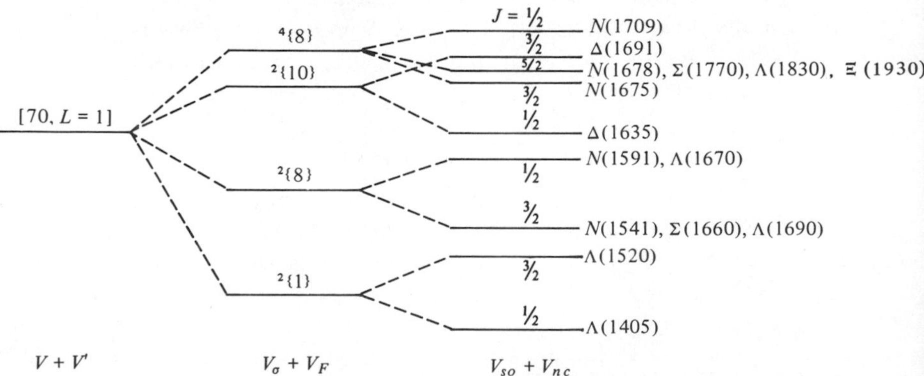

FIGURE 7. Possible breaking pattern for the L = 1, negative parity 3q states. SU(3) splitting is not shown. The forces indicated are supposed to cause the splitting in the corresponding column. The figure is not according to scale.

pion–nucleon resonances are firmly established, and the indicated mass values are often afflicted with considerable uncertainties. With respect to the strange baryon resonances the situation is more obscure. Although for some of the multiplets strange candidates are available, such as the ones shown in Figure 7, many $S = -1, -2, -3$ states have still to be found before all multiplets are complete.

If only V_σ, V_F, and V_{so} account for the symmetry breaking, we are led to the following formula for the central masses of the nine multiplets

$$m = m_0' + a' s(s+1) + b' F^2 + c'[J(J+1) - L(L+1) - s(s+1)] \qquad (9\text{-}5)$$

with a', b', and c' determined by A, B, and C, respectively. Since the $\Lambda(1405)$ is the lowest-lying negative parity baryon resonance known today, the coefficient b' has to be chosen positive in order to shift the octet and decuplet states upwards with respect to the singlet. This puts $^2\{1\}$, $^2\{8\}$, and $^2\{10\}$ in the order indicated in the figure, and, because $N(1678)$ is the lowest $J^P = \frac{5}{2}^-$ resonance known at present, a' has to be large and positive. This leads to the assignments given in the figure. These are further supported by estimates of the level widths and by certain selection rules for photoexcitation[10b] [compare Section 12-2], and are also compatible with the SU(3) breaking mechanism [Eq. (8-1)] in the sense that the parameter Δ emerges as positive and has the correct order of magnitude (see Section 9-4).

Note that the F^2 term in Eq. (9-5) predicts an equal spacing rule for the average masses $m(^2\{1\})$, $m(^2\{8\})$, and $m(^2\{10\})$ in the second column of Figure 7 (see Table 2). The experimental mass values given in this figure are not incompatible with this rule.

It is clear from Figure 7 that, if the assignments made there are correct, the simple spin-orbit term in Eq. (9-5) cannot account for the observed mass splittings between the multiplets in each $^{2s+1}\{\alpha\}$ set. The singlet states $\Lambda(1520)$ with $J^P = \frac{3}{2}^-$ and $\Lambda(1405)$ with $J^P = \frac{1}{2}^-$ require the coefficient c' to be positive. This works for $^2\{10\}$ but not for $^2\{8\}$, which needs a negative c'. For $^4\{8\}$ the situation is even more complicated. This points to a complicated F dependence for the coefficient c' and/or to the presence of other noncentral forces, and perhaps also to three-body forces. We also have to bear in mind that there may be substantial distortions of the pattern due to mixing effects caused by spin-orbit forces and SU(3)-breaking interactions. The former couple $^4\{8\}$ and $^2\{8\}$ states with the same values of J, I, I_z, and S; the latter mix, for instance, the $^2\{1\}$ and $^2\{8\}\,\Lambda$ states, both for $J = \frac{1}{2}$ and $J = \frac{3}{2}$.

The next most obvious negative parity configurations are the odd L rotational excitations of $[70, L = 1]$, namely, $[70, L = 3, 5, 7, \ldots]$, generating for each L SU(3) multiplets with spin $L \pm \frac{3}{2}$ and $L \pm \frac{1}{2}$. There are candidates for some of the $L = 3$ multiplets, all with masses > 1900 MeV.[10]

9-4. POSITIVE PARITY BARYON RESONANCES

We now turn to the positive parity baryon multiplets generated by even values of L. In the case of even L the wave functions can have the symmetry of the ground state configuration ($L = 0$), and it therefore appears natural for the spin-unitary spin wave functions of these states to belong to the 56-plet. Consequently only SU(3) octets and decuplets can occur in this scheme. Again the observed baryon resonance spectrum seems to be compatible with this result. Up to now there has been no need for positive parity unitary singlets, and, apart from a few pathological cases to be treated below, the observed positive parity states can be accommodated in the multiplets contained in [56, L = even]. For each L we obtain a breaking pattern, as shown in Figure 8 for the case $L = 2$, in which the

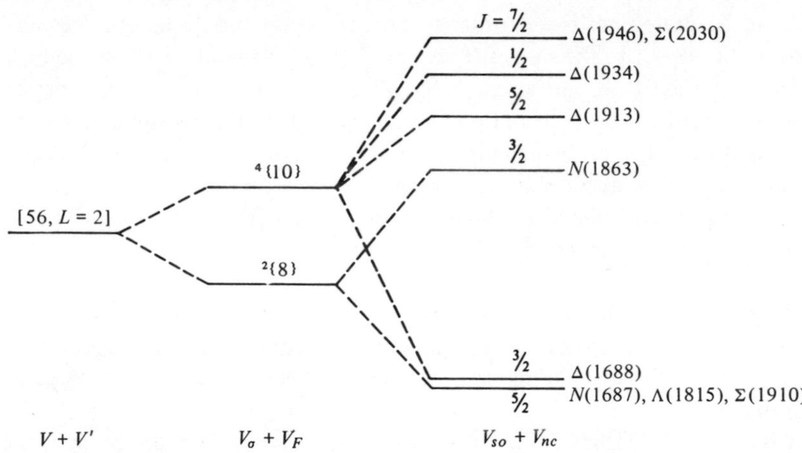

FIGURE 8. Possible breaking pattern for the L = 2, positive parity 3q states. SU(3) splitting is not shown. The forces indicated are supposed to cause the splitting in the corresponding column. The figure is not according to scale.

N's and Δ's are taken from Reference 48. As far as the mass splittings between the SU(3) multiplets are concerned we have to conclude, just as for the negative parity states, that, unless the mass values and assignments of the resonance states given in Figure 8 prove to be incorrect, the mass formula [Eq. (9-5)] is too simple to account for the splitting in the right-hand part of the figure. A more complicated dynamics than expressed by this formula is suggested by the data. (Note that the $^4\{8\}$ octets and $^4\{10\}$ decuplets in Figures 7 and 8 are very close together in mass, except for $\Delta(1688)$. In fact, they are essentially degenerate, their separations being much smaller than their widths. This suggests the vanishing of the spin-orbit interaction in $3q$ states with $s = 3/2$. It is probably not correct therefore to assign $\Delta(1688)$ to $[56, L = 2]$. Perhaps we should consider this state together with $P_{11}(1466)$ as vibrational excitations of $[56, L = 0]$. (Compare Section 9-5 and Reference 10b.) Another $J^P = \frac{3}{2}^+$ Δ resonance should then exist near 1930 MeV to fill up $[56, L = 2]$.) Note that for $L = 0$ Figure 8 correctly represents the actual situation.

From the mass values given in Table 4 and Figures 7 and 8 we see that, turning off SU(3)-breaking interactions, the three groups of SU(3) multiplets generated by $[56, L^P = 0^+]$, $[70, L^P = 1^-]$, and $[56, L^P = 2^+]$, respectively, are clearly separated from each other and appear in this order, the three clusters covering the mass regions 940–1240, 1400–1700, and 1700–1950 MeV.

Before closing this section we remark on SU(3) symmetry breaking in the $L = 1$ and $L = 2$ multiplets. We estimate for the parameter Δ, introduced in Chapter 8, for the $\frac{5}{2}^-$ octet (Figure 7)

$$\Delta = m[\Sigma(1770)] - m[N(1678)] = 92 \text{ MeV}$$

for the $\frac{3}{2}^-$ octet (Figure 7)

$$\Delta = m[\Sigma(1660)] - m[N(1541)] = 119 \text{ MeV}$$

for the $\frac{5}{2}^+$ octet (Figure 8)

$$\Delta = m[\Sigma(1910)] - m[N(1687)] = 223 \text{ MeV}$$

for the $\frac{7}{2}^+$ decuplet (Figure 8)

$$\Delta = m[\Sigma(2030)] - m[\Delta(1946)] = 84 \text{ MeV}$$

Although these values are of the correct order of magnitude when compared with the values obtained in Chapter 8, there are considerable discrepancies between them. Note also that $m(\Lambda) \neq m(\Sigma)$. Just as in the case of the $L = 0$ baryons, the reason for the discrepancies lies, presumably, in SU(3) symmetry breaking in the quark potentials, a fact which appears to be more important in the qq than in the $q\bar{q}$ potentials.

9-5. THE SYMMETRIC MODEL

Supposing that the sequences $[56, L^P = (\text{even})^+]$ and $[70, L^P = (\text{odd})^-]$ are really the only groups of baryonic multiplets realized in nature (at least in the mass region explored up to now; see, however, below), one is faced with the question, which has to be answered by any correct dynamical model, why this is so. In other words, a dynamical theory of quarks has to explain why, for instance, $[20, L = 0, 2, \ldots]$ and $[70, L = 0, 2, \ldots]$ are not seen in the lowest mass region, for example, below 2.5 GeV. In this connection it is interesting to remark that, when applying the nuclear shell model with harmonic oscillator forces to the $3q$ system, one finds that the observed sequence of multiplets $[56, L^P = 0^+]$, $[70, L^P = 1^-]$, and $[56, L^P = 2^+]$ corresponding to the baryon ground state and first excited states follows quite naturally the sequence of expected shell model states.[10b,36,49] The ground state $[56, L^P = 0^+]$ corresponds to the $(1s)^3$ configuration (we use standard notation), which has a fully symmetric space wave function (symmetric model) implying that in this model we must abandon Fermi statistics for the quarks (compare the discussion in Chapter 7). The first excited state has the structure $(1s)^2\,(1p)$, whose nonspurious component has a mixed space wave function and gives rise to $[70, L^P = 1^-]$, in agreement with observations, as we have seen.

The next configuration includes five supermultiplets, namely,

$$[56, L^P = 2^+] \qquad [56, L^P = 0^+] \qquad [70, L^P = 2^+] \qquad [70, L^P = 0^+]$$
$$[20, L^P = 1^+] \tag{9-6}$$

The first of these is the one discussed in Section 9-4 (Figure 8). For the existence of the last three of the above multiplets there is still no experimental evidence. They are not required by the data. Mitra[49] has pointed out that it is possible to construct a symmetric model based on the assumption of short-range S-wave qq forces in which just these unwanted states are kept out and only the states $[56, L^P = (\text{even})^+]$ and $[70, L^P = (\text{odd})^-]$ occur.

The second supermultiplet in the set (9-6) can be considered as the first vibrational excitation of the ground state $[56, L = 0^+]$. Its space wave function has the structure $\sqrt{2/3}\,(1s)^2\,(2s) + \sqrt{1/3}\,(1s)\,(1p)^2$, its spin-unitary spin structure is identical to that of the ground state; that is, it contains a $\frac{1}{2}^+$ octet and a $\frac{3}{2}^+$ decuplet. The most obvious candidates for such radial excitations of the ground state are the P_{11} pion–nucleon resonances (notation: $L_{2I,\,2J}$, where L is the orbital angular momentum of the πN wave) found in phase shift analyses[48] $N(1470)$ and $N(1750)$, which have the same internal quantum numbers as the nucleon. Evidence for the first one also exists from other observations.[50] In the qqq model, each of these states can only be a member of a $\frac{1}{2}^+$ octet. An assignment of the $N(1470)$ to an octet, and not, for instance, to an antidecuplet $\overline{10}$, is strongly favored by the experimental observation of the decay mode $\Delta(1236)\pi$. In the framework of the symmetric model it is natural to consider the $N(1470)$, possibly together with the $\Delta(1688)$ (see foregoing section), as belonging to the first excited $[56, L = 0^+]$ (the one occurring in the sequence (9-6)) and the $N(1750)$ as belonging to the second excited $[56, L = 0^+]$. For other possibilities discussed in the literature we refer to the papers by Dalitz.[10]

If it turns out that one or more of the P_{11} states are of a more exotic nature and belong to other SU(3) multiplets, such as 10, we have to extend the simple

qqq model and admit more complicated quark configurations, such as $qqqq\bar{q}$ (or more than one fundamental triplet). In fact, some evidence for these higher quark states might exist already, namely, the bumps seen in K^+P and K^+ deuteron total cross sections.[51] At present it is by no means clear whether these bumps should be considered as resonances (the so-called Z resonances with positive strangeness and masses in the region 1800–2500 MeV). At least for one of them there is an alternative explanation.[52] Moreover, a search for Z's in bubble chamber pictures has so far given negative results.[53] However, if their interpretation as being resonances proves to be correct, the above-mentioned extension of the model is unavoidable. There is, of course, no *a priori* reason to shrink from the possibility of more complicated quark configurations; on the contrary, as is clear from the discussion in Chapter 7, no theoretical argument exists in favor of the occurrence of only $q\bar{q}$ and qqq composite states.

Summarizing this chapter, we may conclude that the simplest quark model—$q\bar{q}$ and qqq configurations for mesons and baryons with the possibility of rotational and eventually vibrational excitation—can reproduce qualitatively the gross features of the presently established resonance spectra of the hadrons. To be able to generate an SU(3) multiplet spectrum that agrees remarkably well with the observations is a challenging achievement of the model.

Notes added in proof.

1. The fact that meson Regge trajectories appear to be linear can be interpreted by assuming that the $q\bar{q}$ pair interacts through a harmonic oscillator potential and that the system is described by a wave equation that is quadratic in the energy E, as required by the use of $(\text{mass})^2$ in the mass formulas (Chapter 8). This leads to a linear dependence of E^2 on L, that is, to linear Regge trajectories (Dalitz,[10c] Zweig[49]).

2. In the $q\bar{q}$ model with L excitation there are four states for each J, I, Y, and F, except for $J = 0$, where there are two. As a consequence, the model predicts that of the four corresponding positive signature trajectories, connecting states with $J = 0, 2, 4, \ldots$, two must cross the $J = 0$ axis at negative values of m^2 [that is, have positive intercept $\alpha(0)$] or have vanishing residues at $J = 0$. Of the $I = 1$ trajectories, it is known that the A_2 trajectory (which is degenerate with the ρ trajectory) has positive intercept. The same should be true for the $I = 1$ trajectory with physical states $J^{PG} = (\text{even})^{-+}$.

Chapter 10

Weak Decay Processes

10-1. BETA DECAY

Many decay processes of hadrons have been treated in the framework of the quark model. We do not study them all in detail but give a few examples for each type of interaction, thereby trying to mention both the successes and the failures of the model. Much of what we say about decay properties is taken from work by Van Royen and Weisskopf.[54] We restrict our attention to the $L = 0$ states and start in this chapter with the weak decays.

The first class of processes we consider are the β-decay processes

$$A \to B + l + \nu \tag{10-1}$$

in which A and B are hadrons, l is an electron or muon, and ν a neutrino or antineutrino. We now assume that these processes can be described in terms of β-decay processes of the corresponding quarks (Figure 3) and result from a current–current interaction

$$\begin{aligned} H_W = \int d^3 x\bar{q}(x)\,[G'_V \gamma_\mu + G'_A \gamma_\mu \gamma_5]\,(\alpha^+ \cos\theta + \beta^+ \sin\theta)\,q(x) \\ \times\, \bar{l}(x)\,\gamma_\mu(1+\gamma_5)\,\nu(x) + h.c. \end{aligned} \tag{10-2}$$

Here $q(x)$, $l(x)$, and $\nu(x)$ represent the states of quark, lepton, and neutrino, respectively; θ is the Cabibbo angle; and G'_V and G'_A are the renormalized interaction constants of quarks for vector and axial vector coupling. Finally, α^+ (β^+) is an operator which transforms an n-like state (λ-like state) into a p-like state. The hadronic current density in Eq. (10-2) consists of octet elements consistent with the Cabibbo hypothesis.[55] Also, because the strangeness-conserving part $\bar{q}(x)\,\gamma_\mu\alpha^+\,q(x)$ is the I_+ component of the isospin current, Eq. (10-2) gives all the results of the conserved vector current theory.[56] In particular, $G'_V = G_\mu$, when G_μ is the coupling constant for the purely leptonic decay

$$\mu^+ \to e^+ + \nu_e + \bar{\nu}_\mu$$

The insertion of the Cabibbo angle at the quark level ensures universality of this angle for all hadrons, in accordance with the facts.

Under the assumption of nonrelativistic motion for the quarks, only the time component of the γ_μ term and the space component of the $\gamma_\mu\gamma_5$ term survive, which reduce to the unit operator and the spin operator $\boldsymbol{\sigma}$, respectively, giving

$$\begin{aligned} H_W = G_V' \int d^3x\bar{q}(x)\,[\alpha^+\cos\theta + \beta^+\sin\theta]\,q(x)\,\bar{l}(x)\,\gamma_0(1+\gamma_5)\,\nu(x) \\ + G_A' \int d^3x\bar{q}(x)\,[\alpha^+\cos\theta + \beta^+\sin\theta]\,\boldsymbol{\sigma}\cdot q(x)\,\bar{l}(x)\,\boldsymbol{\gamma}(1+\gamma_5)\,\nu(x) \end{aligned} \tag{10-3}$$

We now take this expression between hadron states $|A>$ and $|B>$ belonging to the same SU(3) multiplet. Using Eqs. (5-6), (5-12), and the fact that for β decay $\mathbf{x}\cdot(\mathbf{q}_l + \mathbf{q}_\nu) \ll 1$, we can write

$$\begin{aligned} \langle A|H_W|B\rangle = G_V'\langle\phi(B)|\cos\theta \sum_i \alpha_i^+ + \sin\theta \sum_i \beta_i^+|\phi(A)\rangle\,\bar{l}(0)\,\gamma_0(1+\gamma_5)\,\nu(0) \\ + G_A'\langle\phi(B)|\cos\theta \sum_i \boldsymbol{\sigma}_i\alpha_i^+ + \sin\theta \sum_i \boldsymbol{\sigma}_i\beta_i^+|\phi(A)\rangle \\ \times\, \bar{l}(0)\,\boldsymbol{\gamma}(1+\gamma_5)\,\nu(0) \end{aligned} \tag{10-4}$$

in which the subscript i indicates that the operator in question acts on quark i in the expression for $\phi(A)$. Taking $|A> = |N, s_z = ½>$, and $B = |P, s_z = ½>$ and computing

$$\begin{aligned} \langle P, s_z = \tfrac{1}{2}|\sum_i \alpha_i^+|N, s_z = \tfrac{1}{2}\rangle = 1 \\ \langle P, s_z = \tfrac{1}{2}|\sum_i \alpha_i^+\sigma_i^z|N, s_z = \tfrac{1}{2}\rangle = \tfrac{5}{3} \end{aligned} \tag{10-5}$$

thereby using Eqs. (6-3) and (6-4), we conclude

$$G_V = G_V' \qquad G_A = \tfrac{5}{3}G_A' \tag{10-6}$$

G_V and G_A being the vector and axial vector coupling constants for nucleons. From the experimental result $G_A = 1.2\,G_V$ we obtain

$$G_A' = 0.7\,G_V \tag{10-7}$$

Using these values we can calculate the matrix elements and decay widths for all reactions of type (10-1). The results are those of SU(6) with $D/F = 3/2$ for the axial currents.[57]

10-2. THE RATIO G_A/G_V

At this stage we wish to make a remark about the ratios G_A/G_V and G_A'/G_V'. In the above discussion the point of view was taken that for quarks, as for nucleons, the coupling constant G_A' is affected by the strong interactions so that

G'_A/G'_V differs from the value one. In fact, we just saw that adjusting G'_A/G'_V, so as to reproduce the experimental value $G_A/G_V = 1.2$ for nucleons, gave a value of 0.7. Another point of view, taken especially by the Dubna group,[58] is to assume that the axial constant G'_A for quarks is not renormalized, that is, $G'_A/G'_V = 1$. The underlying idea is a composite model for hadrons in which the basic particles, the quarks, have no structure of their own, while their interaction determines the structure of the composite particles. On the basis of this assumption Bogoliubov[58c] has calculated G_A/G_V for the nucleons taking relativistic corrections into account. Of course, in the nonrelativistic limit one finds in this model $G_A/G_V = 5/3$. Each quark is assumed to move independently of the other quarks in a scalar radially symmetric potential $U(r)$ (compare the discussion in Chapter 4) and is described by a space-spin wave function

$$\Psi_0(\mathbf{r}) = \begin{pmatrix} f(r)\chi \\ ig(r)(\boldsymbol{\sigma}\cdot\mathbf{r})\chi \end{pmatrix} \tag{10-8}$$

in which χ is the normal two-component spinor. All three quarks are put in the same state, an S state, with lowest energy E_0. This supposes a symmetric space wave function and therefore parastatistics for the quarks or a three-triplet model [see Eq. (7-10)]. The total angular momentum for each quark is

$$\mathbf{j} = \tfrac{1}{2}\boldsymbol{\sigma} + \mathbf{l} \tag{10-9}$$

Neither the spin $\boldsymbol{\sigma}$ nor the orbital angular momentum $\mathbf{l}$ have definite values in a relativistic theory, $l = 0$ for the upper component of Ψ_0 (nonrelativistic limit) and $l = 1$ for the lower component. However, since Ψ_0 is an S state, we have of course

$$j^2\,\Psi_0 = \tfrac{1}{2}(\tfrac{1}{2} + 1)\,\Psi_0$$

It is the contribution of $\mathbf{l}$ that gives the relativistic correction to the value $5/3$ for G_A/G_V.

We calculate for nucleons (at zero momentum transfer)

$$\frac{G_A}{G_V} = \frac{5}{3}(1 - 2\delta) \tag{10-10}$$

with

$$\delta = \left.\frac{\int \Psi_0^* l_z \Psi_0\, d\mathbf{r}}{\int \Psi_0^* \Psi_0\, d\mathbf{r}}\right|_{j_z=\frac{1}{2}} = \frac{\frac{2}{3}\int_0^\infty |g(r)|^2 r^4\, dr}{\int_0^\infty \{|f(r)|^2 + r^2|g(r)|^2\} r^2\, dr} \tag{10-11}$$

To compute δ we have to assume a specific form for the scalar potential $U(r)$. Taking the square-well potential of Section 4-3 with $U_0 \approx m_q$, the free quark mass, we find in the limit of very large m_q

$$\delta = 0.17 \tag{10-12}$$

and hence

$$\frac{G_A}{G_V} = 1.1 \tag{10-13}$$

in surprising agreement with experiment. Note that for a scalar potential taking the limit $m_q \to \infty$ does not imply taking the nonrelativistic limit since it is $m_q^* = m_q - U_0$ that enters the dynamical equations (Section 4-3).

10-3. THE VAN ROYEN-WEISSKOPF PARADOX

Let us now look at the reactions[54, 59]

$$K \to l + \nu \qquad \pi \to l + \nu \tag{10-14}$$

From the point of view of the quark model these processes involve the annihilation of a quark and an antiquark. Because of this, a new parameter appears in the squared matrix element for these decays, namely $|f(M, 0)|^2$, in which $f(M, \mathbf{r})$ is the (unknown) space wave function of the quark–antiquark bound state corresponding to the decaying meson M. It is easy to see how this factor enters. Following the discussion by Van Royen and Weisskopf,[54] we write the creation operator $d_M^*(0)$ for meson M with zero momentum in terms of the creation operators $a_r^*(\mathbf{p})$ and $b_s^*(\mathbf{p})$ for the quark and the antiquark with spin-unitary spin components r and s as follows:

$$d_M^*(0) = \sum_{r,s} \int d^3p \tilde{f}(M, \mathbf{p})\, c(r,s)\, a_r^*(\mathbf{p})\, b_s^*(-\mathbf{p})$$

Here $\tilde{f}(M, \mathbf{p})$ is the bound state wave function normalized to

$$\int d^3p |\tilde{f}(M, \mathbf{p})|^2 = 1$$

and $c(r, s)$ is a coefficient depending only on the spin-unitary spin labels r and s. The amplitude for annihilation can be written as

$$\begin{aligned} A &= (2\pi)^{3/2} \langle 0 | H\, d_M^*(0) | 0 \rangle \\ &= (2\pi)^{3/2} \sum_{r,s} \int d^3p \tilde{f}(M, \mathbf{p})\, c(r,s) \langle 0 | H a_r^*(\mathbf{p})\, b_s^*(-\mathbf{p}) | 0 \rangle \end{aligned}$$

in which H is the interaction causing the transition and the factor in front is a normalization factor. Assuming now that the quarks move nonrelativistically, so that we can expand the matrix element in $\mathbf{p}$ and keep only the leading term, we finally get

$$A \simeq f(M,0)(2\pi)^3 \sum_{r,s} c(r,s)\langle 0|Ha_r^*(0)\,b_s^*(0)|0\rangle \tag{10-15}$$

in which we have used

$$f(M,\mathbf{r}) = \frac{1}{(2\pi)^{3/2}}\int \tilde{f}(M,\mathbf{p})\,e^{i\mathbf{p}\cdot\mathbf{r}}\,d^3p$$

The matrix element on the right of formula (10-15) is just that for annihilation of free quarks of zero momentum. The expression $(2\pi)^3 a_r^*(0)\, b_s^*(0)|0\rangle$ represents the properly normalized $q\bar{q}$ state. The effect of the bound state is described by the multiplication factor $f(M, 0)$.

The calculation of the matrix elements for processes (10-14) is now straightfoward. We find

$$\langle l\nu|H_W|\pi\rangle = G'_A f(\pi,0)\sqrt{2}\cos\theta\,\bar{u}_l(\mathbf{p})\,\gamma_0(1+\gamma_5)\,u_\nu(-\mathbf{p}) \tag{10-16}$$

which holds in the rest system of the decaying particle. The corresponding expression for K decay has $\cos\theta$ replaced by $\sin\theta$. From Eq. (10-16) we obtain along standard lines [see, for instance, Källén[60]] for the decay widths

$$\begin{aligned} \Gamma_{\pi^+\to\mu^+\nu} &= \frac{1}{2\pi}|f(\pi,0)|^2 G_A'^2 \cos^2\theta m_\mu^2\left(1-\frac{m_\mu^2}{m_\pi^2}\right)^2 \\ \Gamma_{K^+\to\mu^+\nu} &= \frac{1}{2\pi}|f(K,0)|^2 G_A'^2 \sin^2\theta m_\mu^2\left(1-\frac{m_\mu^2}{m_K^2}\right)^2 \end{aligned} \tag{10-17}$$

Using the experimental numbers $\Gamma_{\pi^+\to\mu^+\nu} = 2.6 \times 10^{-14}$ MeV, $\Gamma_{K^+\to\mu^+\nu} = 3.4 \times 10^{-14}$ MeV, and $\sin\theta = 0.25$, these expressions lead to the surprising result[54]

$$\begin{aligned} |f(\pi,0)|^2 &= 1.4 \times 10^6\ (\text{MeV})^3 \\ |f(K,0)|^2 &= 5.1 \times 10^6\ (\text{MeV})^3 \end{aligned} \tag{10-18}$$

that is, $|f(\pi, 0)|^2$ and $|f(K, 0)|^2$ are almost exactly in the ratio m_π/m_K and $|f(\pi, 0)|^2 \simeq \frac{1}{2}m_\pi^3$. This result is supported by analogous calculations for the electromagnetic decays (Chapter 12). We generally seem to have (M = pseudoscalar or vector meson)[54]

$$|f(\pi,0)|^2 \simeq \tfrac{1}{2}m_\pi^3 \qquad \frac{|f(M,0)|^2}{|f(\pi,0)|^2} \simeq \frac{m_M}{m_\pi} \tag{10-19}$$

This result shows that symmetry breaking has quite a large effect on the space wave functions, especially in the case of the pseudoscalar mesons. There is at present no explanation for this unexpected behavior of the wave functions. However, we should bear in mind that in Eq. (10-15), and hence in result (10-19), form factors for $q\bar{q}$ annihilation are neglected. These form factors are time-like and hard to estimate. Thus we actually do not obtain from Eq. (10-17) the value of $|f(M, 0)|$, but of $|f(M, 0)|$ times a form factor $F(-m_M^2)$. This may modify especially the second of Eqs. (10-19).

The question that immediately arises is how far this result will upset the assumption $F(0) = 1$, made in Eq. (5-12)? We can check this by calculating $F(0)$ with a specific Ansatz for the wave function $f(M, \mathbf{r})$. A simple choice is

$$f(M_i, r) = \left(\frac{b_i^3}{\pi}\right)^{1/2} e^{-b_i r} \tag{10-20}$$

in which r is the interquark distance. We find

$$\begin{aligned} F(0) &= \int f(M_1, \mathbf{r}) f^*(M_2, \mathbf{r})\, d\mathbf{r} \\ &= 8\,\frac{(b_1 b_2)^{3/2}}{(b_1 + b_2)^3} \end{aligned} \tag{10-21}$$

and, according to Eq. (10-19),

$$\left(\frac{b_1}{b_2}\right)^3 = \frac{m_{M_1}}{m_{M_2}} \tag{10-22}$$

This gives

$$F(0) = 0.93 \qquad \text{for } \frac{m_{M_1}}{m_{M_2}} = \frac{1}{4}$$

$$F(0) = 0.89 \qquad \text{for } \frac{m_{M_1}}{m_{M_2}} = \frac{1}{6}$$

showing that $F(0)$ is rather insensitive to the value of m_{M_1}/m_{M_2}.[61]

Is Ansatz (10-20) consistent with the first of Eqs. (10-19) and with what we know about the pion form factor? On the one hand, from Eqs. (10-19) and (10-20), we have

$$b_\pi = \pi^{1/3} |f(\pi, 0)|^{2/3} = \left(\frac{\pi}{2}\right)^{1/3} m_\pi = 0.80 f^{-1} \tag{10-23}$$

On the other hand, from the expression for the form factor following from Eq. (10-20),

$$F_\pi(k^2) = \frac{1}{[1 + (k^2/4b_\pi^2)]^2} \tag{10-24}$$

and from the recently measured[62] rms charge radius of the pion, $r_\pi = 0.80 \pm 0.10\, f$, we expect $b_\pi \geqslant 2.2\, f^{-1}$, in disagreement with Eq. (10-23). The equality sign holds when the quarks are point charges (see also Section 7-3). With this value for b_π we have, instead of Eq. (10-19),

$$|f(\pi, 0)|^2 \geqslant 19(\tfrac{1}{2}m_\pi^3) \tag{10-25}$$

that is, the "measured" value $\frac{1}{2} m_\pi^3$ of $|f(\pi, 0)|^2$ is much smaller than we expect on the basis of Eq. (10-20). It seems, therefore, that this wave function, and in general any wave function that has its maximum value at $\mathbf{r} = 0$, is not correct for $\mathbf{r}$ around zero, and that a mechanism such as a repulsive core in the $\bar{q}q$ potential is operating, which strongly reduces the wave function in that region.[63] Perhaps a better Ansatz for the wave function is

$$f(M_i, r) = N_i[e^{-b_i r} - a_i e^{-c_i r}] \qquad \begin{array}{l} c_i \gg b_i > 0 \\ 0 \leqslant a_i < 1 \end{array} \tag{10-26}$$

For small k^2 this leads again to the form factor Eq. (10-24). Taking $b_\pi = 2.2\, f^{-1}$, so as to reproduce the correct pion charge radius, requires $a_\pi = 0.77$. Thus the pion wave function has a strong dip at $\mathbf{r} = 0$. It is easy to confirm that with this wave function the overlap integrals [Eq. (10-21)] also emerge close to one for m_M/m_π between 1 and 6, and a_M/a_π between 0 and 1.

The above conclusion can clearly be interpreted as an argument in favor of a picture of hadrons in which the bound quarks are small compared to the hadrons and are as far apart in space as possible. Such a picture is not compatible with the usual assumption that the form factors $F(\mathbf{q})$, defined by Eq. (5-11), are approximately constant in the interval $0 < |\mathbf{q}| < 1$ GeV/c (compare the remarks in Sections 5-2, 7-3, and 12-5).

10-4. NONLEPTONIC DECAY

For completeness we note that nonleptonic decays also have been discussed in the framework of the quark model.[64] The basic assumption here is also additivity; that is, one calculates diagrams of the type shown in Figure 3, in which the dotted line is now a pion. The further assumption is then made that we can forget the quark structure of this pion and treat it as a field quantum. We come back to this question in Chapter 13. Some interesting results have been obtained in this way by Badier[64] for the parity-violating (S-wave) transitions.

Chapter 11

Magnetic Moments

11-1. CALCULATION OF HADRON MAGNETIC MOMENTS

Before proceeding with the electromagnetic decay processes, it is necessary to study the magnetic moments of the hadrons in the nonrelativistic quark model. The basic assumption is again that of additivity; the magnetic moment operator $\mathbf{M}_A$ of hadron A is written as the sum of the magnetic moment operators $\mathbf{M}_q$ of the constituent quarks and/or antiquarks. We consider only the case $L = 0$ so that there is no orbital contribution to $\mathbf{M}_A$. Furthermore, we assume the magnetic moment of a quark (including the anomalous part) to be proportional to its charge. We thus write

$$\mathbf{M}_A = \sum_q \mathbf{M}_q \tag{11-1}$$

with

$$\mathbf{M}_q = \mu \frac{e_q}{e} \boldsymbol{\sigma}_q \tag{11-2}$$

in which e_q and $\boldsymbol{\sigma}_q$ are the charge and spin operator of quark q and μ is a scale parameter.

The assumed proportionality of $\mathbf{M}_q$ and e_q is a simple consequence of SU(3) invariance. The latter requires the components within a triplet having the same charge to have the same electromagnetic properties; hence

$$M_n = M_\lambda \tag{11-3}$$

Furthermore, assuming that, just as for the charge operator [see Eq. (2-5)], the current operator transforms as

$$j(x) = j_1(x) I_3 + j_2(x) Y$$

we obtain

$$M_p + M_n + M_\lambda = 0 \tag{11-4}$$

because the expectation values of I_3 and Y summed over the triplet give zero. This, together with Eq. (11-3), proves Eq. (11-2). [SU(3)-breaking forces give rise to correction terms on the right of Eq. (11-2), which we do not consider here.[65]]

Using Eq. (6-3) we obtain, for the expectation value of the proton magnetic moment,

$$\mu_P = \langle \phi(P, s_z = \tfrac{1}{2}) | \sum_i M^z_{q_i} | \phi(P, s_z = \tfrac{1}{2}) \rangle = \mu \tag{11-5}$$

Similarly,

$$\mu_N = -\tfrac{2}{3}\mu \qquad \mu_\Lambda = -\tfrac{1}{3}\mu \tag{11-6}$$

Hence, the quark model predicts[22]

$$\frac{\mu_P}{\mu_N} = -\frac{3}{2} \tag{11-7}$$

while experimentally this ratio is -1.47. The agreement is better than 2%. Equation (11-7) is the famous SU(6) result.[66] In the quark model it is obtained without explicitly assuming SU(6) symmetry in the sense that, although it is essential that the spin-unitary spin parts of the baryon wave functions have the permutation symmetry according to the 56-representation of SU(6), their space parts need not be identical.

Equations (11-5) and (11-6) give

$$\mu_\Lambda / \mu_P = -\tfrac{1}{3} \tag{11-8}$$

to be compared with the experimental value -0.29 ± 0.05.[67] For the decuplet members one finds

$$\mu_A = Q_A \mu \tag{11-9}$$

in which Q_A is the charge of A. In the same way, we calculate the magnetic moments of the mesons.

11-2. THE ANOMALOUS MAGNETIC MOMENT OF A QUARK

From Eq. (11-5) we have the remarkable result

$$\mu = \mu_P = 2.79 \frac{e}{2m_P} \tag{11-10}$$

Writing the magnetic moment of a quark as

$$\mathbf{M}_q = g\mu_q \boldsymbol{\sigma}_q \qquad \mu_q = \frac{e_q}{2m_q} \tag{11-11}$$

we conclude from Eq. (11-10) that

$$g = 2.79 \frac{m_q}{m_P} \tag{11-12}$$

Taking for m_q the mass of a free quark, that is, $M_q \gtrsim 4$ GeV, we have $g \gtrsim 12$, which would imply a highly anomalous quark magnetic moment. One way to "explain" this large g factor for the quarks is to note that Eq. (11-11) is not the appropriate unit in which to measure the quark magnetic moment, the reason being that the latter may be essentially determined by the magnetic moment of the meson cloud surrounding the quark, which is composed of objects much lighter than the quark itself.

Another point of view is to assume that, whereas the magnetic moment of free quarks is very small, of the order $e/2m_q$, when strongly bound inside the hadrons, quarks do have a small effective mass that enhances their magnetic moment with respect to the free value. This, however, is very sensitive to the type of field (scalar or vector) binding the quarks. To illuminate the argument[58, 68] we again use the extremely simplified model discussed in Chapter 4, but now with the presence of a magnetic field. The Dirac Eqs. (4-3) and (4-4) become

for U, the fourth component of a vector field,

$$[m_q + \boldsymbol{\gamma} \cdot (\mathbf{p} - e_q \mathbf{A})]\ \psi_q = (E + U_0)\gamma_0\ \psi_q \tag{11-13}$$

for U, a scalar field,

$$[m_q - U_0 + \boldsymbol{\gamma} \cdot (\mathbf{p} - e_q \mathbf{A})]\ \psi_q = E\gamma_0\ \psi_q \tag{11-14}$$

in which $\mathbf{A}$ is the vector potential describing the external magnetic field. The first of these equations describes essentially a free particle in an external magnetic field. Only the energy scale is shifted, the mass is not affected. The magnetic properties are the same as those for a free particle, and the Dirac magnetic moment is $e_q/2m_q$. Hence, in view of Eqs. (11-10) and (11-11) we must assume that in the case of a vector field most of the magnetic moment of the quark is anomalous ($g \gg 1$). The parameter μ is approximately the same in all hadrons (see below).

The situation is different for a scalar field. Rewriting Eq. (11-14) as

$$[m_q^* + \boldsymbol{\gamma} \cdot (\mathbf{p} - e_q \mathbf{A})]\ \psi_q = E\gamma_0\ \psi_q \tag{11-15}$$

with

$$m_q^* = m_q - U_0 \tag{11-16}$$

we see that this is the Dirac equation for a free particle with mass m_q^* in an external magnetic field. The magnetic moment is that of a Dirac particle with mass m_q^*, so that we have, instead of Eq. (11-11),

$$\mu_q = \frac{e_q}{2m_q^*} \tag{11-17}$$

Assume now the scalar binding forces to be SU(6) invariant [of type (1) and (2) in the notation of Chapter 7]. If the quark motion is nonrelativistic m_q^* is given by Eq. (4-6). In this case we have to replace m_q in Eq. (11-12) by m_q^*, giving $g \simeq 2.79\ m_q^*/m_P \simeq 1$, which means that there is no (or only small) anomalous contribution to the quark magnetic moment. As we will see, this low value of g seems to be favored by the experimental data on electromagnetic decays. Moreover, under these circumstances the parameter μ is about the same in all hadrons and equal to μ_P. This constancy of μ is always assumed in the applications and turns out to be necessary in order to reach reasonable agreement with the data (see Chapter 12), which implies that SU(6)-breaking potentials should be such as not to change the effective quark mass greatly from the value of Eq. (4-6). As we have seen above, we can achieve this by assuming the latter potentials to be of vector character.

We note finally that the scalar potential model predicts, for the value of μ_P,

$$\mu_P = \frac{e}{2m_q^*} \simeq 2.4 \frac{e}{2m_P}$$

to be compared with Eq. (11-10). Here we have used formula (4-6) and assumed that the SU(6)-breaking forces do not affect the value of m_q^*. If the latter are also scalar forces we find

$$\mu_P \simeq 3 \frac{e}{2m_P}$$

For more extensive calculations of the magnetic moments we refer to Reference 58c.

Chapter 12

Electromagnetic Decay Processes

12-1. RADIATIVE DECAY OF VECTOR MESONS

We start with the radiative transitions of the type

$$V \to \Pi + \gamma \tag{12-1}$$

in which V and Π represent a vector and a pseudoscalar meson, respectively. These processes can be considered in the quark model as quark transitions (Figure 3) involving quark spin flip, and are described by transition matrix elements of the form

$$\mu_{V\Pi} = \langle \Pi | \sum_{q_i} \mathbf{M}_{q_i} | V \rangle \tag{12-2}$$

with $\mathbf{M}_q$ given by Eq. (11-2). The operator with subscript q_i acts only on the ith quark in $|V\rangle$. Note that, although the pseudoscalar mesons have, of course, zero magnetic moment, they can have transition moments to the vector mesons. To illustrate the typical approximations that are made and ambiguities that arise in calculating decay widths in the quark model, we study the above processes in some detail, taking as a specific example

$$\omega \to \pi^0 + \gamma \tag{12-3}$$

which at present is the best observed process of type (12-1).

The interaction operator inducing the transition of the ith quark in reaction (12-1) can be written in nonrelativistic form as

$$H_i = \mu \frac{e_i}{e} \boldsymbol{\sigma}_i \cdot (\mathbf{k} \times \boldsymbol{\epsilon}^{(\lambda)}) \, e^{i\mathbf{k}\cdot\mathbf{r}_i} \tag{12-4}$$

in which $\boldsymbol{\epsilon}^{(\lambda)}$ and $\mathbf{k}$ denote the polarization and momentum vector of the emitted photon. We have to calculate matrix elements of the form

$$m_{V\Pi} = \langle \Psi(\Pi) | \sum_i H_i | \Psi(V) \rangle \tag{12-5}$$

in which Ψ is given by Eq. (5-6). The space part leads to an expression of the form of Eq. (5-11) with $A = \Pi$ and $A' = V$. This expression is approximated by unity. For a discussion of this point we refer to Sections 5-2 and 10-3.

The spin-unitary spin parts of the matrix elements are easy to calculate, using the wave functions given in Chapter 5. For the process (12-3) we find, for instance,

$$\langle\phi(\pi^0)|\sum_i \mu\frac{e_i}{e}\boldsymbol{\sigma}_i\cdot(\mathbf{k}\times\boldsymbol{\epsilon}^{(\lambda)})|\phi(\omega, s_z=0)\rangle = -\mu(\mathbf{k}\times\boldsymbol{\epsilon}^{(\lambda)})_z$$
$$= -\mu_P(\mathbf{k}\times\boldsymbol{\epsilon}^{(\lambda)})_z \qquad (12\text{-}6)$$

Only σ_i^z contributes in this case. We see the remarkable result, which cannot be obtained from any symmetry, that the transition magnetic moments involving mesons are expressed in terms of the proton magnetic moment. We should emphasize, however, that the identification $\mu = \mu_P$ in Eq. (12-6) can be made only if we assume that the parameter μ is the same in all hadrons. The conditions under which this is true are discussed in Chapter 11.

Similarly we calculate

$$\langle\phi(\pi^0)|\sum_i \mu\frac{e_i}{e}\boldsymbol{\sigma}_i\cdot(\mathbf{k}\times\boldsymbol{\epsilon}^{(\lambda)})|\phi(\omega, s_z=\pm 1)\rangle$$
$$= \frac{\mu_P}{\sqrt{2}}[\pm(\mathbf{k}\times\boldsymbol{\epsilon}^{(\lambda)})_x - i(\mathbf{k}\times\boldsymbol{\epsilon}^{(\lambda)})_y] \qquad (12\text{-}7)$$

Using these results together with the formula

$$\sum_\lambda \epsilon_i^{(\lambda)}\epsilon_j^{(\lambda)} = \delta_{ij}$$

we find for the squared matrix element, summed over photon polarizations and averaged over the polarizations of the decaying vector meson,

$$|m_{\omega\pi}|^2_{\text{av}} = \tfrac{2}{3}\mu_P^2 k^2 \qquad (12\text{-}8)$$

With nonrelativistic phase space this leads in the rest system of ω to

$$\Gamma_{\omega\to\pi^0\gamma} = \frac{\mu_P^2}{12\pi^2}\int d^3p\int d^3k\, k\delta(p_0+k_0-q_0)\,\delta^{(3)}(\mathbf{p}+\mathbf{q})$$
$$= \frac{\mu_P^2 k^3}{3\pi}\frac{E_\pi}{m_\omega} \qquad (12\text{-}9)$$

in which $\mathbf{q}$, $\mathbf{p}$, and $\mathbf{k}$ refer to ω, π, and γ, respectively, and E_π is the energy of the pion. Here an ambiguity arises concerning the factor E_π/m_ω, which comes from the nonrelativistic phase space. To be consistent with our nonrelativistic calculation, in which k is assumed to be small, we should put $E_\pi/m_\omega \simeq 1$. However, using physical values gives $E_\pi/m_\omega \simeq ½$, implying that k is not small. In the literature[54, 69] the former value for E_π/m_ω is always taken, more or less as a prescription, with an appeal to a relativistic calculation in which this factor does not show up. Indeed, starting from a relativistic effective interaction of the form

$$H_{\text{int}} = g_{V\Pi}\, \epsilon_{\alpha\beta\gamma\delta}\, \partial_\alpha A_\beta\, \partial_\gamma\, V_\delta\, \Pi \tag{12-10}$$

we arrive at

$$\Gamma_{V\Pi\gamma} = \frac{g_{V\Pi}^2\, k^3}{12\pi} \tag{12-11}$$

This shows that in the relativistic phase space the factor E_Π/m_V is missing, and we conclude that formula (12-9) is relativistically correct provided we put E_π/m_ω, or more generally E_Π/m_V, equal to one. Comparing Eq. (12-9) and Eq. (12-11) then gives

$$g_{\omega\pi} = 2\mu_P \tag{12-12}$$

In Eq. (12-11), as in Eq. (12-9), form factor effects are neglected. With

$$k = \frac{m_\omega^2 - m_\pi^2}{2m_\omega} = 380 \text{ MeV}$$

and

$$\mu_P^2 = \left[2.79\frac{e}{2m_P}\right]^2 = (2.79)^2(4\pi/137)/4m_P^2$$

we obtain from Eq. (12-9), putting $E_\pi/m_\omega = 1$,[69]

$$\Gamma_{\omega\to\pi^0\gamma} = 1.17 \text{ MeV} \tag{12-13}$$

The experimental value is about 1.2 MeV, in close agreement with the predicted value. It should be emphasized once more that this result is not merely a direct prediction of the quark hypothesis as such but is obtained under certain additional dynamical assumptions, such as nonrelativistic motion, additivity, the constancy of μ for all hadrons, and the flatness of form factors. Therefore this prediction—and this is true *mutatis mutandis* for all other predictions of the model as well—should never be considered as a test of the quark hypothesis itself.

In a similar way we can calculate other reactions of the Eq. (12-1) type, as well as pseudoscalar meson decays $\Pi \to V + \gamma$. We have collected a few results in Table 8.[69]

Table 8. Results on Radiative Decays of Vector Mesons.

Process	$\lvert m\rvert^2_{av}$	$\Gamma^{th}_{V\to\Pi+\gamma}$	$\Gamma^{exp}_{V\to\Pi+\gamma}$
$\omega \to \pi^0 + \gamma$	$\frac{2}{3}\mu_P^2 k^2$	1.17 MeV	1.20 MeV
$\rho \to \pi + \gamma$	$\frac{2}{27}\mu_P^2 k^2$	0.13 MeV	< 2.5 MeV
$\phi \to \pi^0 + \gamma$	0	0	...
$\omega \to \eta + \gamma$	$\frac{2}{81}\mu_P^2 k^2$	6.3 keV	< 180 keV
$\rho \to \eta + \gamma$	$\frac{2}{9}\mu_P^2 k^2$	50 keV	...

12-2. RADIATIVE DECAY OF BARYON RESONANCES

Radiative decays involving baryons can be treated in the quark model along similar lines. A well-known example is

$$\Delta^+(1236) \to P + \gamma \tag{12-14}$$

which can be either a magnetic dipole (M_1) or an electric quadrupole (E_2) transition. However, the quark model predicts that the E_2 transition is forbidden[70] because we are dealing with an $L = 0 \to L = 0$ transition. This prediction agrees excellently with the facts; from photoproduction data we conclude that the E_2-transition moment is less than 4% of the M_1 moment.[6] The latter can again be expressed in terms of μ_P. We find

$$\langle \phi(P, s_z = \tfrac{1}{2})| \sum_{q_i} M^z_{q_i} |\phi(\Delta^+, s_z = \tfrac{1}{2})\rangle = \frac{2\sqrt{2}}{3}\,\mu_P$$

From the photoproduction process

$$\gamma + P \to \Delta^+ \to \pi^0 + P$$

we extract for this matrix element the empirical value $(1.25 \pm 0.02)\,(2\mu_P\sqrt{2})/3$, which is in reasonable agreement with the above prediction.[71] However, note that the inclusion of form factors makes the agreement worse.

Other quark model predictions for the $N^*N\gamma$ vertex (N = nucleon, N^* = nonstrange resonance) have been given by Moorhouse.[72] He shows that for certain states this vertex vanishes. An example is the $N^+(1678)$ with $J^P = 5/2^-$ in the $^4\{8\}$, $L = 1$ multiplet (Figure 7), which for that reason is predicted not to occur as a γP resonance excitation. On the other hand, neither for the $^2\{8\}$, $L = 1$ (Figure 7) nor the $^2\{8\}$, $L = 2$ states (Figure 8) is photoexcitation forbidden by the quark model. These predictions are borne out by experiment.[10]

12-3. LEPTONIC DECAY OF VECTOR MESONS

Another class of electromagnetic transitions is characterized by the fact that a quark and an antiquark annihilate. Examples are

$$\begin{aligned} &\rho \to l^+ + l^- \qquad \pi^0 \to 2\gamma \\ &\omega \to l^+ + l^- \qquad \eta \to 2\gamma \end{aligned} \tag{12-15}$$

in which l denotes a lepton. We have seen in Chapter 10, in treating the leptonic decays of π and K, that in the nonrelativistic quark model the amplitude for annihilation of a bound quark–antiquark pair can be written as that of two free quarks with momentum zero, multiplied by $f(M, 0)$. For the process $V \to l^+ + l^-$, which we consider as a two-stage process $V \to \gamma \to l^+ + l^-$, we therefore start by calculating the diagram corresponding to free quarks of mass m_q^* (see Figure 9), which

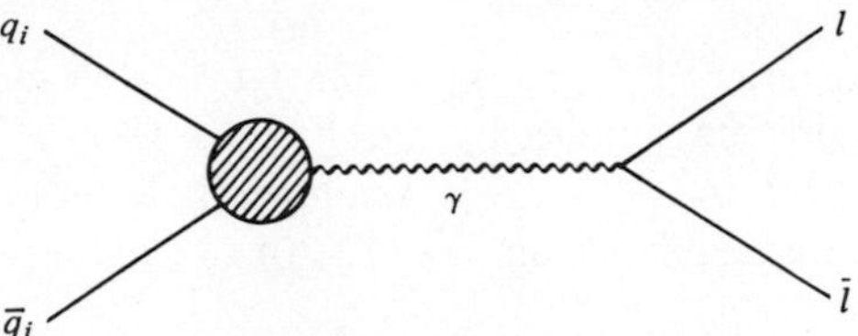

FIGURE 9. Diagram for the process $q\bar{q} \to l\bar{l}$.

from the point of view of the t channel can be considered as Coulomb scattering of a quark and a lepton. For the quark current operator we have the familiar expression

$$j_\mu = ie_q\,\bar{u}_q(\mathbf{p}')\left[\gamma_\mu F_1 + \frac{g-1}{2m_q^*}(p_\nu - p_\nu')\,\sigma_{\mu\nu} F_2\right]u_q(\mathbf{p}) \tag{12-16}$$

in which $e_q(g-1)/2m_q^*$ is the anomalous magnetic moment of the quark (see Chapter 11). We can rewrite this as[60]

$$j_\mu = ie_q\,\bar{u}_q(\mathbf{p}')\,[\gamma_\mu f_1 + (p_\mu + p_\mu') f_2]\,u_q(\mathbf{p}) \tag{12-17}$$

with

$$f_1 = F_1 + (g-1)F_2 \qquad f_2 = \frac{i(g-1)}{2m_q^*}F_2 \tag{12-18}$$

Only the term with f_1 contributes to the above diagram. The corresponding matrix element is

$$m' = ee_q f_1\,\bar{u}_{\bar{q}}\gamma_\mu u_q \frac{1}{k^2}\bar{u}_l\gamma_\mu u_{\bar{l}} \equiv \frac{e_q}{e}m''$$

in which k_μ is the photon four-momentum. In terms of this result the matrix element m for the mesonic decay process $V \rightarrow l^+ l^-$ becomes

$$m = f(V,0)\, c_V\, m'' \tag{12-19}$$

in which

$$c_\rho = \frac{1}{\sqrt{2}} \qquad c_\omega = \frac{1}{3\sqrt{2}} \qquad c_\phi = \frac{1}{3}$$

We have used the quark wave functions of Table 3. A straightforward calculation leads to[54, 73]

$$\Gamma_{V\rightarrow l^+l^-} = f_1^2 |f(V,0)|^2 \frac{e^4}{3\pi} \frac{c_V^2}{m_V^2} + 0\left(\frac{m_l^2}{m_V^2}\right) \tag{12-20}$$

From the branching ratio[74] $\Gamma_{\rho\rightarrow e^+e^-}/\Gamma_\rho = (6.5 \pm 1.4)10^{-5}$ and $\Gamma_\rho = 128$ MeV,[28] we obtain the experimental number $\Gamma_{\rho\rightarrow e^+e^-} = (8.3 \pm 1.8)\, 10^{-3}$ MeV; furthermore, within the errors,[28] $\Gamma_{\rho\rightarrow e^+e^-} = \Gamma_{\rho\rightarrow\mu^+\mu^-}$. Assuming the validity of Eqs. (10-19) for the vector mesons, we calculate from Eq. (12-20) and the first-mentioned experimental numbers

$$f_1^2 = 1.6 \pm 0.4 \tag{12-21}$$

We should remark here that there is some confusion concerning Γ_ρ. A recent measurement[75] of electron–positron annihilation into two pions claims a width for ρ of 93 ± 15 MeV. This would reduce f_1^2 to the value 1.1 ± 0.3.

From $\omega \rightarrow e^+e^-$ and $\phi \rightarrow e^+e^-$ observations[28] we obtain along similar lines the respective values:

$$f_1^2 = 1.1 \pm 0.6 \qquad f_1^2 = 1.5 \pm 0.6 \tag{12-22}$$

These consistent results for f_1^2 indicate that $g \simeq 1$ [see formula (12-18)], that is, that the quark has no (or only a small) anomalous magnetic moment. In view of what has been said in the foregoing chapter, this points toward a mainly scalar binding potential. To repeat, this conclusion only holds if $f(V, 0)$ follows law (10-19).

We can easily verify that by calculating $\Gamma_{V\rightarrow l^+l^-}$ by means of a relativistic effective interaction of the form[76]

$$H = e g_{V\gamma}\, m_V^2\, V_\mu A_\mu \tag{12-23}$$

and comparing the result with Eq. (12-20) for $f_1^2 = 1$ we find for the vector meson–photon coupling constant $g_{V\gamma}$ the expression*

$$g_{V\gamma} = 2c_V f(V,0)/m_V^{3/2} \tag{12-24}$$

The use of Eq. (10-19) gives for $g_{\rho\gamma}$ the value $(m_\pi/m_\rho) = 0.18$, to be compared with the value of 0.183 obtained from the ρ-dominance model for the isovector form factor of the pion.[77]

12-4. ELECTROMAGNETIC DECAY OF π^0 AND η

Finally a few words about the processes $\pi^0 \to 2\gamma$ and $\eta \to 2\gamma$.[54, 73] These processes are supposed to occur according to the diagram in Figure 10,[78] in which V

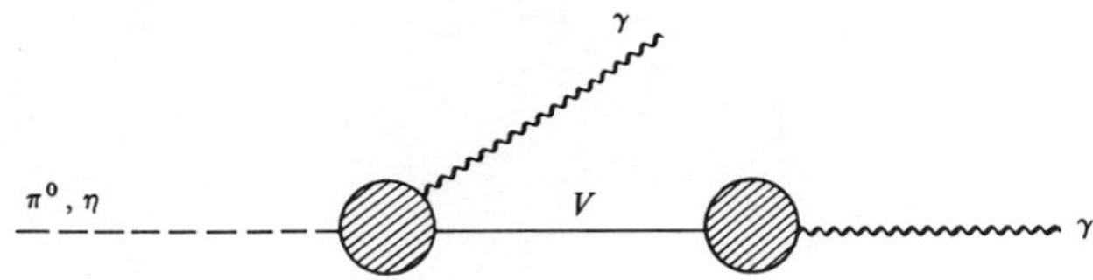

FIGURE 10. Assumed mechanism for $\pi^0 \to 2\gamma$ and $\eta \to 2\gamma$.

is any $L = 0$ neutral vector meson (the higher L states are neglected, which, of course, is an additional dynamical assumption). The emission of the first γ is assumed to occur through the same mechanism as that discussed for the $V \to \Pi\gamma$ decay, namely, spin flip of a quark or antiquark. The second photon results from the annihilation of the $q\bar{q}$ pair in V. Therefore the strength of the left vertex is determined by the parameter μ, which we identify with μ_P, while that of the right vertex is given by $g_{V\gamma}$, defined by Eq. (12-23). For the latter, the quark-model expression [Eq. (12-24)] is used, corresponding to $f_1^2 = 1$, with $f(V, 0)$ determined by Eqs. (10-19). Form factor effects are always neglected. We quote only the results[54]; they are

$$\Gamma_{\pi^0 \to 2\gamma} = 7.5 \text{ eV} \qquad \Gamma_{\eta \to 2\gamma} = 1 \text{ keV} \tag{12-25}$$

* The coupling constant $g_{V\gamma}$ is related to the constant γ_V, introduced in Ref. 77, by $g_{V\gamma} = 1/(2\gamma_V)$.

in which, in the second result, an η-η' mixing angle of -10° is used [see Eq. (8-19)]. The experimental value for $\Gamma_{\pi^0 \to 2\gamma}$ lies between 6.3 ± 1 and 9.2 ± 1.2 eV,[79] while for $\Gamma_{\eta \to 2\gamma}$ it is 0.88 ± 0.19 keV.[80] The agreement is suggestive and confirms results (12-21) and (12-22).

12-5. CONCLUSIONS

We can perhaps best summarize the results of the last three chapters by saying that the weak leptonic and electromagnetic decays considered here are consistently described by the nonrelativistic, independent quark model provided the following "rules of the game" are observed:

Neglect form factors and put overlap integrals equal to one.
Assume the validity of Eq. (10-19).
Assume that μ is the same for all hadrons.
Assume $g \simeq 1$; that is the anomalous magnetic moment of the quark is small.

Chapter 13

Strong Decay Processes

13-1. GENERAL REMARKS

When considering strong decay processes in the quark model, we are immediately faced with a number of fundamental difficulties. First, the interaction binding the quarks together and the one giving rise to the decay are both strong interactions, and it is in general not possible to isolate one from the other as we can for the weak and electromagnetic decays. Second, in the foregoing chapters processes of the type

$$A \rightarrow B + c \tag{13-1}$$

in which A and B are hadrons (either mesons or baryons) could simply be treated as the transition of a quark in A into a quark in B, thereby flipping its spin and/or changing its internal quantum numbers, accompanied by the emission of the system c, which was either a photon or a lepton pair. In strong decays, however, c is, for instance, a pion; that is, c is itself a quark–antiquark bound state, and the proper treatment of reaction (13-1) would require the solution of a many-body problem. Since this goes beyond our skill, the only thing we can do is to treat reaction (13-1) as analogous to the weak and electromagnetic decays, and consider c as a field quantum, ignoring its quark structure. This implies that in the decay process

$$\rho \rightarrow \pi + \pi$$

For instance, one of the pions is treated as a quark–antiquark system, the other as a field quantum emitted during the q–q or $\bar{q}$–$\bar{q}$ transition. In view of the first mentioned difficulty, this seems reasonable only if the emitted pion is soft, that is, has small momentum, and if the quark motion is nonrelativistic. Then, as is well known from nuclear physics, the coupling constant governing the emission process is strongly reduced and is small compared to the normal pion–nucleon coupling constant [see Eqs. (13-4) and (13-5) below]. In other words, the relevant interaction is essentially "weak" and can be treated as separate from the normal strong interactions.

We assume a nonrelativistic quark–pion interaction of the form

$$H^{q}_{\text{int}} = \pm \frac{f_q}{m_\pi} \int d^3x \bar{q}(x)\, \boldsymbol{\sigma} \alpha_k q(x) \cdot \boldsymbol{\nabla} \phi_k(x) \tag{13-2}$$

with ϕ_k the pion field with isotopic spin label k, and α_k ($k = 1, 2, 3$) the Pauli isospin matrices. The +(–) sign applies when the pion is emitted by a quark (antiquark). For the pion–nucleon interaction we have in the same limit

$$H_{int}^{N} = \pm \frac{f}{m_\pi} \int d^3 x \bar{N}(x) \boldsymbol{\sigma} \alpha_k N(x) \cdot \nabla \phi_k(x) \tag{13-3}$$

in which

$$f = \frac{m_\pi}{2m_P} g_{\pi N} \qquad \frac{f^2}{4\pi} = 0.082 \qquad \frac{g_{\pi N}^2}{4\pi} = 14.6 \tag{13-4}$$

Note, as mentioned above, that $f^2 \ll g_{\pi N}^2$. Now using Eq. (13-2) between nucleon states and comparing with Eq. (13-3) gives for the static pion–quark coupling constant

$$f_q = \tfrac{3}{5} f \tag{13-5}$$

The knowledge of this coupling constant enables us to obtain various decay widths by calculating the matrix element of H_{int}^{q} between the relevant hadron states.

13-2. DECAY OF BARYON RESONANCES

As a first example we compute the $B\Delta\pi$ vertex, in which B is a baryon and Δ a baryon resonance (with $L = 0$). We can restrict ourselves to $\Delta^{++} \to P + \pi^+$, all other transitions following by means of SU(3) transformations. The matrix element for (Δ^{++}, $s_z = 3/2$) $\to$ (P, $s_z = 1/2$) is easily seen to be

$$2i \frac{f_q}{m_\pi} (k_x + ik_y) \tag{13-6}$$

in which $\mathbf{k}$ is the pion center-of-mass momentum and in which we have used Eq. (5-12), thereby neglecting form factor effects, as usual. Similar expressions can be written for the other spin states. The spin-averaged squared matrix element becomes

$$|m|_{av}^2 = \frac{8}{3} k^2 \left(\frac{f_q}{m_\pi}\right)^2 = \frac{24}{25} k^2 \left(\frac{f^2}{m_\pi^2}\right) \tag{13-7}$$

leading to[29, 54, 81]

$$\Gamma_{\Delta^{++} \to P + \pi^+} = \frac{f^2}{4\pi} \frac{48}{25} \frac{k^3}{m_\pi^2} \frac{E_N}{m_\Delta} \tag{13-8}$$

In contrast to the radiative decays of the vector mesons, the factor E_N/m_Δ has to be retained in this expression because it also appears in the relativistic calculation. Substituting numbers we find

$$\Gamma_{\Delta^{++} \to P + \pi^+} = 80 \text{ MeV}$$

Without the factor E_N/m_Δ we would get 100 MeV. The experimental value is 120 MeV.

13-3. DECAY OF VECTOR MESONS

Along completely similar lines we treat the processes $V \to \Pi\Pi$, in which V is a vector meson and Π a pseudoscalar meson. We devote a few words to the decay $\rho^+ \to \pi^+ + \pi^0$. One of the pions is considered to be a $q\bar{q}$ state and one a field quantum. We can take either π^+ or π^0 as the $q\bar{q}$ state; the matrix element is the same in either case and is given for a $(\rho, s_z = 0) \to \pi$ transition by

$$m = \frac{f_q}{m_\pi} 2i\, k_z \tag{13-9}$$

in which $\mathbf{k}$ is the final center-of-mass momentum. The matrix element for the decay is the average of these two matrix elements and not their sum. This can be made clear from an argument based on the hypothesis of a partially conserved axial vector current (*PCAC*, see below). Consequently, the total matrix element for the decay of $(\rho, s_z = 0)$ is given by Eq. (13-9). Averaging over spins leads to[29, 54, 81]

$$|m|^2_{\text{av}} = \left(\frac{f_q}{m_\pi}\right)^2 \frac{4k^2}{3} \tag{13-10}$$

from which we calculate

$$\Gamma_{\rho \to \pi\pi} = 185 \text{ MeV} \tag{13-11}$$

form factor effects again being neglected. As stated before, there is a lot of confusion about the experimental value for the width of the ρ. The numbers vary between 95 and 170 MeV. At present the most probable value seems to be $\Gamma_{\rho \to \pi\pi} = 128$ MeV.[82]

It is interesting to note that the above results can also be obtained from the *PCAC* hypothesis.[54] This is another dynamical assumption, different from the one discussed in the first section, enabling us to calculate a strong decay $A \rightarrow B + \pi$ in terms of a transition matrix element between A and B. In this case this is the weak transition matrix element of the form

$$2\frac{f_q}{m_\pi} k_\mu \langle B | J^A_{\mu,k}(0) | A \rangle \tag{13-12}$$

in which $J^A_{\mu,k}$ is the axial vector current

$$J^A_{\mu,k} = i\bar{q}(x)\gamma_5\gamma_\mu\alpha_k q(x)$$

and k_μ is the pion four-momentum. In the nonrelativistic quark model this leads to matrix elements of the type given by Eq. (10-4). It is easy to see that for the decay $\rho^+ \rightarrow \pi^+ + \pi^0$ we obtain a matrix element identical to Eq. (13-9).

Finally, we note that several authors have calculated the decay widths of the L-excited states in the framework of the quark model.[83]

Note added in proof.

For an ideal meson nonet [in which the mixing angle between the $I = Y = 0$ states is equal to the value arctan ($\frac{1}{2}\sqrt{2}$) so that one of these states, call it D, contains only strange quarks (Chapter 5)], the additivity scheme (Figure 3) forbids decays of the type $D \rightarrow A + c$, where $c = \pi$ or γ and A is a hadron containing only non-strange quarks. This explains the experimental observation that the strong decay of ϕ and $f'(1500)$ occurs mainly in $K\bar{K}$ channels. [The fact that $\phi \rightarrow \rho\pi$ has been observed at all indicates a deviation of ϑ_V from the value arctan ($\frac{1}{2}\sqrt{2}$)]. For the same reason D-like particles are not produced in pion–nucleon reactions (Chapter 17).

Chapter 14

The Additivity Assumption For High-Energy Scattering

14-1. FORMULATION OF ADDITIVITY

In this and subsequent chapters we discuss another interesting and often surprisingly successful application of the quark model, namely, high-energy scattering of hadrons.[84-98] With "high energy" we have in mind the region $p_L \gtrsim 4$ GeV/c, in which p_L is the laboratory momentum of the incident particle. The highest value for p_L available with present accelerators is about 30 GeV/c for protons. This region is characterized by the fact that elastic and total cross sections are found to be smooth, slowly varying, in certain cases nearly constant, functions of p_L, without noticeable structure. At present, experimental high-energy data are available for hadron–hadron reactions with incident $\pi^{\pm}, K^{\pm}, P, \bar{P}$ on proton and neutron targets, the latter in the form of deuterons.

We begin with elastic reactions, that is, reactions of the type

$$A + B \rightarrow A + B \tag{14-1}$$

in which A and B are hadrons. (We neglect for the moment the complications due to spins.) The elastic scattering amplitude $T_{AB}(s, t)$ is defined by

$$\langle A, p_A'; B, p_B'|\tau|A, p_A; B, p_B\rangle = i\,\delta^{(4)}(p_A' + p_B' - p_A - p_B)\,T_{AB}(s,t) \tag{14-2}$$

$$s = -(p_A + p_B)^2 \qquad t = -(p_A' - p_A)^2$$

in which $\tau = i(1 - S)$ is the scattering operator, and p and p' are the initial and final four-momenta. In the center-of-mass system s = (total energy)^2 and t = −(momentum transfer)^2. Note that T_{AB} and the quark amplitude T_{ij} introduced below are noncovariant amplitudes, that is, S-matrix elements.* This means that their normalization is such that at high energy, s independence of the amplitudes implies s independence of total and elastic cross sections. The optical theorem reads, in the high-energy limit,

$$\sigma_T(AB) = 4\pi^2\, Im\, T_{AB}(s, 0) \tag{14-3}$$

* Because of this T_{AB} does not depend only on the invariants s and t, but also explicitly on the energies of A and B. For the following, however, the notation T_{AB} (s, t) does not give rise to confusion.

in which $\sigma_T(AB)$ is the total cross section for scattering of hadrons A and B, while for the differential elastic cross section $d\sigma_{el}(AB)/dt$ we have

$$\frac{d\sigma_{el}(AB)}{dt} = \pi^3 |T_{AB}(s,t)|^2 \tag{14-4}$$

The basic assumption we make in applying the quark model to high-energy scattering is the additivity assumption[84, 85] expressed by Figure 3, in which T_{AB} is written as the sum of all possible elastic amplitudes T_{ij} for the scattering of a quark or antiquark i in A with a quark or antiquark j in B, as follows[86] (see Appendix):

$$T_{AB}(s,t) = \sum_{ij} F_i^A(t) F_j^B(t) T_{ij}(s,t) \tag{14-5}$$

This amounts to the so-called impulse approximation. Each quark i in hadron A is considered to act as a quasifree particle whose binding within the hadron is described by a form factor $F_i^A(t)$ with $F_i^A(0) = 1$, giving the overlap between the quark wave function of the final hadron A and the wave function obtained by action of the quark scattering operator on quark i in the initial hadron A, the remaining quarks of A being unaffected. Similarly, we have form factors $F_j^B(t)$ for the quarks in B. We are of course not yet able to calculate the shape of these form factors. The quark amplitudes T_{ij} are assumed not to depend on the labels A and B; that is, for fixed i and j they are assumed the same for all hadrons. This amounts to a kind of universality assumption, stating the equivalence of quarks constituting mesons and quarks constituting baryons.

We expect that Eq. (14-5) is applicable only at high energy ($s \gtrsim 10$ GeV^2), at which effects due to s-channel resonances are unimportant, and small momentum transfer [$|t| \lesssim 1$ (GeV/c)^2]. It should be mentioned that SU(3) or SU(6) need not be exact symmetries of the S matrix; as noted before, the only point at which they intervene in the quark model is in the construction of the bound-state wave functions.

The energy dependence of T_{ij} in Eq. (14-5), describing an elastic quark–quark, quark–antiquark, or antiquark–antiquark reaction, deserves a comment. The value of $T_{ij}(s, t)$ for given s and t, and fixed quark labels i and j will, in general, not be the same for a nucleon–nucleon and a meson–nucleon collision, the reason being that the c.m. energy of the $q_i + q_j$ collision is different for the two cases and unequal to the energy of the $A + B$ collision. If the meson and baryon have the same laboratory momentum p_L, the effective momenta of the constituting quarks should be on the average $\frac{1}{2} p_L$ and $\frac{1}{3} p_L$, respectively. This makes sense only if the scattering quarks can be considered as having effective masses of the order m_A/n or m_B/n, in which n is the number of quarks in A or B. Therefore, in checking relations obtained from Eq. (14-5) by eliminating quark amplitudes that involve both meson–baryon and baryon–baryon cross sections, these cross sections should be taken at laboratory momenta in the ratio 2 to 3, respectively.[86, 88]

14-2. NONADDITIVITY OF BARYON-ANTIBARYON ANNIHILATION PROCESSES

Before applying the additivity assumption to specific processes, we have to make an important restriction concerning its applicability to antibaryon–baryon and baryon–baryon reactions.[91] Consider the imaginary parts of the elastic amplitudes together with the unitarity condition

$$Im\, T_{AB}(s,t) = \sum_n \langle AB|\tau^\dagger|n\rangle\langle n|\tau|AB\rangle \qquad (14\text{-}6)$$

in which the sum extends over all elastic and inelastic intermediate states and where τ is the properly normalized scattering operator. Conservation of energy and momentum is assumed to be taken into account. In the forward direction we have, using Eq. (14-3),

$$\sigma_T(AB) = 4\pi^2 \sum_n \langle AB|\tau^\dagger|n\rangle\langle n|\tau|AB\rangle|_{t=0} \qquad (14\text{-}7)$$

If in Eqs. (14-6) and (14-7) $A = \bar{B}'$ = antibaryon and B = baryon, at finite energies, an appreciable contribution to the sum over n comes from annihilation channels $\bar{B}' + B \rightarrow$ mesons (Figure 11). Since such processes involve baryon, or triple quark,

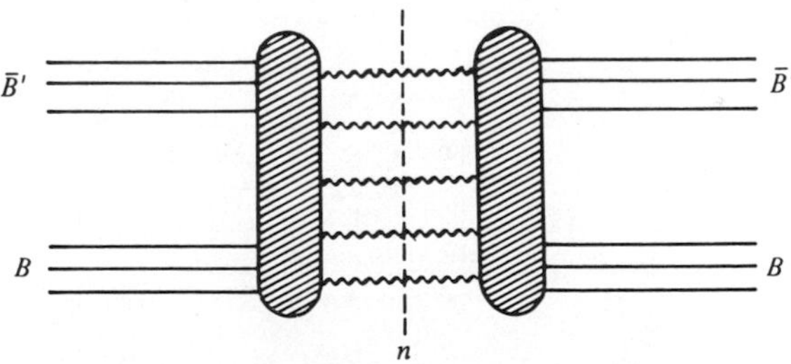

FIGURE 11. Diagram representing antibaryon–baryon annihilation contributions to the sum in Eqs. (14-6) and (14-7). The solid lines represent quarks and antiquarks, the wavy lines mesons.

exchange, they can clearly not be described by the additivity formula. In other words, Figure 12, which describes Eqs. (14-6) or (14-7) under the additivity assumption, cannot be a good approximation of the annihilation process of Figure 11. Consequently, $\bar{B}'B$ annihilation contributions have to be excluded from the additivity assumption for the *imaginary part* of the $\bar{B}'B$ amplitude [a similar restriction applies to meson–baryon backward scattering: its contribution to the sum in Eq. (14-6) for small angle meson–baryon scattering is, however, very small. Also negligible are effects due to double charge and/or strangeness exchange, which fall under this restriction too]. For these contributions an assumption of a multiplicative, rather than an additive, type to express them in terms of quarks seems more natural (see Chapter 18). The exclusion of annihilation processes from the additivity assumption for $Im\ T_{\bar{B}'B}$ may in general affect $Im\ T_{B'B}$, as well as $Re\ T_{\bar{B}'B}$ and $Re\ T_{B'B}$, because these amplitudes are related by crossing relations. As long as we consider only total cross sections this question is of no importance, because for $t = 0$ the correction due to the annihilation part of $Im\ T_{\bar{B}'B}$ is reflected mainly in $Re\ T_{B'B}$.[91] It may become very important for differential cross sections and for inelastic reactions (Chapter 17).

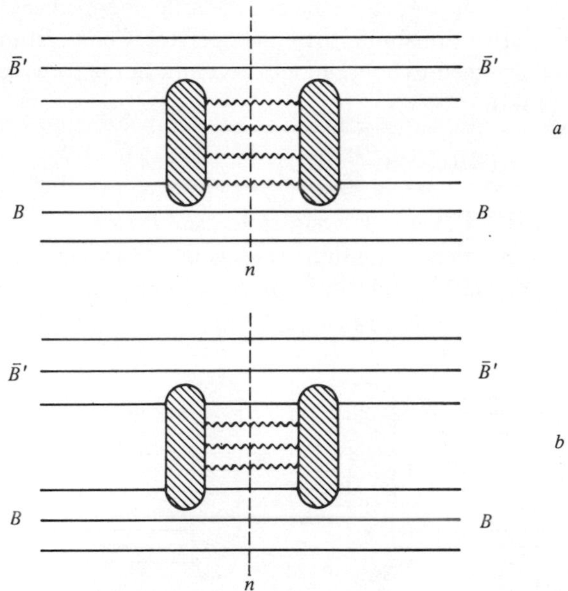

FIGURE 12. Diagrams describing, for antibaryon-baryon scattering, the sum in Eqs. (14-6) and (14-7) under the additivity assumption for quark amplitudes, with (diagram a) and without (diagram b) quark-antiquark annihilation. Similar diagrams can be drawn for baryon-baryon and meson-baryon scattering.

The part to be excluded in the additivity scheme from the sum in Eq. (14-7) for $\sigma_T(\bar{B}'B)$ is the cross section for annihilation $\sigma_A(\bar{B}'B)$,

$$\sigma_A(\bar{B}'B) = \sum_{n'} \langle \bar{B}'B|\tau^\dagger|n'\rangle\langle n'|\tau|\bar{B}'B\rangle|_{t=0} \tag{14-8}$$

in which $|n'\rangle$ contains only mesons. This is an experimental quantity, however, only one high-energy annihilation cross section has been measured so far,* namely $\sigma_A(\bar{P}P) =$

*See also T. Ferbel *et al.*, *Phys. Rev.* **173,** 1307 (1968), who report a measurement at 6.94 GeV.

22.5 ± 2 mb at $p_L = 5.7$ GeV/c.[99] At this momentum we have $\sigma_T(\bar{P}P) = 62.5 \pm 1$ mb and $\sigma_T(PP) = 41.0 \pm 1$ mb, so that

$$\sigma_A(\bar{P}P) = [\sigma_T(\bar{P}P) - \sigma_T(PP)] \pm (1-2)\text{mb} \tag{14-9}$$

In order to be able to compare our theoretical results with experiment, we assume that Eq. (14-9) continues to hold for $p_L \gtrsim 6$ GeV/c, and that the part of the total cross section $\sigma_T(\bar{B}'B)$, which is additive in the quark amplitudes, is $\sigma_T(\bar{B}'B) - \sigma_A(\bar{B}'B)$. As long as accurate data on annihilation cross sections are lacking, a more rigorous procedure, which takes care of small corrections owing to the fact that annihilation and nonannihilation contributions are not completely independent,[100] does not make much sense.

The diagrams of Figure 12 describe the two types of contributions for $B\,B'$ reactions that approximate the nonannihilation part of Eq. (14-6) in the additivity scheme. Similar diagrams can be drawn for baryon–baryon and meson–baryon scattering. The right-hand side of Figure 12a contains antiquark–quark annihilation, that is, single quark exchange between hadrons A and B in $\langle AB|\tau|n\rangle$. Such inelastic reactions, however, have never been found to occur experimentally. We therefore expect that only the diagrams of the type depicted in Figure 12b, and not those of Figure 12a, can provide a good approximation of the nonannihilation part of the sum in Eq. (14-6). Hence, we also exclude antiquark–quark annihilation contributions of the type given by Figure 12a from the additivity scheme. We come back to this point in Section 16-2. Note that if quarks do not exist as separate particles but only in bound combinations,[21] it would be clear *a priori* that a process similar to that shown in Figure 12a cannot exist.

14-3. THREE CLASSES OF INELASTIC FINAL STATES

For future purposes it is useful to make a few more remarks about the different types of channels n that make up the total cross section $\sigma_T(AB)$ according to Eq. (14-7). Consider the reaction

$$A + B \rightarrow \text{inelastic final state } n$$

in the c.m. system. The jet structure of high-energy inelastic collisions (small transverse momenta in c.m.) suggests that the particles in the final state may be roughly divided into two groups A' and B', one containing the particles that go forward in the c.m. system and one containing the particles going backward. In general, A' and B' are many-particle systems. In analogy with two-body reactions, we can now, according to the possible exchanges in the t channel in reactions of the type $A + B \rightarrow A' + B'$, roughly subdivide the contributions to the sum in Eq. (14-7), that is, to $\sigma_T(AB)$, into three classes [the same, of course, holds for Eq. (14-6)]:

(1) annihilation or baryon exchange contributions $\sigma_A(AB)$;
(2) charge, isospin, and strangeness exchange contributions $\sigma_E(AB)$; and
(3) Pomeranchuk contributions $\sigma_P(AB)$.

Class (1) contributes only when A and B have opposite baryon number. Class (3) refers to those contributions for which vanishing internal quantum numbers are exchanged in the t channel of $A + B \to A' + B'$. Since cross sections for exchange reactions are always found to decrease with increasing energy, one expects that at very high energies only the contributions from class (3) survive, that is,

$$\frac{\sigma_A}{\sigma_P} \to 0 \qquad \frac{\sigma_E}{\sigma_P} \to 0 \qquad \text{for } s \to \infty \tag{14-10}$$

and that at finite energies the measured differences $\sigma_T(\bar{A}B) - \sigma_T(AB)$ are mainly determined by contributions of classes (1) and (2).

As a consequence of the above subdivision we may write approximately

$$\sigma_T(AB) = \sigma_P(AB) + \sigma_A(AB) + \sigma_E(AB) \tag{14-11}$$

(We neglect the fact that, in general, the three types of contributions affect each other due to absorption corrections.[100] For instance, the presence of σ_A affects σ_{el} and hence σ_P.) The contribution from elastic final states in Eq. (14-7), being mainly diffractive, is supposed to be included in σ_P. From Eq. (14-11) simple inequalities between total cross sections follow.[88] For instance:

$$\sigma_T(PN) > \sigma_T(PP) \tag{14-12}$$

which one obtains by noting that $\sigma_P(PP) \simeq \sigma_P(PN)$, $\sigma_A(PP) = \sigma_A(PN) = 0$, and $\sigma_E(PN) > \sigma_E(PP)$, the last inequality arising from the fact that charge can be exchanged in more ways between N and P than between P and P. Similarly, because of strong annihilation contributions in $\bar{P}N$, we have

$$\sigma_T(\bar{P}N) > \sigma_T(PP) \tag{14-13}$$

Similar inequalities can be obtained for meson–baryon scattering. Although these considerations are very crude, all inequalities between measured high-energy cross sections derived on the basis of Eq. (14-11) appear to agree with the facts.[88]

Chapter 15

Elastic Scattering in the Limit $s \to \infty$

We briefly discuss the implications of Eq. (14-5) in the limit $s \to \infty$ and for small scattering angles, corresponding to a t interval of, for example, $0 \leqslant |t| \lesssim 1\ (\mathrm{GeV/c})^2$, which is the region of the forward diffraction peak. This peak is known to dominate high-energy elastic scattering, making up almost all of the total elastic cross section. It is generally believed that for the above values of s and t the elastic scattering amplitude $T_{AB}(s, t)$ becomes purely imaginary (purely diffractive or shadow scattering). (For a review of general questions concerning high-energy scattering, see, for instance, Reference 88.) In fact, the recent Brookhaven measurements[101] on $\pi^{\pm}P$ and PP scattering in the momentum interval $8 \lesssim p_L \lesssim 26$ GeV/c have clearly shown that the ratio $Re\, T_{AB}(s, 0)/Im\, T_{AB}(s, 0)$ is quite small at high energies, about -0.13 for $\pi^- P$, -0.19 for $\pi^+ P$, and -0.27 for PP at 14 GeV/c, and is steadily decreasing in absolute magnitude with increasing energy. The total cross sections and the differential elastic cross sections $d\sigma/dt$ in the region of the forward diffraction peak seem to become energy-independent in the asymptotic limit, and are believed to satisfy the Pomeranchuk theorems[102]

$$\left.\begin{aligned} \sigma_T(AB) &= \sigma_T(\bar{A}B) \\ \frac{d\sigma_{el}(AB)}{dt} &= \frac{d\sigma_{el}(\bar{A}B)}{dt} \end{aligned}\right\} s \to \infty \tag{15-1}$$

whereas the cross sections for exchange reactions σ_A and σ_E, defined in Section 14-3, are expected to vanish in this limit.

We assume that the above properties also hold for quark–quark and antiquark–quark scattering. Restricting ourselves to pion–nucleon and nucleon–nucleon scattering, that is, to nonstrange quarks, we can then write asymptotically

$$T_{AB}(s,t) \overset{s\to\infty}{=} ig(t)\Big[\sum_i F_i^A(t)\Big]\Big[\sum_j F_j^B(t)\Big] \tag{15-2}$$

with

$$T_{ij}(s,t) \overset{s\to\infty}{=} ig_{ij}(t), \quad g_{ij} \text{ real} \tag{15-3}$$

$$g_{\bar{p}p} = g_{\bar{n}n} = g_{pp} = g_{nn} = g_{pn} = g_{\bar{p}n} = g_{p\bar{n}} = g \tag{15-4}$$

in which we have used isospin and charge conjugation invariance. Equation (15-2) and the analogous equations for T_{AA} and T_{BB} immediately imply the factorization property,[86] valid for $s \to \infty$,

$$[T_{AB}(s,t)]^2 = T_{AA}(s,t)\, T_{BB}(s,t) \tag{15-5}$$

predicted before in the Regge pole model.[103]

As another interesting implication, we can obtain from Eq. (15-2) in two extreme cases an understanding of why additivity can be a good approximation.[86–88] Case I is obtained when the entire t dependence of $\lim_{s\to\infty} T_{AB}(s, t)$ in the region of the diffraction peak, that is, $|t| \lesssim 1\ (\mathrm{GeV}/c)^2$, comes from the quark amplitude $g(t)$, that is, when in that region the form factors F are approximately constant and equal to one. In that case Eq. (15-2) becomes

$$T_{AB}(s,t) \overset{s\to\infty}{=} ig(t)\, n_A n_B \tag{15-6}$$

in which n_A and n_B are the number of quarks composing A and B. This equation implies that all nonstrange hadrons have asymptotic diffraction curves ($d\sigma_{el}/dt$ versus t) of the same shape, which is in accordance with the experimental facts. Indeed, all high-energy hadron diffraction curves measured so far can be parametrized in the form[104]

$$\frac{d\sigma_{el}}{dt} = \left(\frac{d\sigma_{el}}{dt}\right)_{t=0} e^{at+bt^2} \qquad b^2/a \ll 1 \tag{15-7}$$

with the slopes a for pion–nucleon and nucleon–nucleon scattering varying not at all or only slowly with the energy and tending to a common asymptotic value of about $9(\mathrm{GeV}/c)^{-2}$ Moreover, it follows from Eq. (15-6) that this common value of a for the hadrons is identical to that for quark scattering, since both for quarks and for hadrons the t dependence of the scattering is described by the same function $g(t)$. Since the size of a particle is related to the slope of its diffraction curve, this means that in this extreme case quarks have roughly the same size as hadrons. At the same time, however, we have from additivity and the Pomeranchuk theorem [Eq. (15-1)] (applied to quarks)

$$\sigma_T^{(\infty)}(qq) = \tfrac{1}{9}\,\sigma_T^{(\infty)}(PP) \tag{15-8}$$

in which $\sigma_T^{(\infty)}(AB)$ is the asymptotic value of the AB total cross section. These two conclusions can be compatible only if the quarks have very weak absorption, that is, are very transparent, about nine times more than protons. It is this high transparency that in the present picture may give an *a posteriori* justification for the additivity assumption.

Case II is the opposite of Case I. The t dependence of $\lim_{s\to\infty} T_{AB}(s, t)$ in the diffraction peak is assumed now to be entirely determined by the form factors in Eq. (15-2); that is, $g(t)$ is constant in t. In this case the quarks have spatial dimensions that are small compared to those of the corresponding hadrons. This small size of the quarks makes multiple scattering effects rare, so that also in this extreme picture we can understand why additivity works.

A remarkable relation is obtained[87, 88] by noting that the form factors $F_i^{A,B}(t)$ should, in this limiting case of small quarks composing large hadrons with the quarks carrying the charge, be proportional to the electromagnetic form factors $G_E^{A,B}(t)$ for hadrons A and B. Using this in Eq. (15-2) with $g(t) \equiv g(0)$ for small t we obtain, for the case of proton–proton scattering,

$$\frac{d\sigma_{el}(PP)}{dt} = \left[\frac{d\sigma_{el}(PP)}{dt}\right]_{t=0} [G_E^P(t)]^4 \qquad (15\text{-}9)$$

which, as shown by Figure 13, is in excellent agreement with experiment for the range $|t| \lesssim 1$ (GeV/c)^2. (Using completely different arguments, Wu and Yang[105]

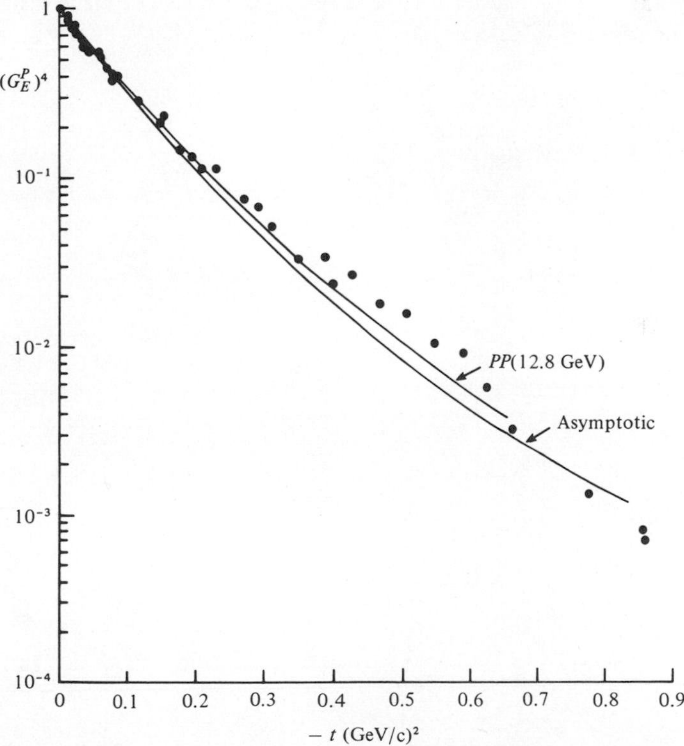

FIGURE 13. Demonstration of relation (15-9). The full lines represent $[d\sigma_{el}(PP)/dt]/[d\sigma_{el}(PP)/dt]_{t=0}$ at 12.8 GeV and the asymptotic curve obtained by extrapolating measured PP and $\bar{P}P$ diffraction curves to infinite energy. The dots give the fourth power of the nucleon electromagnetic form factor.

derived this relation for the case of large t, corresponding to scattering angles near 90°. Here agreement with experiment seems to be less good.) For πP scattering, the corresponding relation is

$$\frac{d\sigma_{el}(\pi P)}{dt} = \left[\frac{d\sigma_{el}(\pi P)}{dt}\right]_{t=0} [G_E^P(t)]^2 \, [G_E^\pi(t)]^2 \tag{15-10}$$

From the above-mentioned experimental fact that the πP and PP diffraction curves have similar slopes at very high energies, we may conclude, on the basis of these relations, that the same should be true for $G_E^P(t)$ and $G_E^\pi(t)$. The shape of the latter is not yet fully measured; however, a recent experiment[62] has shown that the rms charge radius of the pion is, within the experimental uncertainties, equal to that of the proton, the two values being 0.80 ± 0.10 and 0.81 ± 0.01 f, respectively, in support of the above conclusion.

It should be mentioned that the above relations can also be made plausible in the extreme case I.[88]

Chapter 16

Relations Between Total Cross Sections

16-1. DISCUSSION OF THE VARIOUS RELATIONS

We now use the additivity assumption, limited to nonannihilation contributions as discussed in Chapter 14, to derive certain relations between hadron spin-averaged total cross sections. The latter provide a clean test for additivity, because, since we only need the elastic amplitudes at $t = 0$ [see Eq. (14-3)], all form factors can be put equal to one, and, since we consider spin-averaged cross sections, spin couplings are rigorously taken into account by simply ignoring them. From Eqs. (14-3) and (14-5), the following expressions for the spin-averaged cross sections are obtained

$$\tilde{S}^{\pm}(PP) = 5\tilde{S}^{\pm}(pp) + 4\tilde{S}^{\pm}(np) \tag{16-1a}$$

$$\tilde{S}^{\pm}(PN) = 4\tilde{S}^{\pm}(pp) + 5\tilde{S}^{\pm}(np) \tag{16-1b}$$

$$S^{+}(\pi^{+}P) = 3\tilde{S}^{+}(pp) + 3\tilde{S}^{+}(np) \tag{16-1c}$$

$$S^{-}(\pi^{+}P) = \tilde{S}^{-}(pp) - \tilde{S}^{-}(np) \tag{16-1d}$$

$$S^{\pm}(K^{+}P) = 2\tilde{S}^{\pm}(pp) + \tilde{S}^{\pm}(np) \pm 3\tilde{S}^{\pm}(\lambda p) \tag{16-1e}$$

$$S^{\pm}(K^{+}N) = \tilde{S}^{\pm}(pp) + 2\tilde{S}^{\pm}(np) \pm 3\tilde{S}^{\pm}(\lambda p) \tag{16-1f}$$

with the definitions

$$\begin{aligned} \tilde{S}^{\pm}(AB) &= S^{\pm}(AB) - \sigma_A(\bar{A}B) \\ S^{\pm}(AB) &= \sigma_T(\bar{A}B) \pm \sigma_T(AB) \end{aligned} \tag{16-2}$$

in which A and B may refer to hadrons as well as to quarks. In all equations the upper or the lower signs have to be taken simultaneously. For A = meson and B = baryon, $\tilde{S}^{\pm}(AB)$ and $S^{\pm}(AB)$ are of course identical. In writing Eqs. (16-1) we used isospin and charge conjugation invariance, but no higher symmetries. These equations, which involve only measured cross sections on the left-hand side, imply four relations between the quantities $\tilde{S}^{\pm}$, namely

$$S^{-}(K^{+}P) - S^{-}(K^{+}N) = S^{-}(\pi^{+}P) \tag{16-3a}$$

$$\tilde{S}^{+}(PP) + \tilde{S}^{+}(PN) = 3S^{+}(\pi^{+}P) \tag{16-3b}$$

$$\tilde{S}^{+}(PP) - \tilde{S}^{+}(PN) = S^{+}(K^{+}P) - S^{+}(K^{+}N) \tag{16-3c}$$

$$\tilde{S}^{-}(PP) - \tilde{S}^{-}(PN) = S^{-}(\pi^{+}P) \tag{16-3d}$$

It goes without saying that the neglect of contributions of type a in Figure 12, as a consequence of which $\tilde{S}^{\pm}(qq')$, rather than $S^{\pm}(qq')$, appears on the right of Eq. (16-1), has no bearing on the resulting sum rules for hadronic cross sections (compare Section 16-2).

When comparing relations (16-3) with experiment, we use the data of Galbraith *et al.*,[106] because here we have a single experiment in which all cross sections occurring on the left of Eqs. (16-1) are measured in the range $6 \leqslant p_L \leqslant 18$ GeV/c. The recent, more accurate data of Foley *et al.*[101, 107] unfortunately concern only $\pi^{\pm}P$ and PP total cross sections.

Relation (16-3a) is the so-called "good" Johnson–Treiman relation.[85] It agrees very well with the data, as shown by Table 9 in which the comparison with experiment is made.

Table 9. Comparison of Relation (16-3a) with Experiment.

p_L	$S^-(K^+P) - S^-(K^+N)$	$S^-(\pi^+P)$
6	2.6 ± 0.4 mb	2.3 ± 0.2 mb
12	1.7 ± 0.4	1.7 ± 0.2
18	1.2 ± 0.6	1.5 ± 0.2

As to relations (16-3b, c, d)[91] a detailed comparison with experiment has to await better data on nucleon–antinucleon annihilation at high energy. In particular, this is true for relations (16-3c) and (16-3d), which involve cross-section differences of the order of the error in Eq. (14-9), so that a significant test is not possible at present; these relations are, however, fully compatible with the data. To compare relation (16-3b) with the data we make use of Eq. (14-9), which can be written as $\tilde{S}^-(PP) \simeq 0$. Using this in relation (16-3d), we obtain $\tilde{S}^-(PN) \simeq - S^-(\pi^+P)$, so that $\tilde{S}^+(PP) \simeq 2\sigma_T(PP)$ and $\tilde{S}^+(PN) \simeq 2\sigma_T(PN) - S^-(\pi^+P)$. Remembering that we have to compare nucleon–nucleon and meson–nucleon cross sections at laboratory momenta in the ratio 3/2 (compare Section 14-1), we find for the left- and right-hand sides of relation (16-3b), respectively:

$$157 \pm 3 \text{ mb} \qquad 157.8 \pm 0.6 \text{ mb at } p_L^{\pi} = 8 \text{ GeV/c}, \quad p_L^{P} = 12 \text{ GeV/c}$$

$$154 \pm 3 \text{ mb} \qquad 150.0 \pm 0.6 \text{ mb at } p_L^{\pi} = 12 \text{ GeV/c}, \quad p_L^{P} = 18 \text{ GeV/c}$$

Hence this sum rule is satisfied to within a few per cent. Note that the agreement would have been poor if annihilation contributions had been included on the left-hand side of this relation, increasing the latter by 15–20%.

In the limit $s \to \infty$, relation (16-3b) becomes[84, 85]

$$\frac{\sigma_T^{(\infty)}(\pi P)}{\sigma_T^{(\infty)}(PP)} = \frac{2}{3} \tag{16-4}$$

in which we have used Eq. (14-10) and the Pomeranchuk theorem for total cross sections [Eq. (15-1)]. A recent Regge pole fit by Rarita *et al.*[108] to the new cross-section data obtained by Foley *et al.*,[101, 107] as well as to all the previous high-energy πP, PP, and $\bar{P}P$ scattering data, predicts $\sigma_T^{(\infty)}(\pi P) = 21.4$ mb and $\sigma_T^{(\infty)}(PP) =$ 34.8 mb, and hence, for the ratio in Eq. (16-4), the value 0.62, very close to the quark model prediction. From Eq. (15-5) we have, of course,

$$[\sigma_T^{(\infty)}(\pi P)]^2 = \sigma_T^{(\infty)}(\pi\pi)\,\sigma_T^{(\infty)}(PP) \tag{16-5}$$

Relations between asymptotic total cross sections involving strange baryons are given in Reference 86.

Of the many other sum rules for high-energy total cross sections following directly from additivity (plus, eventually, isospin and charge conjugation invariance) only three involve measured cross sections. They can be written in the form

$$\sigma_T(\Lambda P) = \sigma_T(PP) + \sigma_T(K^- N) - \sigma_T(\pi^+ P) \tag{16-6a}$$

$$\sigma_T(\rho^0 P) = \tfrac{1}{2} S^+(\pi^+ P) \tag{16-6b}$$

$$\sigma_T(\phi P) = \tfrac{1}{2}[S^+(K^+ P) + S^+(K^+ N) - S^+(\pi^+ P)] \tag{16-6c}$$

The first one predicts for $\sigma_T(\Lambda P)$ at 6 GeV/c the value 36 ± 1 mb, in agreement with recent measurements at $p_L \leqslant 5$ GeV/c.[109] The neutral vector meson–proton cross sections on the left of Eqs. (16-6b, c) were obtained recently in a beautiful experiment[110] by measuring the cross section for photoproduction of vector mesons on complex nuclei. In the momentum range $2.7 < p_L < 4.5$ GeV/c the experimental values are found to be $\sigma_T(\rho^0 P) = 31.3 \pm 2.3$ mb and $\sigma_T(\phi P) =$ 13.3 ± 2.7 mb. This is in excellent agreement with the theoretical values, averaged over the same range, of about 30 and 14 mb respectively, obtained from the above relations by using the results of Reference 106.

From formula (16-1) we can obtain further relations between measured cross sections if we make some extra assumptions concerning $\tilde{S}^{\pm}(qq')$. In the first place, assuming in Eq. (16-1) the condition

$$\tilde{S}^+(pp) + \tilde{S}^+(np) = 4\tilde{S}^+(\lambda p) \tag{16-7}$$

we obtain[91]

$$3S^{+}(\pi^{+}P) = 2[S^{+}(K^{+}P) + S^{+}(K^{+}N)] \tag{16-8}$$

This relation is remarkably successful in the whole range $6 \lesssim p_L \lesssim 18$ GeV/c. For instance, at 10 GeV/c we have 154 and 156 mb at left and right, respectively. We thus have the empirical fact that the quark cross sections satisfy condition (16-7); its dynamical meaning, however, is unclear. It is interesting to write relations (16-3b) and (16-8) in slightly different form by introducing the average cross sections S_P, S_π, S_K, S_p, S_λ, defined as

$$\begin{aligned} \tilde{S}_P &= \tfrac{1}{4}[\tilde{S}^{+}(PP) + \tilde{S}^{+}(PN)] \\ S_\pi &= \tfrac{1}{2}S^{+}(\pi^{+}P) \\ S_K &= \tfrac{1}{4}[S^{+}(K^{+}P) + S^{+}(K^{+}N)] \\ \tilde{S}_p &= \tfrac{1}{4}[\tilde{S}^{+}(pp) + \tilde{S}^{+}(pn)] \\ \tilde{S}_\lambda &= \tfrac{1}{2}\tilde{S}^{+}(\lambda p) \end{aligned} \tag{16-9}$$

We can then write formulas (16-3b), (16-7), and (16-8) as

$$\begin{aligned} \tilde{S}_P : S_\pi : S_K &= 6:4:3 \\ \tilde{S}_p : \tilde{S}_\lambda &= 2:1 \end{aligned} \tag{16-10}$$

Extrapolating to $s \to \infty$ gives, as a generalization of Eq. (16-4),

$$\begin{aligned} \sigma_T^{(\infty)}(PP) : \sigma_T^{(\infty)}(\pi P) : \sigma_T^{(\infty)}(KP) &= 6:4:3 \\ \sigma_T^{(\infty)}(pp) &= 2\sigma_T^{(\infty)}(\lambda p) \end{aligned} \tag{16-11}$$

Note that the smallness of $\tilde{S}_\lambda$ as compared to $\tilde{S}_p$, which is here derived from the π- and K-nucleon scattering data, is reflected in the smallness of $\sigma_T(\phi P)$ with regard to $\sigma_T(\rho^{\circ} P)$. (Remember that ϕ contains only strange quarks.) In fact, Eqs. (16-6) and (16-10) correspond to

$$\frac{\sigma_T(\phi P)}{\sigma_T(\rho^0 P)} = \frac{1}{2}$$

As seen above, recent experiments support this result.

Next, SU(3) invariance, that is,

$$\tilde{S}^{\pm}(np) = \tilde{S}^{\pm}(\lambda p) \tag{16-12}$$

gives two further relations, namely,

$$\tfrac{1}{2}S^-(K^+P) = S^-(\pi^+P) \tag{16-13}$$

$$\tilde{S}^+(PP) = 2S^+(\pi^+P) - \tfrac{1}{2}S^+(K^+P) \tag{16-14}$$

Comparing formula (16-12) with (16-16) below shows that SU(3) is badly broken for the quark cross sections, reflecting the well-known fact that the Johnson–Treiman relation [Eq. (16-13)] is not as good as Eq. (16-3a). [Strictly speaking, SU(3) is not needed to obtain Eq. (16-13); what is required is the condition $S^-(\lambda p) = S^-(np)$, which is not necessarily a reflection of SU(3) symmetry.[90]] Relation (16-14) agrees very well with the facts because it is much less sensitive to symmetry breaking than relation (16-13). Again the agreement would have been much worse if annihilation contributions were included on the left-hand side.

Finally, we briefly consider reactions involving deuterons. Treating the deuteron (denoted by D) as a single isoscalar object and using additivity and isospin invariance, we obtain the relation, analogous to formula (16-3b),

$$\tilde{S}^+(PD) = \tfrac{3}{2}S^+(\pi^+D) \tag{16-15}$$

in which the tilde on the left-hand side indicates that contributions due to annihilation of P with one of the nucleons composing the deuteron should be subtracted from $\sigma_T(\ D)$. Because of lack of data for these contributions, we cannot test formula (16-15) directly. However, using the Glauber formula[111]

$$\sigma_T(AD) = \sigma_T(AP) + \sigma_T(AN) - \frac{\langle r^{-2}\rangle}{4\pi}\,\sigma_T(AP)\,\sigma_T(AN)$$

in which r measures the separation of the nucleons inside the deuteron, and noting that, for the nonannihilation parts, the Glauber correction terms are to first approximation the same for $A = P$ and $A = \bar{P}$, we have

$$\tilde{S}^-(PD) \simeq \tilde{S}^-(PP) + \tilde{S}^-(PN) \simeq -S^-(\pi^+P)$$

in which we have used formulas (14-9) and (16-1). Therefore $\tilde{S}^+(PD) \simeq 2\sigma_T(PD) - S^-(\pi^+P)$. With this result we find, using the data of Reference 106, at $p_L^\pi = 10$, 12, 14 GeV/c and $p_L^{\bar{P}} = {}^3\!/_2\, p_L^\pi$, $\tilde{S}^+(PD)/S^+(\pi^+D) = 1.48$, 1.50, 1.51, respectively, to be compared with the value of 1.50 predicted by relation (16-15).

We may conclude that the quark model with additivity assumption for the nonannihilation parts of the elastic amplitudes is in excellent agreement with the data as far as high-energy total cross sections are concerned. Why this simple model works so well is a mystery. Although, as we saw in Chapter 15, in certain extreme cases we may obtain *a posteriori* justifications for the additivity hypothesis, *a priori* dynamical justifications are lacking.

16-2. CROSS SECTIONS FOR QUARK SCATTERING

By inserting the data on the left of relation (16-1) we can obtain numbers for the quark "cross sections." At 10 GeV/c one gets, taking $\tilde{S}^-(PP) = 0$ and using the data of Reference 106,

$$\tilde{S}^-(pp) \simeq 0.9 \text{ mb} \qquad \tilde{S}^-(np) \simeq -1.1\text{mb} \qquad \tilde{S}^-(\lambda p) \simeq -1.5 \text{ mb}$$
$$\tilde{S}^+(pp) \simeq 9.5 \text{ mb} \qquad \tilde{S}^+(np) \simeq 7.7 \text{ mb} \qquad \tilde{S}^+(\lambda p) \simeq 4.4 \text{ mb} \tag{16-16}$$

From this we find for the nonannihilation parts, $\sigma(qq')$, of the quark "cross sections"

$$\sigma(\bar{p}p) \simeq 5.2 \text{ mb} \qquad \sigma(\bar{p}n) \simeq 3.3 \text{ mb} \qquad \sigma(\bar{\lambda}p) \simeq 1.5 \text{ mb}$$
$$\sigma(pp) \simeq 4.3 \text{ mb} \qquad \sigma(pn) \simeq 4.4 \text{ mb} \qquad \sigma(\lambda p) \simeq 3 \text{ mb} \tag{16-17}$$

These results show that the quark cross sections do not satisfy SU(3) symmetry. Note the near equality of $\sigma(pp)$ and $\sigma(pn)$, implying that the imaginary part of the amplitude of the charge exchange reaction $n + p \to p + n$ is almost negligible. From the relation

$$\sigma_T(K^+ P) - \sigma_T(K^+ N) = \sigma(pp) - \sigma(pn)$$

which follows from Eq. (14-5), we see that this corresponds to the well-known, observed, approximate equality of $\sigma_T(K^+P)$ and $\sigma_T(K^+N)$.[89]

At this stage we must consider the signs of $\tilde{S}^-(qq')$. It is reasonable to assume that the considerations of Section 14-3 can also be applied to quark scattering. Remembering that, by definition, $\tilde{S}^-(qq')$ does not involve quark–antiquark annihilation contributions, so that it can be only nonzero because of a difference in the number of ways (integral) charge and/or hypercharge can be exchanged in $q + q'$ and $\bar{q} + q'$ collisions, we predict, as in Eqs. (14-12) and (14-13),

$$\tilde{S}^-(pp) > 0 \qquad \tilde{S}^-(np) < 0 \qquad \tilde{S}^-(\lambda p) < 0 \tag{16-18}$$

For instance, the first inequality arises because charge can be exchanged in more ways between p and $\bar{p}$ than between p and p. We see that these predictions are satisfied by Eq. (16-16); it can be verified, assuming Eq. (14-9), that this is true for the whole momentum range $6 \leqslant p_L \leqslant 18$ GeV/c. This is consistent with the fact that quark–antiquark annihilation contributions in the sense of Figure 12a are not included on the right of Eq. (16-1). If we would have found from Eq. (16-1) $\tilde{S}^-(\lambda p)$ or $\tilde{S}^-(np)$ positive, this would have been an indication that the quantities $S^\pm(qq')$, which include $q\bar{q}$ annihilation, rather than $S^\pm(qq')$, should have occurred. [See the remark following Eqs. (16-3).] Of course, the results given by Eq. (16-16) do not by themselves necessarily require the complete absence of $q\bar{q}$ annihilation on the right-hand side of Eq. (16-1), but indicate that annihilation could certainly not dominate, at least for np and λp. We should always have $\sigma_A(\bar{n}p) < |\tilde{S}^-(np)|$ and $\sigma_A(\bar{\lambda}p) < |\tilde{S}^-(\lambda p)|$. We should stress again that $\sigma_A(\bar{q}q')$ represents here the cross section for annihilation in the sense of Figure 12a, in which, during a baryon–antibaryon collision, one quark–antiquark pair $\bar{q}q'$ annihilates, while the other quarks remain unaffected. This should be contrasted with the situation in baryon–antibaryon annihilation (Chapter 18).

16-3. REMARKS

Several authors[112] have tried to extend the additivity scheme by including multiple scattering corrections that produce nonadditive terms in cross sections. This is done by means of the eikonal method introduced by Glauber[111] (see Appendix) to calculate multiple scattering corrections to the scattering of hadrons from deuterons. Although the existence of such corrections in the quark model is a natural possibility, it is difficult to compute them because of our ignorance concerning the quark space wave functions. The various estimates are therefore not very reliable. Moreover, they seem to go in the wrong direction. Harrington[112] obtains for the double scattering correction to the asymptotic formula [Eq. (16-4)]

$$2\sigma_T^{(\infty)}(PP) - 3\sigma_T^{(\infty)}(\pi P) = -\delta \qquad (16\text{-}19)$$

in which δ is positive and ≈ 5 mb, whereas the extrapolations to the data give, for the left-hand side, 5.4 mb. Perhaps this is another indication that quarks inside hadrons do not behave in the same way as nucleons inside nuclei, and that the calculation of multiple scattering corrections in the conventional way is too far-fetched. It is interesting to note that we have an example of a situation in which particles do not follow the Glauber formula, namely, that of particles that are not on the mass shell.[113]

More direct information about multiple quark scattering might be obtained by studying processes that are forbidden in the additive quark model, namely, processes that involve double charge or strangeness exchange or both in the t-channel, such as $\pi^-P \to \pi^+\Delta^-$ and $K^-P \to K^0\Xi^0$ (Dean[112]). Processes of this type are known to be rare as compared with those with single exchange.

Some of the relations between total cross sections obtained in this chapter have also been derived in other models for high-energy scattering.[114, 115] In particular, in the model of Cabibbo *et al.* (*CHN*),[115] which consists essentially of the Regge pole model endowed with an algebraic structure for the vertex strength functions, we obtain relations (16-3), but with the important difference that everywhere

$\tilde{S}^{\pm}(AB)$ is replaced by $S^{\pm}(AB)$, because it is common practice to assume that in the Regge pole description of total baryon–antibaryon cross sections the annihilation contributions are included. An intriguing question is raised here. In the quark model different mechanisms control the annihilation and nonannihilation parts of the total cross sections. This rests on the fact that annihilation effects correspond to baryon exchange, while all nonannihilation processes are of a different type, corresponding to exchange of vanishing baryon number. We might also say that the latter processes are peripheral and the annihilation processes nonperipheral (or central). This difference in the nature of the two types of processes may require different descriptions for them, not only in the quark model, but also in other dyanmical models.[91, 116] This may be true, in particular, for the Regge pole model. In fact, from the observation that additivity of quark amplitudes corresponds to t-channel exchanges of singlet and octet type, we might speculate about the possibility that the Regge pole model, in which only singlet and octet trajectories are exchanged, such as the *CHN* model, describes only the nonannihilation part of the total cross sections. If this were true, the relations obtained in the quark model and the *CHN* model would become identical. Further questions about the compatibility of quark and Regge pole models are studied in papers by Daboul and Lipkin.[117]

Chapter 17

Inelastic Two-Body Processes

17-1. GENERAL REMARKS

The simplest inelastic procedure of the type

$$A + B \rightarrow C + D \tag{17-1}$$

in which the target particle B is usually a proton, and each of the particles C and D is a stable or unstable hadron. If the latter is the case, the observed final state contains more than two particles, $C + D$ representing an intermediate two-body state due to resonance production, for example, $\pi^+P \rightarrow (\rho^+P \text{ or } \pi\Delta) \rightarrow \pi^+\pi^0P$ (quasi two-body reactions). It is a well-known experimental fact[118] that often quasi two-body reactions account for a large fraction of a given many-body reaction channel, even at rather high energies. For the above example, this fraction is at least 50% at 8 GeV/c, so that less than 50% of the $\pi^+\pi^0P$ channel consists of genuine three-body states. In a quark picture this can be qualitatively understood by noting that in a two-particle scattering process two-body states, arising simply from a rearrangement of the incident quarks with or without spin flip (their number being conserved), are likely to be produced more easily than many-body states in which the number of final quarks differs from the number of initial quarks.[119]

It is found, in general,[118] that high-energy two-body reactions exhibit strong forward diffraction-like peaks, that is, for small t [$|t_{\min}| \leqslant |t| \lesssim 1\ (\text{GeV/c})^2$, $t = -(p_A - p_C)^2$] the differential cross sections are found to have the form of Eq. (15-7) with the slopes a in most cases of the same order of magnitude as for elastic scattering. In other words, these processes are strongly peripheral. The total cross section for a given reaction is dominated by the region of the forward peak. It is just in this region that the additivity assumption is expected to hold. It is clear that a theoretical relation between two reactions obtained from additivity can only be meaningfully tested if peripheralism is observed in both cases.

In dealing with inelastic processes in the additivity model, we are faced with a number of complicating features that often make it more difficult than in the case of total cross sections to test additivity proper without recourse to further assumptions.[93a] We note the following.

(1) Spin couplings have to be properly taken into account in writing down the additivity formula for the amplitude of a given process. [Note that, since the cross section for reaction (17-1) contains the amplitude squared, additivity for the amplitude does not imply additivity for the cross section.] This will increase the

number of independent quark amplitudes. For the mesons, the quark spin couplings are determined by the spins of the mesons; for the baryons they are assumed to be given by the SU(6) wave functions discussed in Chapter 6.

(2) Form factors, defined as in Eq. (14-5), enter the expressions for the cross sections. To get rid of them we usually assume their shape to be the same for all corresponding particles in a given sum rule, so that they drop out of the sum rule. This amounts to making symmetry assumptions about the space wave functions of these particles.[93a] If the mass differences between the particles in the initial and final states are nonzero and different for related cross sections, we still have to make a correction that takes into account the nonzero momentum transfer in the forward direction. Lipkin *et al.*[93] propose to determine the form factors from elastic diffraction scattering by assuming that the angular dependence of elastic and inelastic quark scattering can be neglected. This is what we called the extreme case II in Chapter 15. It is by no means clear, however, whether this limiting case corresponds to the actual situation.

(3) We have to make the appropriate corrections for phase space. Additivity leads to relations between the amplitudes squared for the various reactions. Calling the latter $\bar{\sigma}$, summed over the angles and, if polarizations are not detected, over spin directions its relation with the corresponding experimental cross section σ is given by

$$\bar{\sigma} = \sigma/F \tag{17-2}$$

in which F contains the phase space correction and possible form factor corrections [point (2)].

(4) It is not quite clear how to compare the relations obtained by experiment. For different initial states (meson–baryon and baryon–baryon) we may use the rule discussed in Section 14-1. For reactions with the same initial state but with the masses of the final particles varying from one reaction to the other, the prescription is to compare them at the same Q value, in which Q is the kinetic c.m. energy in the final state, $Q = \epsilon_C + \epsilon_D - m_C - m_D$, ϵ_C and ϵ_D being the c.m. energies of the final particles.

(5) The test of additivity in the case of inelastic reactions is further hampered by the scarcity of accurate data. In addition, most experiments have been performed at lower momenta, $p_L \lesssim 8$ GeV/c.

17-2. RELATIONS BETWEEN CROSS SECTIONS

Numerous relations between inelastic cross sections follow from the additivity assumption for scattering amplitudes.[84, 92–98] Also, predictions for spin density matrices are made when resonances of higher spins are produced.[95, 96, 120] We only discuss a few typical examples here. An excellent review on the application of the quark model to inelastic processes has been written recently by Białas and Zalewski,[97] to which we refer for many details.

As mentioned before (Chapter 14), additivity can be applied neither to baryon–antibaryon annihilation nor to two-body amplitudes that correspond to the exchange of nonzero baryon number or more than two units of charge (i.e., $|\mathbf{I}| > 1$) and/or strangeness in the t channel. Regarding the latter, the available experimental information[118] suggests that, in the energy region in which additivity is supposed to be applicable, we can safely neglect their effect; that is, we need not worry about possible nonadditive corrections of this type.

With respect to annihilation effects, the situation is less clear. Consider processes of the type

$$\bar{\mathcal{N}}' + \mathcal{N} \to \bar{B}' + B \tag{17-3}$$

in which $\mathcal{N}$ and $\mathcal{N}'$ are nucleons and B and B' baryons or baryon resonances. Just as for the case of elastic nucleon–antinucleon scattering (Section 14-2), we may expect that for these processes even at rather high energies a considerable contribution to the right-hand side of an equation similar to Eq. (14-6) comes from annihilation channels $\bar{\mathcal{N}}' + \mathcal{N} \to$ mesons and $\bar{B}' + B \to$ mesons, implying lack of additivity for these processes. Since, contrary to the case of baryon–antibaryon total cross sections, we do not know how to correct for these annihilation effects, the additivity model does not make much sense for the inelastic processes (17-3). The same holds for the nucleon–nucleon processes

$$\mathcal{N}' + \mathcal{N} \to B' + B \tag{17-4}$$

Indeed, because analyticity and crossing properties of scattering amplitudes imply relations between baryon–baryon and baryon–antibaryon reactions, any corrections to process (17-3) are reflected in the crossed reaction (17-4). It should therefore not be too surprising that, by substituting experimental cross sections into sum rules obtained from additivity that involve, in addition to meson–baryon cross sections, cross sections for reaction (17-3) or (17-4), in almost all cases strong disagreement between theory and experiment is found in the momentum range $4 \lesssim p_L \lesssim 8$ GeV/c.[93, 95, 97] To conclude, the most direct test of additivity is provided by those relations that involve meson-baryon processes in which only the quantum numbers of $q\bar{q}$ can be exchanged in the t channel.

Let us therefore turn to this type of processes. Relations between the cross sections for meson–baryon charge-exchange reactions are readily obtained. From additivity it follows that

$$\begin{aligned}
\langle \pi^- X | \pi^0 X' \rangle &= T_1 - T_2 \\
\langle \pi^- X | \eta X' \rangle &= -(T_1 + T_2) \sin \Psi_P \\
\langle \pi^- X | \eta' X' \rangle &= -(T_1 + T_2) \cos \Psi_P \\
\langle K^- X | \bar{K}^0 X' \rangle &= \sqrt{2} T_2 \\
\langle K^0 X | K^+ X' \rangle &= \sqrt{2} T_1
\end{aligned} \tag{17-5}$$

with

$$T_1 = \frac{1}{2\sqrt{2}}\left[\langle n\uparrow X|p\uparrow X'\rangle + \langle n\downarrow X|p\downarrow X'\rangle\right]$$
$$T_2 = \frac{1}{2\sqrt{2}}\left[\langle \bar{p}\uparrow X|\bar{n}\uparrow X'\rangle + \langle \bar{p}\downarrow X|\bar{n}\downarrow X'\rangle\right] \tag{17-6}$$

in which X and X' are any particles allowed by the conservation laws. We do not make assumptions regarding the quark structure of these particles. In Eq. (17-5) the wave functions of Chapter 5 are used and $\Psi_P = \arctan(\frac{1}{2}\sqrt{2}) - \vartheta_P$, ϑ_P being the η–η' mixing angle defined by Eq. (5-4). We obtain the relations

$$\frac{\bar{\sigma}(\pi^- X \to \eta X')}{\bar{\sigma}(\pi^- X \to \eta' X')} = \tan^2 \Psi_P \tag{17-7}$$

$$\bar{\sigma}(\pi^- X \to \pi^0 X') + \bar{\sigma}(\pi^- X \to \eta X') + \bar{\sigma}(\pi^- X \to \eta' X')$$
$$= \bar{\sigma}(K^- X \to \bar{K}^0 X') + \bar{\sigma}(K^0 X \to K^+ X') \tag{17-8}$$

in which $\bar{\sigma}$ is defined by Eq. (17-2). Differences in form factors are neglected [see remark (2) in Section 17-1].

In exactly the same way we obtain sum rules involving strangeness-exchange processes. For instance,

$$\bar{\sigma}(K^- X \to \eta X') + \bar{\sigma}(K^- X \to \eta' X') = \bar{\sigma}(K^- X \to \pi^0 X')$$
$$+ \bar{\sigma}(\pi^- X \to K^0 X') \tag{17-9}$$

All these relations remain unchanged when the pseudoscalar mesons in the final state are replaced by the corresponding vector mesons and Ψ_P is replaced by $\Psi_V = \arctan(\frac{1}{2}\sqrt{2}) - \vartheta_V$.

In the reactions measured until now, X is always a proton and X' can be any baryon or baryon resonance. From Eq. (17-7) and analogous expressions we obtain[92]

$$\frac{\bar{\sigma}(\pi^- P \to \eta N)}{\bar{\sigma}(\pi^- P \to \eta' N)} = \frac{\bar{\sigma}(\pi^+ P \to \eta \Delta^{++})}{\bar{\sigma}(\pi^+ P \to \eta' \Delta^{++})} = \tan^2 \Psi_P \tag{17-10}$$

$$\frac{\bar{\sigma}(\pi^- P \to \phi N)}{\bar{\sigma}(\pi^- P \to \omega N)} = \frac{\bar{\sigma}(\pi^+ P \to \phi \Delta^{++})}{\bar{\sigma}(\pi^+ P \to \omega \Delta^{++})} = \tan^2 \Psi_V \tag{17-11}$$

Similar expressions can be written for the production cross sections of the higher L mesons. We know from the mass formulas (Chapter 8) that, for the vector mesons, ϑ_V is close to the value $\arctan(\frac{1}{2}\sqrt{2})$ for which the right-hand side of Eq. (17-11) vanishes. This agrees very well with the experimental fact that ϕ production is very small compared to ω production. On the other hand, using experimental data for the cross sections, the above and similar relations can be used as an independent way of determining the mixing angles.[92] This, then, indeed gives estimates for ϑ_V in the neighborhood of $\arctan(\frac{1}{2}\sqrt{2})$, that is, $\Psi_V \simeq 0$.[10] For ϑ_P we find in this way[10] values in the range $-19 \pm 7°$ to $-31 \pm 5°$, that is, definitely opposite in sign compared to ϑ_V, in accordance with the quark model analysis of the masses discussed in Chapter 8. There is a second solution for ϑ_P, around $+90°$, which, however, is too far from the expected value. Similar estimates[10] for the f-f' mixing angle are compatible with result (9-3).

Of the many relations following from Eqs. (17-7) to (17-9), and from similar expressions involving vector mesons or baryons, we mention only four, namely,

$$\bar{\sigma}(K^- P \to \omega\Lambda) = \bar{\sigma}(K^- P \to \rho^0 \Lambda) \tag{17-12a}$$

$$\bar{\sigma}(K^- P \to \phi\Lambda) = \bar{\sigma}(\pi^- P \to K^{*0} \Lambda) \tag{17-12b}$$

which hold when $\Psi_V = 0$,[92]

$$\bar{\sigma}(X\mathcal{N} \to X' \Lambda) = 27\bar{\sigma}(X\mathcal{N} \to X' \Sigma^0) \tag{17-12c}$$

for processes involving baryon spin flip,[94] and

$$\bar{\sigma}(X\mathcal{N} \to X' \Lambda) > 3\bar{\sigma}(X\mathcal{N} \to X' \Sigma^0) \tag{17-12d}$$

for processes in which no polarization measurements are made.[94] As before, X and X' are arbitrary particles for which no quark structure is assumed. Results (17-12c) and (17-12d) are particularly interesting because the suppression of Σ^0 production with respect to Λ production, expressed by these relations, results from the properties of the baryon spin-unitary spin wave functions and should therefore be a test for the assumption that the latter are the SU(6) wave functions corresponding to representation [56]. These relations follow also from a meson exchange model with higher symmetry.[94]

The first of relations (17-12) is in good agreement with the data at 4.1 and 5.5 GeV/c.[121] Both ω and ρ^0 production are found to be strongly peripheral at these energies, and the total forward hemisphere cross sections are, respectively, 43 ± 12 and 44 ± 19 μb at 4.1 GeV/c, and 19 ± 6 and 17 ± 6 μb at 5.5 GeV/c. Note that, m_ρ and m_ω being approximately the same, the kinematical corrections cancel out in Eq. (17-12a). No data for K^{*0} production are available above 4 GeV/c; at 3 GeV/c relation (17-12b) is found to agree reasonably with experiment.[92]

As to relations (17-12c) and (17-12d), recent data[122] on peripheral photoproduction of Λ and Σ^0 from protons ($X = \gamma$, $X' = K^+$, $\mathcal{N} = P$) in the photon energy range 2.4–16 GeV give, for the ratio of the two cross sections, a value around one, in clear disagreement with the above predictions. At the moment no explanation for this discrepancy exists.

We remark that the cross-section relations discussed in this section are of a relatively simple type in that no assumptions concerning the equivalence between quarks constituting mesons and quarks constituting baryons are necessary. Assuming this equivalence (which we also did in Chapter 16!) leads to another class of sum rules for meson–baryon reactions, for a discussion of which we refer to the literature.[93, 95-97]

17-3. SPIN-DENSITY MATRICES

A promising way to test the quark model with additivity for scattering amplitudes has been introduced by Friar and Trefil.[95] Applying the model to reactions in which a resonance with higher spin is produced, they are able to make predictions about its spin density matrix elements. The latter offer an advantage with respect to cross sections in that we deal with ratios of amplitudes rather than with amplitudes themselves, so that form factors and other kinematical factors tend to cancel out in these ratios. In many cases, therefore, predictions for the density matrix elements may provide a cleaner test for additivity than do predictions for cross sections. Predictions are also made[120] for the joint decay distributions in double resonance production, such as $\pi P \to \rho\Delta$. Just as in the case of single decay distributions, it is possible to derive results that involve only additivity and no secondary assumptions. Because such relations are vital for the additivity model, it is important to test them carefully. In all cases in which a comparison with existing data can be made, consistency between theory and experiment is observed. Consider for instance processes of the type

$$\pi + P \to V + \Delta(1236)$$

The following relations between the spin density matrix elements $\rho^{mm'}_{nn'}$, where the upper indices refer to V and the lower to Δ, follow directly from additivity.[120]

$$\frac{1}{3}(\rho^{11} - \rho^{00}) + \rho^{1,-1} = \frac{2}{3}(\rho_{33} - \rho_{11}) + \frac{4}{\sqrt{3}}\, Re\, \rho_{3,-1} \tag{17-16a}$$

$$\sqrt{3}(Re\,\rho^{1,-1}_{3,-1} + Re\,\rho^{-1,1}_{3,-1}) + \tfrac{1}{2}\underline{\rho^{1,-1}} - \sqrt{3}\, Re\,\overline{\rho_{3,-1}} - \tfrac{1}{2}(\rho_{\overline{33}} - \rho_{\overline{11}})$$
$$= \tfrac{1}{2}(\rho^{11} - \rho^{00}) - \tfrac{1}{2}\rho^{1,-1} \tag{17-16b}$$

$$\sqrt{3}(Re\,\rho^{1,-1}_{3,-1} + Re\,\rho^{-1,1}_{3,-1}) + \frac{1}{\sqrt{3}} Re\,\overline{\rho_{3,-1}} - \frac{3}{2}\underline{\rho^{1,-1}} - \frac{1}{2}(\rho_{\overline{33}} - \rho_{\overline{11}})$$
$$= \rho_{33} - \rho_{11} - \frac{2}{\sqrt{3}} Re\,\rho_{3,-1} \tag{17-16c}$$

$$3\sqrt{3}(Re\,\rho^{1,-1}_{3,-1} + Re\,\rho^{-1,1}_{3,-1}) + \tfrac{3}{2}\underline{\rho^{1,-1}} + \sqrt{3}\, Re\,\overline{\rho_{3,-1}} + \tfrac{1}{2}(\rho_{\overline{33}} - \rho_{\overline{11}})$$
$$= 1 + \rho_{33} - \rho_{11} + 2\sqrt{3}\, Re\,\rho_{3,-1} \tag{17-16d}$$

$$-\sqrt{3}\,Re\,\rho^{10}_{\underline{\quad}} - 3[Re(\rho^{10}_{3,-1} - \rho^{0,-1}_{3,-1}) + Re(\rho^{01}_{3,-1} - \rho^{-1,0}_{3,-1})]$$
$$= \sqrt{3}\,Re\,\rho^{10} \qquad (17\text{-}16e)$$

$$-\sqrt{2}\,Re\,\rho_{\overline{31}} - 3\sqrt{2}(Re\,\rho^{1,-1}_{31} + Re\,\rho^{-1,1}_{31})$$
$$= 2\sqrt{2}\,Re\,\rho_{31} \qquad (17\text{-}16f)$$

in which

$$\rho_{\overline{nn'}} = \rho^{11}_{nn'} + \rho^{-1,-1}_{nn'} - 2\rho^{00}_{nn'}$$
$$\rho^{mm'}_{\underline{\quad}} = \rho^{mm'}_{33} + \rho^{mm'}_{-3,-3} - \rho^{mm'}_{11} - \rho^{mm'}_{-1,-1}$$
$$\rho^{mm'} = \sum_n \rho^{mm'}_{nn},\ \rho_{nn'} = \sum_m \rho^{mm}_{nn'}$$

[For brevity we have written $\rho^{mm'}_{33}$ instead of $\rho^{mm'}_{(3/2)(3/2)}$, and so on.] In deriving Eq. (17-16) the spin-unitary spin wave functions described in Chapters 5 and 6 are used. Parity conservation, but not time-reversal invariance, is assumed for the quark scattering amplitudes. The spin quantization axis is taken in the production plane.

These relations were tested experimentally for the reactions $\pi^+P \to \rho\Delta$ and $\pi^+P \to \omega\Delta$ at 5 GeV/c by one of the European bubble chamber collaborations.[123] The results are shown in Table 10.

It should be noted that agreement between theory and experiment is also found to exist when baryon–baryon and antibaryon–baryon reactions are involved. This is quite understandable if we remember that the density matrix elements and decay parameters involve ratios of amplitudes and are therefore not expected to be strongly affected by the presence of annihilation channels.

17-4. PHOTOPRODUCTION OF VECTOR MESONS

Another class of two-body processes, which have been studied in the quark model, comprises photoproduction processes.[98, 124] Here we will consider briefly the photoproduction of vector mesons

$$\gamma + P \to V + P \qquad V = \rho^0, \omega, \phi$$

and assume (1) that the mechanism of this reaction is that given by Figure 14, (vector dominance model), and (2) that the hadronic process $V' + P \to V + P$ can be described by the additivity assumption for high-energy scattering, neglecting the fact that V' is off the mass shell. At high energies, for example, photon

Table 10. Comparison of Relations (17-16) with Experiment. Both Resonances are Described in their Jackson Frames.[123]

Relation	$\pi^+ P \to \rho\Delta$			$\pi^+ P \to \omega\Delta$		
	Left-hand side	Right-hand side	Left-hand side − Right-hand side	Left-hand side	Right-hand side	Left-hand side − Right-hand side
(17-16a)	-0.26 ± 0.02	-0.24 ± 0.04	-0.02 ± 0.05	0.06 ± 0.04	-0.03 ± 0.07	0.09 ± 0.07
(17-16b)	-0.37 ± 0.09	-0.31 ± 0.02	-0.06 ± 0.09	0.04 ± 0.13	-0.08 ± 0.03	0.12 ± 0.13
(17-16c)	-0.28 ± 0.08	-0.26 ± 0.04	-0.02 ± 0.08	0.14 ± 0.14	-0.07 ± 0.06	0.21 ± 0.15
(17-16d)	0.52 ± 0.13	0.64 ± 0.07	-0.12 ± 0.17	0.84 ± 0.24	0.96 ± 0.11	-0.12 ± 0.24
(17-16e)	0.04 ± 0.12	-0.15 ± 0.03	0.19 ± 0.12	-0.29 ± 0.15	-0.18 ± 0.03	-0.11 ± 0.15
(17-16f)	-0.16 ± 0.10	-0.15 ± 0.05	-0.01 ± 0.10	-0.10 ± 0.17	-0.14 ± 0.08	$0.04 \pm 0 18$

energies $E_\gamma > 4$ GeV, it is reasonable to neglect inelastic processes of the type $V + P \rightarrow V' + P$ as compared to elastic reactions in which $V' \equiv V$. Furthermore we neglect the possible dependence of the elastic VP amplitudes on the helicities. We then have the relation[125]

$$\sigma(\gamma P \rightarrow VP) = 4\alpha\pi g_{V\gamma}^2 \sigma_{el}(VP) \tag{17-17}$$

in which α is the fine structure constant and $g_{V\gamma}$ the γ-V coupling constant defined by Eqs. (12-23) and (12-24). Note that since high-energy elastic scattering is strongly peaked in the forward direction (Chapter 15), the same should be true for the photoproduction of vector mesons according to this model. This is indeed what is observed experimentally.[126]

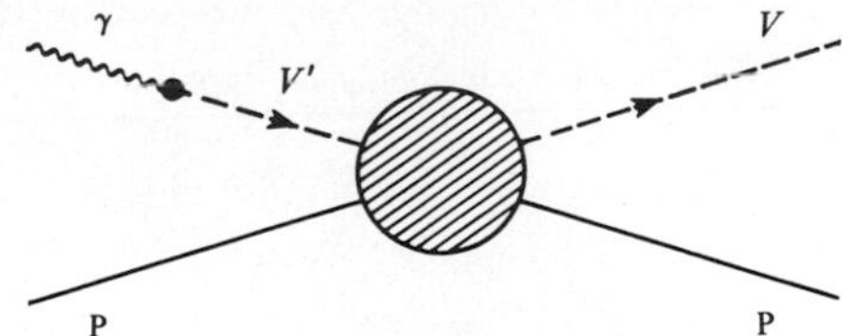

FIGURE 14. Mechanism of the reaction $\gamma + P \rightarrow V + P$.

Additivity gives, for the spin-averaged cross sections [Eqs. (16-6)],

$$\begin{aligned} \sigma_T(\omega P) = \sigma_T(\rho^0 P) = \tfrac{1}{2}S^+(\pi^+ P) \\ \sigma_T(\phi P) = \tfrac{1}{2}[S^+(K^+ P) + S^+(K^+ N) - S^+(\pi^+ P)] \end{aligned} \tag{17-18}$$

Assuming the elastic amplitudes at high energies and near forward directions to be dominantly imaginary, we have, from Eqs. (14-3), (14-4), and (15-7),

$$\sigma_{el}(VP) = \frac{[\sigma_T(VP)]^2}{16\pi a} \tag{17-19}$$

We take the slope a the same for ρ^0, ω, and ϕ scattering, which, in view of what we know experimentally about hadron diffraction scattering, is not unreasonable (see Chapter 15).

Combining all these results and using Eq. (10-19) we obtain, abbreviating $\sigma(\gamma P \rightarrow VP)$ by σ_V and neglecting the mass difference between ρ^0 and ω,

$$\sigma_{\rho^0} : \sigma_\omega : \sigma_\phi = 9:1:2\beta \tag{17-20}$$

with the symmetry-breaking factor β given by

$$\beta = \left[\frac{S^+(K^+ P) + S^+(K^+ N) - S^+(\pi^+ P)}{S^+(\pi^+ P)}\right]^2 \left(\frac{m_{\rho^0}}{m_\phi}\right)^2 \tag{17-21}$$

According to Eq. (16-8) the first factor on the right of the latter expression has the value ¼ in the range $6 \leqslant p_L \leqslant 18$ GeV/c. It accounts for the symmetry breaking in quark–proton scattering, that is, for the fact that the coupling to the proton of the λ quarks making up ϕ is weaker than that of the p and n quarks making up ρ^0 and ω [compare Eqs. (16-7) and (16-11)]. Hence $\beta = 0.15$, giving

$$\frac{\sigma_\phi}{\sigma_{\rho^0}} = 0.033, \quad 6 \leqslant E_\gamma \leqslant 18\,\text{GeV} \tag{17-22}$$

The experimental value, averaged over the energy range $3.5 \leqslant E_\gamma \leqslant 5.8$ GeV, is 0.026 ± 0.010.[126] In this range β is expected to be somewhat smaller (about 0.10), which would decrease the right-hand side of Eq. (17-22). However, this is compensated by the somewhat smaller slope a of ϕ production as compared with ρ^0 production [see Eq. (17-19)].[126] In the same range the value for $\sigma_\omega/\sigma_{\rho^0}$ is found to be 0.19 ± 0.06, to be compared with the theoretical value 0.11. Here the agreement is less good. However, this may be due to the neglect of the inelastic amplitudes $\langle \omega P | \rho P \rangle$, which can be shown to affect mostly σ_ω.[98]

The use of Eqs. (10-19) to determine $g_{V\gamma}$ enables us to estimate the magnitude of the cross sections σ_V. From Eqs. (17-17), (17-18), and (17-19) we obtain

$$\sigma_{\rho^0} = \frac{\alpha}{16a}\left[\frac{m_\pi}{m_p} S^+(\pi^+ P)\right]^2 \tag{17-23}$$

Taking for a the value found for $\pi^\pm P$ scattering, that is, about $8(\text{GeV}/c)^{-2}$, which is also the value fitting $d\sigma(\gamma P \to \rho^0 P)/dt$ at small momentum transfers,[126] and using the cross-section data of Reference 106, we have at 4.5 GeV

$$\sigma_{\rho^0} = 15.7\,\mu b$$

in remarkable agreement with the experimental result of 16 μb, which represents an average over the range $3.5 \leqslant E_\gamma \leqslant 5.5$ GeV.[126]

These results show that the quark model combined with vector meson dominance works quite well for photoproduction of vector mesons. This should be contrasted with the situation for K^+ photoproduction mentioned in Section 17-2.

Chapter 18

Baryon–Antibaryon Annihilation and Multiparticle Production

18-1. BARYON-ANTIBARYON ANNIHILATION

The application of the quark model to more complicated reactions, such as baryon–antibaryon annihilation and high-energy production processes with high multiplicities, has yielded some useful results. Let us first briefly consider nucleon-antinucleon annihilation at rest as discussed by Rubinstein and Stern.[127] Their basic assumption is that this process, which takes place mainly from S states, is essentially a rearrangement of the three quarks in the nucleon and the three antiquarks in the antinucleon into three quark–antiquark $L = 0$ pairs, without any annihilation or creation of pairs or emission of particles through bremsstrahlung, and with each quark conserving all its quantum numbers. This extremely simplified picture leads immediately to the following qualitative predictions:

(1) The final state contains three nonstrange pseudoscalar and/or vector mesons (of course, if the latter are produced they subsequently decay into pions and the observed final state will contain more than three particles).

(2) Particles containing strange quarks cannot be produced. So, in addition to strange particle production, ϕ production is also forbidden.

The second prediction agrees reasonably well with experiment [I quote, here and below, from recent, preliminary, and as yet unpublished, CERN data on $\bar{P}P$ annihilations at rest (L. Montanet, private communications)]. The total number of $\bar{P}P$ annihilation channels containing strange particles amounts to about 10% of all channels. Of these the $K\bar{K}\ 2\pi$ channel takes 80%, 10% of which goes via $\phi\pi\pi$ formation. As to the first prediction, it does not seem to represent the present-day experimental situation regarding $\bar{P}P$ annihilation at rest very well. Although there is a strong tendency towards low multiplicities, probably not more than about 60 or 70% of all $\bar{P}P$ annihilation channels is of the three-body type (body means stable or unstable particle). There is a considerable fraction of two-body final states. For instance, more than 80% of the decays into $\pi^+\pi^-\pi^\circ$, that is, about 6% of all decays, goes via $\rho\pi$ formation; of the $2\pi^+2\pi^-$ channels, which make up about 7% of the total, roughly 50% goes via $\rho\pi\pi$ and roughly 40% via $f^0\rho^0$ and $A_2\pi$ formation, and so on. Moreover, the distribution of three-body final states is not correctly described by the model.[128] The conclusion has to be that baryon–antibaryon annihilation at rest is more than a simple quark rearrangement.

It should be mentioned at this stage that the quark rearrangement idea has recently been used quite successfully to discuss hadron S-wave scattering lengths.[129] The assumption here is that the S-wave scattering amplitude is proportional to the number of all possible permutations of two quarks, one in each of the interacting hadrons, without changing any of their quantum numbers. If no such permutation is possible, the amplitude is put equal to zero.

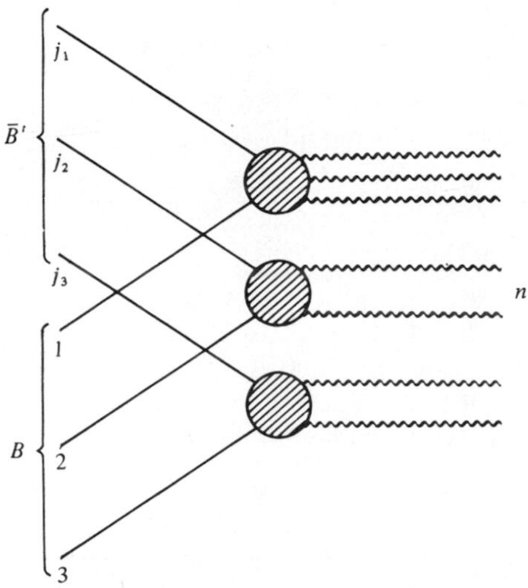

FIGURE 15. Diagram showing the factorization of antibaryon-baryon annihilation into three antiquark-quark annihilations.

Whereas the above considerations may still provide a very rough qualitative picture for annihilations at rest, they are certainly too simple to describe annihilations in flight. In fact, toward higher energies, the number of bodies (stable or unstable particles) in the final state seems to increase and becomes definitely more than three. For instance, for $\bar{P}P$ annihilations at 5.7 GeV/c, the dominant contributions to $\sigma_A(\bar{P}P)$ seem to come from channels containing six or more bodies.[99] In the simplest model we can propose for high-energy annihilation,[91] we write the $\bar{B}'B$ annihilation amplitude as a product of three $\bar{q}'q$ annihilation amplitudes, momentum and energy being approximately conserved in each of the latter, that is, one approximates the left-hand part of Figure 11 by Figure 15. No assumptions are made about the particles produced in each vertex. Since each $\bar{q}'q$ annihilation produces at least two bodies in the final state, this model makes sense only if the $\bar{B}'B$ annihilation process produces six or more final bodies. This is what seems to happen at high energies, as demonstrated by the above-mentioned 5.7 GeV/c experiment.

We thus write

$$\sigma_A(\bar{B}' B) = \sum_{\{j_1 j_2 j_3\}} \prod_{i=1,2,3} Z(j_i, i) \tag{18-1}$$

in which j_1, j_2, j_3 run over the permutations of 1, 2, 3, and $Z(j_i, i)$ describes the contribution of all annihilations of antiquark j_i in $\bar{B}'$ with quark i in B (see Figure 15). Each Z, which has dimension of $(\text{mb})^{1/3}$, is the product of an antiquark–quark annihilation cross section and a factor of dimension $(\text{length})^{-4/3}$ determined by the wave functions of the baryon and antibaryon as three-quark bound states. This factor is assumed to be the same for all baryons. Its explicit form is not needed for our purpose. It follows from isospin and charge conjugation invariance that only four of the Z's are independent, namely,

$$Z_1 = Z(\bar{p}p) \qquad Z_2 = Z(\bar{p}n) \qquad Z_3 = Z(\bar{\lambda}p) \qquad Z_4 = Z(\bar{\lambda}\lambda) \tag{18-2}$$

The last one does not enter if only reactions with proton targets are considered. The following expressions are obtained

$$\begin{aligned}
\sigma_A(\bar{P}P) &= 2Z_1^3 + 4Z_1 Z_2^2 \\
\sigma_A(\bar{N}P) &= 2Z_2^3 + 4Z_1^2 Z_2 \\
\sigma_A(\bar{\Lambda}P) &= \sigma_A(\bar{\Sigma}^0 P) = 2Z_1 Z_2 Z_3 + 2Z_1^2 Z_3 + 2Z_2^2 Z_3
\end{aligned} \tag{18-3}$$

and so on. At present, experimental information at high energy exists only for the first cross section of the list. This means that we cannot yet compare the factorization assumption with experiment.

It is clear that neither the additivity assumption as used here nor the factorization assumption by themselves can produce relations for hadron cross sections that connect annihilation and nonannihilation effects. Relations of that type can only be obtained if we make such a connection *ad hoc* on the level of the quarks. Examples of such are the Freund relations[89, 90, 130]

$$\begin{aligned}
S^-(PP) &= 5S^-(\pi^+ P) \\
S^-(PN) &= 4S^-(\pi^+ P)
\end{aligned} \tag{18-4}$$

and the Levinson–Wall–Lipkin relations[131]

$$\begin{aligned}
S^-(PP) &= 2S^-(K^+ P) + S^-(K^+ N) \\
S^-(PN) &= S^-(K^+ P) + 2S^-(K^+ N)
\end{aligned} \tag{18-5}$$

which essentially express nucleon–antinucleon annihilation in terms of meson–nucleon scattering, $S^{-}(PP)$ and $S^{-}(PN)$ being dominated by annihilation contributions. It is easy to see, using Eqs. (16-1), (16-2), and (18-3), that Eqs. (18-4) and (18-5) are obtained provided the following relations between quark annihilation and nonannihilation cross sections are assumed:

$$\text{from Eq. (18-4)} \qquad Z_1^{\bar{3}} = Z_2^{\bar{3}} = -\tfrac{3}{2}\tilde{S}^{-}(np) \tag{18-6}$$

$$\text{from Eq. (18-5)} \qquad Z_1^{3} = Z_2^{3} = -\tfrac{3}{2}\tilde{S}^{-}(\lambda p) \tag{18-7}$$

Remember that both right-hand sides are positive [see Eq. (16-16)]. The dynamical meaning of these conditions is not clear; they should be regarded as expressing within the model the empirical facts that Eq. (18-4) is rather well and Eq. (18-5) very well satisfied by the data. As such their status is analogous to, for instance, the result given by Eq. (16-7). The equality of Z_1 and Z_2 implies

$$\sigma_A(\bar{P}N) = \sigma_A(\bar{P}P)$$

18-2. MULTIPARTICLE PRODUCTION PROCESSES

Finally, a few words about nonannihilation production processes, such as

$$\pi^- P \rightarrow P 2\pi^- \pi^+ \pi^0$$

involving many produced particles (high multiplicities). In the framework of the additivity assumption, these multiparticle production processes are described by the left-hand part of diagram b in Figure 12 for the particular case of $\bar{B}'B$ scattering. The wavy lines in this diagram represent the particles produced in a quark–quark or quark–antiquark collision. During the act of scattering, the interacting quarks can of course change their charge and/or strangeness. We neglect resonance effects. Some qualitative features of the above processes follow quite naturally from this model.[132a] Starting from an equidistribution of c.m. energy among the incident quarks, it is clear that the two final particles arising from recombination of the spectator quarks with the two scattering quarks will carry much more energy than any of the produced particles (wavy lines). Hence the occurrence of so-called "leading particles," which are fast in the c.m. system, carrying off a relatively large fraction of the kinetic energy, is here a natural consequence of additivity. Note that in this picture the leading particles can differ from the incident ones only by one unit of charge and/or strangeness. Besides, the model predicts

$$K_{\pi P}^{\max} = \tfrac{5}{12} \qquad K_{PP}^{\max} = \tfrac{1}{3} \tag{18-8}$$

in which K_{AB} is the inelasticity of the $A + B$ collision, that is, the fraction of available kinetic energy that goes into particle production. Its maximum value K_{AB}^{max} is obtained if for the corresponding quark–quark or quark–antiquark production process the inelasticity is 1. Therefore, assuming a statistical picture for

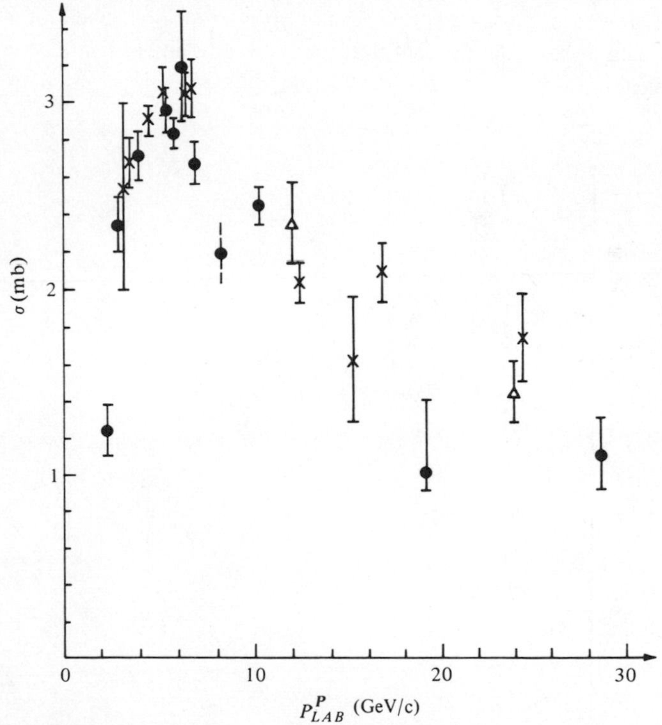

FIGURE 16. Test of a relation of type (18-9) for n = 3. ● *= measured values of* $\sigma(PP \to PP\, \pi^+\pi^-)$. × *= predictions of* $\sigma(PP \to PP\, \pi^+\pi^-)$ *from* $\sigma(\pi^- P \to P\, \pi^+ 2\pi^-)$. Δ *= predictions of* $\sigma(PP \to PP\, \pi^+\pi^-)$ *from* $\sigma(\pi^+ P \to P\, 2\pi^+\pi^-)$. *For the references to the experimental papers, see Reference 132b.*

the latter process, we expect this value to be reached in the limit of very high energies. Cosmic-ray data are compatible with the result expressed by Eq. (18-8).[133]

The model can be used to connect pion–nucleon with nucleon–nucleon induced multipion production cross sections.[132] Explicitly,

$$\sigma[\mathcal{N}\mathcal{N} \to \mathcal{N}\mathcal{N}(n-1)\pi] = \tfrac{3}{2}\sigma[\pi\mathcal{N} \to \mathcal{N}n\pi] \qquad (18\text{-}9)$$

in which $n - 1$ is the number of produced pions. The σ's in this expression denote the cross sections for particles without charge and isospin. In obtaining this relation it is assumed that (1) the overlap integrals on the left and right are independent of quark and hadron labels (see Section 17-1), (2) the transition probability is the incoherent sum of the possible individual quark–quark contributions, and (3) for given n the latter are the same for all qq and $\bar{q}q$ interactions. The factor 3/2 in Eq. (18-9) then arises from the fact that there are nine terms for $\mathcal{N}\mathcal{N}$ and six for $\pi\mathcal{N}$ scattering.

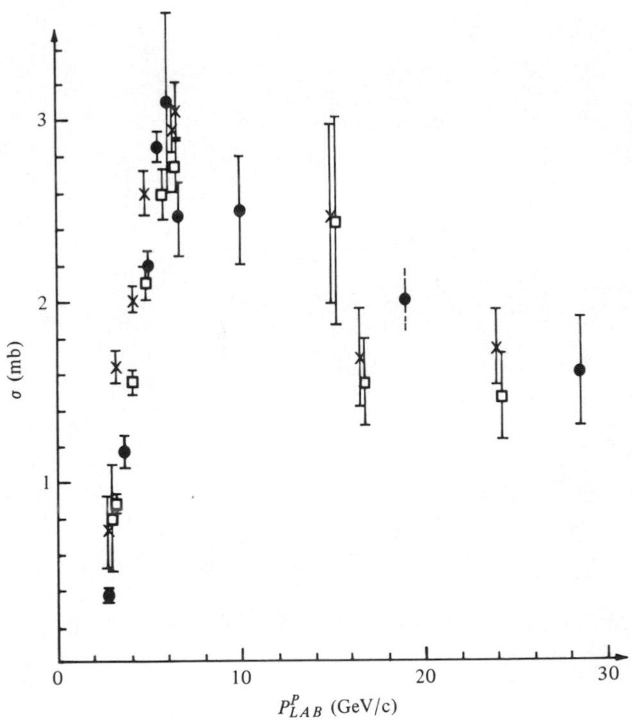

FIGURE 17. Test of a relation of type (18-9) for n = 4. ● *=measured values of* $\sigma(PP \to PN\ 2\pi^+\pi^-)$. × *= predictions of* $\sigma(PP \to PN\ 2\pi^+\pi^-)$ *from* $\sigma(\pi^-P \to P\ 2\pi^-\pi^+\pi^0)$. □ *= predictions of* $\sigma(PP \to PN\ 2\pi^+\pi^-)$ *from* $\sigma(\pi^-P \to N\ 2\pi^+2\pi^-)$. *For the references to the experimental papers, see Reference 132b.*

To obtain from Eq. (18-9) relations between reactions with specific charge configurations we assume that the $(n - 1)$-particle production channel is statistically distributed over all charge configurations allowed by isospin conservation;

the weight of each configuration is then calculated from isospin Clebsch–Gordon coefficients. This assumption seems to be supported by analyses of various multipion experiments.[134] In this way we obtain from Eq. (18-9) relations such as

$$\frac{\sigma(PP \to PP\pi^+\pi^-\pi^0)}{\sigma(\pi^-P \to P2\pi^-\pi^+\pi^0)} = 1.12 \qquad (18\text{-}10)$$

The measured cross sections turn out to satisfy these relations excellently in the range $3 \lesssim p_L^P \lesssim 24$ GeV/c, provided we compare the cross sections for $\mathcal{N}\mathcal{N}$ and $\pi\mathcal{N}$ induced reactions at laboratory momenta in the ratio 3:2, as proposed in Chapter 14. This is demonstrated clearly by Figures 16 and 17, which are taken from the paper by Satz.[132b] The explanation is given in the figure captions. Relations of this type are expected to make sense only well beyond the threshold for production of the channels in question.

By combining this model with the photoproduction model of Section 17-4, we are led to relations between high-energy cross sections for processes of the type $\pi\mathcal{N} \to X$ and $\gamma\mathcal{N} \to X$, in which X represents any allowed multipion hadronic state.[132c] Again, remarkable agreement with the available data is observed.

Appendix

We demonstrate briefly how one can arrive at additivity formula [Eq. (14-5)] for the high-energy scattering amplitude of the elastic reaction

$$A(\mathbf{p}) + B(-\mathbf{p}) = A(\mathbf{p}+\mathbf{q}) + B(-\mathbf{p}-\mathbf{q})$$

in which the momenta indicated are those in the center-of-mass system; we have $|\mathbf{q}|^2 = -t$. We do this in the framework of the impact parameter formalism developed by Glauber[111] for the case of hadron–nucleus scattering.

Let $\mathbf{r}_i(\mathbf{r}_j)$ be the position vector of quark $i(j)$ in hadron $A(B)$ with respect to the center of mass of $A(B)$ [$i(j)$ runs over the number $n_A(n_B)$ of quarks in $A(B)$]; let $\mathbf{b}$ be the impact parameter of the center of mass of A with respect to that of B; and let $\mathbf{b}_{ij}$ be the impact parameter of the center of mass of quark i in A with respect to that of quark j in B. Since for high energies and small scattering angles the vector $\mathbf{q}$ lies in the impact parameter plane, that is, the plane perpendicular to $\mathbf{p}$, we evidently have

$$\mathbf{b}_{ij}\cdot\mathbf{q} = (\mathbf{b} + \mathbf{r}_i - \mathbf{r}_j)\cdot\mathbf{q} \tag{A-1}$$

After having extracted the center-of-mass motion of the hadrons, which gives rise to a delta function expressing momentum conservation [see Appendix of Reference[111c]], we can write the full amplitude defined by Eq. (14-2) as the following two-dimensional Fourier transform (we leave out the energy variable)

$$T_{AB}(\mathbf{q}) = \frac{i}{2\pi}\int d\mathbf{b}\, e^{-i\mathbf{q}\cdot\mathbf{b}}\, \eta_{AB}(\mathbf{b}) \tag{A-2}$$

with

$$\begin{aligned}
\eta_{AB}(\mathbf{b}) &\equiv 1 - \exp[2i\delta_{AB}(\mathbf{b})] \\
&= \int d\tau_A \int d\tau_B |f(A, \{\mathbf{r}_i\})|^2\, |f(B, \{\mathbf{r}_j\})|^2\, \eta_{AB}(\{\mathbf{b}_{ij}\}) \\
\eta_{AB}(\{\mathbf{b}_{ij}\}) &= 1 - \exp[2i\delta_{AB}(\{\mathbf{b}_{ij}\})] \\
d\tau_A &= \prod_i d\mathbf{r}_i\, \delta\left(\frac{1}{n_A}\sum \mathbf{r}_i\right) \qquad d\tau_B = \prod_j d\mathbf{r}_j\, \delta\left(\frac{1}{n_B}\sum_j \mathbf{r}_j\right)
\end{aligned} \tag{A-3}$$

in which $\{\mathbf{x}\}$ stands for the set of all possible vectors $\mathbf{x}$. The f's are the *internal* space wave functions; the delta functions express the fact that in performing the integration the hadronic centers of mass remain fixed at the origin. Finally, the

δ_{AB}'s represent the scattering phase shifts as continuous functions of the impact parameters.

Additivity amounts to writing

$$\eta_{AB}(\{\mathbf{b}_{ij}\}) = \sum_{ij} \eta_{ij}(\mathbf{b}_{ij}) = \sum_{ij} [1 - e^{2i\delta_{ij}(\mathbf{b}_{ij})}] \tag{A-4}$$

in which $\eta_{ij}(\mathbf{b}_{ij})$ is related to the amplitude $T_{ij}(\mathbf{q}')$ for elastic scattering of two quasifree quarks i and j by a formula analogous to Eq. (A-2),

$$T_{ij}(\mathbf{q}') = \frac{i}{2\pi} \int d\mathbf{b}_{ij}\, e^{-i\mathbf{q}'\cdot\mathbf{b}_{ij}}\, \eta_{ij}(\mathbf{b}_{ij}) \tag{A-5}$$

Combining Eqs. (A-1)–(A-5) leads to the desired result,

$$T_{AB}(\mathbf{q}) = \sum_{ij} T_{ij}(\mathbf{q})\, F_i^A(\mathbf{q})\, F_j^B(-\mathbf{q}) \tag{A-6}$$

with the form factor $F_i^A(\mathbf{q}) \equiv F_i^{AA}(\mathbf{q})$ given by

$$F_i^A(\mathbf{q}) = \int d\tau_A |f(A, \{\mathbf{r}_i\})|^2 e^{-i\mathbf{r}_i\cdot\mathbf{q}} \tag{A-7}$$

and a similar expression for F_j^B. The form factors or overlap integrals involved in inelastic processes or in decay processes are identical to Eq. (A-7) except for the replacement of $|f(A, \{\mathbf{r}_i\})|^2$ by $f^*(A, \{\mathbf{r}_i\}) f(A', \{\mathbf{r}_i\})$ with A' different from A [compare Eq. (5-11)].

If instead of Eq. (A-4) (additivity of amplitudes) we use the Glauber Ansatz[111]

$$\delta_{AB}(\{\mathbf{b}_{ij}\}) = \sum_{ij} \delta_{ij}(\mathbf{b}_{ij}) \tag{A-8}$$

(additivity of phase shifts) a series expansion for T_{AB} in powers of the quark–quark amplitudes is obtained, of which Eq. (A-6) is the first term and the second and higher terms represent multiple scattering corrections. This expansion has been the starting point for several authors[112] who discuss such corrections (which are known to be important in scattering of hadrons by nuclei) in the quark model (see Section 16-3).

References

1. M. Gell-Mann, *Phys. Letters* **8**, 214 (1964).
2. G. Zweig, CERN Preprints TH 401, 412 (1964) (unpublished).
3. E. Fermi and C. N. Yang, *Phys. Rev.* **76**, 1739 (1949).
4. V. F. Weisskopf, $SU_2 \to SU_3 \to SU_6$, CERN lectures, CERN Rept. 66-19 (May 1966).
5. (a) J. J. de Swart, *Rev. Mod. Phys.* **35**, 916 (1963); (b) *Proceedings of the 1966 CERN School of Physics,* CERN Rept. 66-29 (December 1966).
6. R. H. Dalitz, in *High Energy Physics,* Ecole d'Ete de Physique Theorique, C. DeWitt and M. Jacob, Eds., Les Houches, 1965 (Gordon and Breach, New York, 1966).
7. An excellent collection of papers on SU(3) has been reprinted in M. Gell-Mann and Y. Ne'eman, *The Eightfold Way* (W. A. Benjamin, Inc., New York, 1964).
8. F. Gürsey and L. A. Radicati, *Phys. Rev. Letters* **13**, 173 (1964); B. Sakita, *Phys. Rev.* **136**, B1756 (1964); F. Gürsey, A. Pais, and L. A. Radicati, *Phys. Rev. Letters* **13**, 299 (1964).
9. For a recent review of the situation, see L. Lederman, *Comments Nucl. Particle Phys.* **1**, 155 (1967); see also, T. Massam, CERN Report 68-24 (July 1968).
10. (a) R. H. Dalitz, in *XIIIth International Conference on High-Energy Physics, Berkeley 1966* (University of California Press, 1967); (b) Report presented at the Topical Conference on πN Scattering, Irvine, California (Dec. 1967); (c) Report presented at the Topical Conference on Meson Spectroscopy, Philadelphia (May 1968).
11. Y. B. Zel'dovich, L. B. Okun, and S. B. Pikelner, *Phys. Letters* **17**, 1964 (1965); *Soviet Phys.–Usp.* (English Transl.) **8**, 702 (1966); A. Nir, *Phys. Rev. Letters* **19**, 337 (1967).
12. W. A. Chupka, J. P. Schiffer, and C. M. Stevens, *Phys. Rev. Letters* **17**, 60 (1966).
13. G. Domokos and T. Fulton, *Phys. Letters* **20**, 546 (1966).
14. C. Becchi, G. Gallinaro, and G. Morpurgo, *Nuovo Cimento* **39**, 409 (1965).
15. R. A. Leacock, W. I. Beavers, and C. T. Daub, Preprint, Iowa State University (1967).
16. T. Massam *et al., Nuovo Cimento* **40**, 589 (1965); H. Kasha *et al., Phys. Rev.* **154**, 1263 (1967); G. Damgaard *et al., Phys. Letters* **17**, 152 (1965); R. C. Lamb *et al., Phys. Rev. Letters* **17**, 1068 (1966).

17. L. B. Leipuner *et al.*, *Phys. Rev. Letters* **12**, 423 (1964); W. Blum *et al.*, *Phys. Rev. Letters* **13**, 353a (1964); D. E. Dorfan *et al.*, *Phys. Rev. Letters* **14**, 999 (1965).
18. V. M. Maximenko *et al.*, *Soviet Phys–JETP Letters* **3**, 8, 15 (1966); R. Hagedorn, CERN Preprint TH 751 (1967), to be published in *Nuovo Cimento Suppl.*
19. A. Buhler-Broglin *et al.*, *Nuovo Cimento* **49**, 209 (1967); H. Kasha *et al.*, *Phys. Rev. Letters* **20**, 217 (1968).
20. J. J. de Swart, *Phys. Rev. Letters* **18**, 618 (1967).
21. L. I. Schiff, *Phys. Rev. Letters* **17**, 612, 714 (1966).
22. G. Morpurgo, *Physics* **2**, 95 (1965).
23. Y. Nambu, in *Symmetry Principles at High-Energy,* Proceedings of the Second Coral Gables Conference, B. Kursunoglu, A. Perlmutter, and I. Sakmar, Eds. (W. H. Freeman and Company, London, 1967).
24. O. W. Greenberg, *Phys. Rev.* **147**, 1077 (1966).
25. H. J. Lipkin, *Nucl. Phys.* **B1**, 597 (1967).
26. (a) H. Bacry, J. Nuyts, and L. Van Hove, *Phys. Letters* **9**, 279 (1964); (b) M. Y. Han and Y. Nambu, *Phys. Rev.* **139**, B1006 (1965).
27. (a) N. Cabibbo, L. Maiani, and G. Preparata, *Phys. Letters* **25B**, 132 (1967); (b) S. Okubo, *Progr. Theor. Phys. (Kyoto) Suppl.* **37**, **38**, 114 (1966).
28. A. H. Rosenfeld *et al.*, "Particle Properties", UCRL–8030 (August 1968).
29. W. Thirring, *Acta Phys. Austriaca, Suppl.* **II**, 205 (1965); *Proceedings of the 5th International University Meeting at Schladming 1966* (Julius Springer-Verlag, Vienna, 1966).
30. G. Morpurgo, *Phys. Letters* **20**, 684 (1966).
31. O. W. Greenberg and D. Zwanziger, *Phys. Rev.* **150**, 1177 (1966).
32. T. K. Kuo and L. A. Radicati, *Phys. Rev.* **139**, B746 (1965); J. Werle, Warsaw Preprint (June 1966).
33. A. N. Mitra and R. Majumdar, *Phys. Rev.* **150**, 1194 (1966).
34. R. E. Kreps and J. J. de Swart, *Phys. Rev.* **162**, 1729 (1967).
35. D. H. Coward *et al.*, *Phys. Rev. Letters* **20**, 292 (1968).
36. (a) O. W. Greenberg, *Phys. Rev. Letters* **13**, 598 (1968); (b) O. W. Greenberg and M. Resnikoff, *Phys. Rev.* **163**, 1844 (1967).
37. R. Delbourgo, A. Salam, and J. Strathdee, *Phys. Letters* **21**, 455 (1966); J. Fischer, N. Limic, J. Niederle, and R. Raczka, *Nuovo Cimento* **55**, 33 (1968); C. H. Llewellyn Smith, Preprint, University of Oxford (November 1967); A. Pagnamento, *Nuovo Cimento* **53**, 30 (1968).
38. P. Federman, H. R. Rubinstein, and I. Talmi, *Phys. Letters* **22**, 208 (1966).
39. H. R. Rubinstein, *Phys. Letters* **22**, 210 (1966).
40. H. R. Rubinstein, *Phys. Rev. Letters* **17**, 41 (1966); A. Gal and F. Scheck, *Nucl. Phys.* **B2**, 110 (1967).
41. D. R. O. Morrison, *Phys. Letters* **25B**, 238 (1967).
42. G. Chikovani *et al.*, *Phys. Letters* **25B**, 44 (1967).

43. G. Goldhaber, A. Firestone, and B. C. Shen, *Phys. Rev. Letters* **19**, 972 (1967).
44. M. N. Focacci *et al., Phys. Rev. Letters* **17**, 890 (1966); L. Dubal *et al., Nucl. Phys.* **B3**, 435 (1967).
45. G. Goldhaber, in *Proceedings of the 1967 CERN School of Physics* (CERN 67-24, Sept. 1967), Vol. 3.
46. D. G. Sutherland, *Nucl. Phys.* **B2**, 157 (1967). We refer to this paper for earlier references.
47. G. Goldhaber, *Phys. Rev. Letters* **19**, 976 (1967).
48. A. Donnachie, R. G. Kirsopp, and C. Lovelace, *Phys. Letters* **26B**, 161 (1967).
49. D. Faiman and A. W. Hendry, *Phys. Rev.* **173**, 1720 (1968); A. N. Mitra, CERN Preprint TH 902 (May 1968); G. Zweig, paper presented at the Topical Conference on Meson Spectroscopy, Philadelphia (May 1968). See also the Reports by H. Harari and G. Morpurgo in *Proceedings of the 14th International Conference on High Energy Physics,* J. Prentki and J. Steinberger, Eds. (CERN, Geneva 1968).
50. G. Belletini *et al., Phys. Letters* **18**, 167 (1965); K. Foley *et al., Phys. Rev. Letters* **19**, 397 (1967); R. B. Bell *et al., Phys. Rev. Letters* **20**, 164 (1968).
51. J. Meyer, in *Proceedings of the Heidelberg International Conference on Elementary Particles* (North-Holland Publishing Co., Amsterdam 1968), p. 117.
52. M. Krammer and E. L. Lomon, *Phys. Rev. Letters* **20**, 71 (1968).
53. G. Bassompierre *et al., Phys. Letters* **27 B**, 468 (1968).
54. R. van Royen and V. F. Weisskopf, *Nuovo Cimento* **50**, 617 (1967); **51**, 583 (19
55. N. Cabibbo, *Phys. Rev. Letters* **10**, 531 (1963).
56. S. S. Gerstein and J. B. Zel'dovich, *Soviet Phys.–JETP* (English Transl.) **2**, 576 (1956); R. P. Feynman and M. Gell-Mann, *Phys. Rev.* **109**, 193 (1958).
57. A. Dar, Preprint, MIT (1967).
58. (a) N. N. Bogoliubov, B. V. Struminskij, and A. N. Tavkhelidze, JINR Preprint D-1968 (1965); (b) N. N. Bogoliubov, V. A. Matveyev, and A. N. Tavkhelidze, *Nuovo Cimento* **48**, 132 (1967); (c) P. N. Bogoliubov, JINR Preprint (1967).
59. V. A. Matveyev, B. V. Struminskij, and A. N. Tavkhelidze, JINR Preprint P-2524 (1965).
60. G. Källén, *Elementary Particle Physics* (Addison-Wesley Publishing Company, Inc., London, 1964).
61. R. Van Royen, private communication.
62. C. W. Akerlof *et al., Phys. Rev.* **163**, 1482 (1967).
63. This has been remarked by J. J. de Swart, private communication.
64. S. Badier, *Phys. Letters* **24B**, 157 (1967); A. Dar, Preprint MIT (1967); M. K. Aliev and B. V. Struminskij, JINR Preprint P-3603 (November 1967).
65. S. B. Gerasimov, *Soviet Phys.–JETP* (English Transl.) **23**, 1040 (1966); E. M. Levin and L. L. Frankfurt, *Soviet J. Nucl. Phys.* **3**, 825 (1966); H. R. Rubinstein, F. Scheck, and R. Socolow, *Phys. Rev.* **154**, 1608 (1967).

66. M. A. Bég, B. W. Lee, and A. Pais, *Phys. Rev. Letters* **13**, 514 (1964).
67. J. Combe *et al., Z. Naturforsch.* **21a**, 1757 (1966).
68. H. J. Lipkin and A. N. Tavkhelidze, *Phys. Letters* **17**, 331 (1965).
69. C. Becchi and G. Morpurgo, *Phys. Rev.* **140B**, 687 (1965); V. V. Anisovich *et al., Phys. Letters* **16**, 194 (1965); W. Thirring, *Phys. Letters* **16**, 335 (1965); L. D. Soloviev, *Phys. Letters* **16**, 345 (1965).
70. C. Becchi and G. Morpurgo, *Phys. Letters* **17**, 352 (1965).
71. R. H. Dalitz and D. G. Sutherland, *Phys. Rev.* **146**, 1180 (1966).
72. R. G. Moorhouse, *Phys. Rev. Letters* **16**, 772, 968 (1966).
73. H. Pietschmann and W. Thirring, Preprint, University of Vienna, Scientific Note No. 32 (1965).
74. J. G. Asbury *et al., Phys. Rev. Letters* **19**, 869 (1967).
75. V. L. Auslander *et al., Phys. Letters* **25B**, 433 (1967).
76. Y. Nambu and J. J. Sakurai, *Phys. Rev. Letters* **8**, 79 (1962).
77. M. Gell-Mann and F. Zachariasen, *Phys. Rev.* **124**, 953 (1961).
78. M. Gell-Mann, D. H. Sharp, and W. Wagner, *Phys. Rev. Letters* **8**, 261 (1962).
79. G. von Dardel *et al., Phys. Letters* **4**, 51 (1963); G. Belletini *et al., Nuovo Cimento* **40A**, 1139 (1965).
80. I. Butterworth, in *Proceedings of the Heidelberg International Conference On Elementary Particles,* Heidelberg (September 1967) (North-Holland Publishing Company, Amsterdam, 1968), p. 11; C. Bemporad *et al., Phys. Letters* **25B**, 380 (1967).
81. C. Becchi and G. Morpurgo, Preprint, University of Genova (January 1966).
82. M. Roos, *Nucl. Phys.* **B2**, 615 (1967).
83. A. N. Mitra and M. Ross, *Phys. Rev.* **158**, 1630 (1967); H. J. Lipkin, H. R. Rubinstein, and H. Stern, *Phys. Rev.* **161**, 1502 (1967).
84. E. M. Levin and L. L. Frankfurt, *Soviet Phys.–JETP Letters* **2**, 65 (1965).
85. H. J. Lipkin and F. Scheck, *Phys. Rev. Letters* **16**, 71 (1966).
86. J. J. J. Kokkedee and L. Van Hove, *Nuovo Cimento* **42**, 711 (1966).
87. L. Van Hove, paper presented at the Conf. on High-Energy Two-Body Reactions, Stony Brook (April, 1966) (unpublished).
88. L. Van Hove, in *Particle Physics at High Energies,* T. W. Priest and L. L. J. Vick, Eds. (Oliver and Boyd, Edinburgh, 1967).
89. H. J. Lipkin, *Phys. Rev. Letters* **16**, 1015 (1966).
90. J. J. J. Kokkedee, *Phys. Letters* **22**, 88 (1966).
91. J. J. J. Kokkedee and L. Van Hove, *Nucl. Phys.* **B1**, 169 (1967).
92. G. Alexander, H. J. Lipkin, and F. Scheck, *Phys. Rev. Letters* **17**, 412 (1966).
93. (a) H. J. Lipkin, F. Scheck, and H. Stern, *Phys. Rev.* **152**, 1325 (1966); (b) C. Itzykson and M. Jacob, *Nuovo Cimento* **48A**, 909 (1967); (c) M. P. Locher and H. Römer, *Phys. Letters* **23**, 496 (1966).
94. H. J. Lipkin and F. Scheck, *Phys. Rev. Letters* **18**, 347 (1967).

95. J. L. Friar and J. S. Trefil, *Nuovo Cimento* **49**, 642 (1967); K. Kajantie and J. S. Trefil, *Nucl. Phys.* **B2**, 243 (1967).
96. A. Bialas, A. Gula, and B. Muryn, *Acta Phys. Polon.* **32**, 443 (1967); B. Gorczyca, *Acta Phys. Polon.* (to be published).
97. A. Bialas and K. Zalewski, *Nucl. Phys.* **B6**, 449 (1968).
98. H. Joos, *Phys. Letters* **24B**, 103 (1967); K. Kajantie and J. S. Trefil, *Phys. Letters* **24B**, 106 (1967).
99. K. Böckmann *et al.*, *Nuovo Cimento* **42A**, 954 (1966).
100. J. J. J. Kokkedee, *Nuovo Cimento* **43**, 919 (1966).
101. K. Foley *et al.*, *Phys. Rev. Letters* **19**, 193, 857 (1967).
102. I. Pomeranchuk, *Soviet Phys.–JETP* **34**, 499 (1958); L. Van Hove, *Phys. Letters* **5**, 252 (1963).
103. M. Gell-Mann, *Phys. Rev. Letters* **8**, 263 (1962). V. N. Gribov and I. Pomeranchuk, *Phys. Rev. Letters* **8**, 343 (1962).
104. See, for instance, A. Wetherell, in *Proceedings of the XIIIth International Conference on High Energy Physics, Berkeley, 1966* (University of California Press, Berkeley, 1967), p. 272.
105. T. T. Wu and C. N. Yang, *Phys. Rev.* **137**, B708 (1965).
106. W. Galbraith *et al.*, *Phys. Rev.* **138**, B913 (1965); W. F. Baker *et al.*, *Phys. Rev.* **129**, 2285 (1963); A. Citron *et al.*, *Phys. Rev. Letters* **13**, 205 (1964).
107. K. Foley *et al.*, *Phys. Rev. Letters* **19**, 330 (1967).
108. W. Rarita, R. J. Riddell, C. B. Chiu, and R. J. N. Phillips, *Phys. Rev.* **165**, 1615 (1968).
109. D. Bassano *et al.*, *Phys. Rev.* **160**, 1239 (1967).
110. J. G. Asbury *et al.*, *Phys. Rev. Letters* **19**, 865 (1967); E. Lohrmann, in *Proceedings of the Topical Conference on High Energy Collisions of Hadrons* (CERN-Rept. 68-7, February 1968) Vol. I, p. 556.
111. R. J. Glauber, in *Lectures in Theoretical Physics* (Interscience Publishers, Inc., New York, 1959), Vol. I, p. 315. See also, V. Franco and R. J. Glauber, *Phys. Rev.* **142**, 1195 (1966); R. J. Glauber, in *High Energy Physics and Nuclear Structure,* G. Alexander, Ed. (North Holland Publishing Company, Amsterdam, 1967), p. 311.
112. D. R. Harrington, Preprint Rutgers University (1967); V. Franco, *Phys. Rev. Letters* **18**, 1159 (1967); M. V. Barnhill, *Phys. Rev.* **163**, 1735 (1967); A. Deloff, *Nucl. Phys.* **B2**, 597 (1967); D. R. Harrington and A. Pagnamento, *Phys. Rev.* **173**, 1599 (1968); N. W. Dean, *Nucl. Phys.* **B4**, 534 (1968); **B7**, 311 (1968).
Dean, *Nucl. Phys.* **B4**, 534 (1968).
113. J. S. Bell, *Phys. Rev. Letters* **13**, 57 (1964).
114. P. G. O. Freund, *Phys. Rev. Letters* **15**, 929 (1965); *Nuovo Cimento* **46A**, 563 (1966).

115. N. Cabibbo, L. Horwitz, and Y. Ne'eman, *Phys. Letters* **22**, 336 (1966); N. Cabibbo, J. J. J. Kokkedee, L. Horwitz, and Y. Ne'eman, *Nuovo Cimento* **45**, 275 (1966).
116. A. Bialas and K. Zalewski, *Nuovo Cimento* **46A**, 425 (1966).
117. J. Daboul, *Nuovo Cimento* **50**, 850 (1967); H. J. Lipkin, in *High-Energy Physics and Nuclear Structure,* G. Alexander, Ed. (North-Holland Publishing Company, Amsterdam, 1967), p. 363.
118. D. R. O. Morrison, "Review of Inelastic Two-Body Reactions," CERN TC 66-20 (August 1966).
119. Z. Koba, *Prog. Theor. Phys. Suppl.* Extra Number (1965); L. Van Hove, in *Preludes in Theoretical Physics,* A. de-Shalit, H. Feshbach, and L. Van Hove, Eds. (North-Holland Publishing Company, Amsterdam, 1966), p. 44.
120. A. Bialas and K. Zalewski, *Phys. Letters* **26B**, 170 (1967); *Nucl. Phys.* **B6**, 465, 478 (1968).
121. J. Mott *et al., Phys. Rev. Letters* **18**, 355 (1967).
122. W. H. K. Panowsky, *Proceedings of the Heidelberg International Conference on Elementary Particles* (North-Holland Publishing Company, Amsterdam, 1968), p. 37; J. S. Greenberg, *et al., Phys. Rev. Letters* **20**, 221 (1968).
123. Bonn-Durham-Nijmegen-Paris-Strasbourg-Turin-Collaboration, *Proceedings of the Topical Conference on High Energy Collisions of Hadrons* (CERN- Rept. 68-7, February 1968), Vol. II, p. 150; *Phys. Letters* **28B**, 72 (1968). I am indebted to Prof. R. T. Van de Walle for discussions on the experimental results.
124. J. Kupsch, *Phys. Letters* **22**, 690 (1966); K. Kajantie and J. S. Trefil, *Nucl. Phys.* **B1**, 648 (1967); A. Bialas, A. Gula, B. Muryn, and K. Zalewski, *Nucl. Phys.* **B6**, 483 (1968).
125. S. M. Berman and S. D. Drell, *Phys. Rev.* **133**, B791 (1964). For a recent review, see H. Joos, in *Special Problems in High-Energy Physics,* P. Urban, Ed. (Julius Springer-Verlag, Vienna, 1967), p. 320.
126. German Bubble Chamber Collaboration, *Phys. Letters* **27B**, 54 (1968).
127. H. R. Rubinstein and H. Stern, *Phys. Letters* **21**, 447 (1966). See also, J. Patera and V. Simak, Preprint Prague 67-1 (1967).
128. J. Harte, R. H. Socolow, J. Vandermeulen, and K. Zalewski, CERN Preprint TH.701 (1966); J. Harte, R. Socolow, and J. Vandermeulen, *Nuovo Cimento* **49**, 555 (1967).
129. M. Elitzur and H. R. Rubinstein, *Phys. Rev. Letters* **18**, 417 (1967).
130. P. G. O. Freund, *Phys. Rev. Letters* **15**, 929 (1965).
131. C. A. Levinson, N. S. Wall, and H. J. Lipkin, *Phys. Rev. Letters* **17**, 1122 (1966).
132. H. Satz (a) *Phys. Letters* **25B**, 27 (1967); (b) *Phys. Rev. Letters* **19**, 1453 (1967) and Addendum; (c) *Phys. Letters* **25B**, 220 (1967).
133. K. Rybicki, *Nuovo Cimento* **49**, 233 (1967).
134. K. Zalewski and J. A. Danysz, *Nucl. Phys.* **B2**, 249 (1967).

Volume 8, number 3 PHYSICS LETTERS 1 February 1964

A SCHEMATIC MODEL OF BARYONS AND MESONS *

M. GELL-MANN
California Institute of Technology, Pasadena, California

Received 4 January 1964

If we assume that the strong interactions of baryons and mesons are correctly described in terms of the broken "eightfold way" [1-3], we are tempted to look for some fundamental explanation of the situation. A highly promised approach is the purely dynamical "boot trap" model for all the strongly interacting particles within which one may try to derive isotopic spin and strangeness conservation and broken eightfold symmetry from self-consistency alone [4]. Of course, with only strong interactions, the orientation of the asymmetry in the unitary space cannot be specified; one hopes that in some way the selection of specific components of the F-spin by electromagnetism and the weak interactions determines the choice of isotopic spin and hypercharge directions.

Even if we consider the scattering amplitudes of strongly interacting particles on the mass shell only and treat the matrix elements of the weak, electromagnetic, and gravitational interactions by means of dispersion theory, there are still meaningful and important questions regarding the algebraic properties of these interactions that have so far been discussed only by abstracting the properties from a formal field theory model based on fundamental entities [3] from which the baryons and mesons are built up.

If these entities were octets, we might expect the underlying symmetry group to be SU(8) instead of SU(3); it is therefore tempting to try to use unitary triplets as fundamental objects. A unitary triplet t consists of an isotopic singlet s of electric charge z (in units of e) and an isotopic doublet (u, d) with charges z+1 and z respectively. The anti-triplet $\bar{t}$ has, of course, the opposite signs of the charges. Complete symmetry among the members of the triplet gives the exact eightfold way, while a mass difference, for example, between the isotopic doublet and singlet gives the first-order violation.

For any value of z and of triplet spin, we can construct baryon octets from a basic neutral baryon singlet b by taking combinations $(b t \bar{t})$, $(b t t \bar{t} \bar{t})$, etc. **. From $(b t \bar{t})$, we get the representations **1** and **8**, while from $(b t t \bar{t} \bar{t})$ we get **1**, **8**, **10**, $\overline{\mathbf{10}}$, and **27**. In a similar way, meson singlets and octets can be made out of $(t \bar{t})$, $(t t \bar{t} \bar{t})$, etc. The quantum number $n_t - n_{\bar{t}}$ would be zero for all known baryons and mesons. The most interesting example of such a model is one in which the triplet has spin $\frac{1}{2}$ and $z = -1$, so that the four particles d^-, s^-, u^0 and b^0 exhibit a parallel with the leptons.

A simpler and more elegant scheme can be constructed if we allow non-integral values for the charges. We can dispense entirely with the basic baryon b if we assign to the triplet t the following properties: spin $\frac{1}{2}$, $z = -\frac{1}{3}$, and baryon number $\frac{1}{3}$. We then refer to the members $u^{\frac{2}{3}}$, $d^{-\frac{1}{3}}$, and $s^{-\frac{1}{3}}$ of the triplet as "quarks" [6] q and the members of the anti-triplet as anti-quarks $\bar{q}$. Baryons can now be constructed from quarks by using the combinations $(q q q)$, $(q q q q \bar{q})$, etc., while mesons are made out of $(q \bar{q})$, $(q q \bar{q} \bar{q})$, etc. It is assuming that the lowest baryon configuration $(q q q)$ gives just the representations **1**, **8**, and **10** that have been observed, while the lowest meson configuration $(q \bar{q})$ similarly gives just **1** and **8**.

A formal mathematical model based on field theory can be built up for the quarks exactly as for p, n, Λ in the old Sakata model, for example [3] with all strong interactions ascribed to a neutral vector meson field interacting symmetrically with the three particles. Within such a framework, the electromagnetic current (in units of e) is just

$$i\{\tfrac{2}{3}\, \bar{u}\, \gamma_\alpha\, u - \tfrac{1}{3}\, \bar{d}\, \gamma_\alpha\, d - \tfrac{1}{3}\, \bar{s}\, \gamma_\alpha\, s\}$$

or $\mathscr{F}_{3\alpha} + \mathscr{F}_{8\alpha}/\sqrt{3}$ in the notation of ref. [3]. For the weak current, we can take over from the Sakata model the form suggested by Gell-Mann and Lévy [7], namely $i\, \bar{p} \gamma_\alpha (1+\gamma_5)(n \cos\theta + \Lambda \sin\theta)$, which gives in the quark scheme the expression ***

$$i\, \bar{u}\, \gamma_\alpha (1 + \gamma_5)(d \cos\theta + s \sin\theta)$$

* Work supported in part by the U.S. Atomic Energy Commission.

** This is similar to the treatment in ref. [1]. See also ref. [5].

*** The parallel with $i\, \bar{\nu}_e\, \gamma_\alpha (1 + \gamma_5)\, e$ and $i\, \bar{\nu}_\mu\, \gamma_\alpha (1 + \gamma_5) \mu$ is obvious. Likewise, in the model with d^-, s^-, u^0, and b^0 discussed above, we would take the weak current to be $i(\bar{b}^0 \cos\theta + \bar{u}^0 \sin\theta)\, \gamma_\alpha (1 + \gamma_5)\, s^- + i(\bar{u}^0 \cos\theta - \bar{b}^0 \sin\theta)\, \gamma_\alpha (1 + \gamma_5)\, d^-$. The part with $\Delta(n_t - n_{\bar{t}}) = 0$ is just $i\, \bar{u}^0\, \gamma_\alpha (1+\gamma_5)(d^- \cos\theta + s^- \sin\theta)$.

or, in the notation of ref. [3]),

$$[\mathscr{F}_{1\alpha} + \mathscr{F}^5_{1\alpha} + i(\mathscr{F}_{2\alpha} + \mathscr{F}^5_{2\alpha})] \cos\theta$$
$$+ [\mathscr{F}_{4\alpha} + \mathscr{F}^5_{4\alpha} + i(\mathscr{F}_{5\alpha} + \mathscr{F}^5_{5\alpha})] \sin\theta .$$

We thus obtain all the features of Cabibbo's picture [8]) of the weak current, namely the rules $|\Delta I| = 1$, $\Delta Y = 0$ and $|\Delta I| = \frac{1}{2}$, $\Delta Y/\Delta Q = +1$, the conserved $\Delta Y = 0$ current with coefficient $\cos\theta$, the vector current in general as a component of the current of the F-spin, and the axial vector current transforming under SU(3) as the same component of another octet. Furthermore, we have [3]) the equal-time commutation rules for the fourth components of the currents:

$$[\mathscr{F}_{j4}(x) \pm \mathscr{F}^5_{j4}(x),\ \mathscr{F}_{k4}(x') \pm \mathscr{F}^5_{k4}(x')] =$$
$$- 2 f_{jkl}\, [\mathscr{F}_{l4}(x) \pm \mathscr{F}^5_{l4}(x)]\, \delta(x-x') ,$$
$$[\mathscr{F}_{j4}(x) \pm \mathscr{F}^5_{j4}(x),\ \mathscr{F}_{k4}(x') \mp \mathscr{F}^5_{k4}(x')] = 0 ,$$

$i = 1, \ldots 8$, yielding the group SU(3) × SU(3). We can also look at the behaviour of the energy density $\theta_{44}(x)$ (in the gravitational interaction) under equal-time commutation with the operators $\mathscr{F}_{j4}(x') \pm \mathscr{F}_{j4}{}^5(x')$. That part which is non-invariant under the group will transform like particular representations of SU(3) × SU(3), for example like $(3, \bar{3})$ and $(\bar{3}, 3)$ if it comes just from the masses of the quarks.

All these relations can now be abstracted from the field theory model and used in a dispersion theory treatment. The scattering amplitudes for strongly interacting particles on the mass shell are assumed known; there is then a system of linear dispersion relations for the matrix elements of the weak currents (and also the electromagnetic and gravitational interactions) to lowest order in these interactions. These dispersion relations, unsubtracted and supplemented by the non-linear commutation rules abstracted from the field theory, may be powerful enough to determine all the matrix elements of the weak currents, including the effective strengths of the axial vector current matrix elements compared with those of the vector current.

It is fun to speculate about the way quarks would behave if they were physical particles of finite mass (instead of purely mathematical entities as they would be in the limit of infinite mass). Since charge and baryon number are exactly conserved, one of the quarks (presumably $u^{\frac{2}{3}}$ or $d^{-\frac{1}{3}}$) would be absolutely stable *, while the other member of the doublet would go into the first member very slowly by β-decay or K-capture. The isotopic singlet quark would presumably decay into the doublet by weak interactions, much as Λ goes into N. Ordinary matter near the earth's surface would be contaminated by stable quarks as a result of high energy cosmic ray events throughout the earth's history, but the contamination is estimated to be so small that it would never have been detected. A search for stable quarks of charge $-\frac{1}{3}$ or $+\frac{2}{3}$ and/or stable di-quarks of charge $-\frac{2}{3}$ or $+\frac{1}{3}$ or $+\frac{4}{3}$ at the highest energy accelerators would help to reassure us of the non-existence of real quarks.

These ideas were developed during a visit to Columbia University in March 1963; the author would like to thank Professor Robert Serber for stimulating them.

References

1) M.Gell-Mann, California Institute of Technology Synchrotron Laboratory Report CTSL-20 (1961).
2) Y.Ne'eman, Nuclear Phys.26 (1961) 222.
3) M.Gell-Mann, Phys.Rev.125 (1962) 1067.
4) E.g.: R.H.Capps, Phys.Rev.Letters 10 (1963) 312; R.E.Cutkosky, J.Kalckar and P.Tarjanne, Physics Letters 1 (1962) 93; E.Abers, F.Zachariasen and A.C .Zemach, Phys. Rev.132 (1963) 1831; S.Glashow, Phys.Rev.130 (1963) 2132; R.E.Cutkosky and P.Tarjanne, Phys.Rev.132 (1963) 1354.
5) P.Tarjanne and V.L.Teplitz, Phys.Rev.Letters 11 (1963) 447.
6) James Joyce, Finnegan's Wake (Viking Press, New York, 1939) p.383.
7) M.Gell-Mann and M.Lévy, Nuovo Cimento 16 (1960) 705.
8) N.Cabibbo, Phys.Rev.Letters 10 (1963) 531.

* There is the alternative possibility that the quarks are unstable under decay into baryon plus anti-di-quark or anti-baryon plus quadri-quark. In any case, some particle of fractional charge would have to be absolutely stable.

* * * * *

Volume 9, number 3 PHYSICS LETTERS 15 April 1964

BASIC SU_3 TRIPLETS WITH INTEGRAL CHARGE AND UNIT BARYON NUMBER

H. BACRY, J. NUYTS and L. VAN HOVE
CERN, Geneva

Received 2 March 1964

The success encountered by the octet model of SU_3 symmetry [1] has given increased interest to speculations about the possible existence and properties of hitherto undiscovered particles which would belong to the basic representations 3 and $\bar{3}$ of SU_3, and would be through strong binding forces the building blocks of mesons and baryons. Up to now the SU_3 multiplets established for mesons belong to the representations 1 and 8, while representations 1, 8 and 10 have been found for baryons. Just these representations are obtained in an elegant triplet model of SU_3 symmetry recently proposed by Gell-Mann [2] and Zweig [3], where mesons are given the structure $A \times \bar{A}(3 \times \bar{3} = 1 + 8)$ and baryons the structure $AAA(3 \times 3 \times 3 = 1 + 8 + 8 + 10)$ in terms of one basic triplet A of spin $\frac{1}{2}$ particles. The latter, however, must then be assigned the unusual values $\frac{2}{3}$, $-\frac{1}{3}$, $-\frac{1}{3}$ for the electric charge Q and $N = \frac{1}{3}$ for the baryon number N.

Our aim is to show that consideration of two basic triplets instead of one allows to eliminate in a simple way the occurrence of fractional Q and N, without losing the elegant structures $3 \times \bar{3}$ for mesons and $3 \times 3 \times 3$ for baryons. We introduce two triplets T and Θ of spin $\frac{1}{2}$ particles, which we call trions. They all have $N = 1$ and are distinguished by a new additive quantum number D. The trions are listed in tables 1 and 2.

For a given SU_3 multiplet the value of D is related to its main charge $\langle Q \rangle$ by

$$D = 3\langle Q \rangle$$

and the corresponding generalized Gell-Mann - Nishijima formula is

$$Q = I_3 + \tfrac{1}{2}Y + \tfrac{1}{3}D \, .$$

Consequently D is conserved in strong and electromagnetic interactions.

It is natural to assume that all particles observed up to now have the quantum number D equal to zero, or more generally that $D = 0$ characterizes the most stable particles built up from trions. This raises the question of the possible composite particles having $D = 0$. Those among them which are obtained as products of two and three triplets are listed in table 3.

Table 1
T-trions ($N = 1$, $D = 1$, spin $s = \frac{1}{2}$).

States	T^+	T^0	T'^0
charge Q	1	0	0
hypercharge Y	$\frac{1}{3}$	$\frac{1}{3}$	$-\frac{2}{3}$
isospin I	$\frac{1}{2}$	$\frac{1}{2}$	0
I_3	$\frac{1}{2}$	$-\frac{1}{2}$	0

Table 2
Θ-trions ($N = 1$, $D = 2$, spin $s = \frac{1}{2}$).

States	Θ^0	Θ^+	Θ'^+
Q	0	1	1
Y	$-\frac{1}{3}$	$-\frac{1}{3}$	$\frac{2}{3}$
I	$\frac{1}{2}$	$\frac{1}{2}$	0
I_3	$-\frac{1}{2}$	$\frac{1}{2}$	0

Table 3

Number of trions in composite particles	Representations	Baryonic number N	Spin and parity
2	$\bar{T}T = 1+8$	0	0^- or 1^-
	$\bar{\Theta}\Theta = 1+8$	0	0^- or 1^-
3	$\bar{\Theta}TT = 1+8+8+10$	1	$\frac{1}{2}$ or $\frac{3}{2}$
	$\Theta\bar{T}\bar{T} = 1+8+8+10$	-1	$\frac{1}{2}$ or $\frac{3}{2}$

spin and parity have been given for s-state binding

It is interesting to note that products of more than three trions, when they have $D = 0$, can always be obtained as products of the composite particles in table 3.

The model here discussed has the following properties:

Table 4

Representations of C_3	1	6		14				14'			21				56						64							
Submultiplets A_2	1	3	$\bar{3}$	1	$\bar{6}$	6	1	$\bar{3}$	8	3	6	1	8	$\bar{6}$	10	3	15	$\overline{15}$	$\bar{3}$	$\overline{10}$	8	3	6	$\overline{15}$	$\overline{15}$	6	$\bar{3}$	8
Z	0	$\frac{1}{3}$	$-\frac{1}{3}$	1	$\frac{1}{3}$	$-\frac{1}{3}$	-1	$\frac{2}{3}$	0	$-\frac{2}{3}$	$\frac{2}{3}$	0	0	$-\frac{2}{3}$	1	$\frac{1}{3}$	$\frac{1}{3}$	$-\frac{1}{3}$	$-\frac{1}{3}$	-1	1	$\frac{1}{3}$	$\frac{1}{3}$	$\frac{1}{3}$	$-\frac{1}{3}$	$-\frac{1}{3}$	$-\frac{1}{3}$	-1

1. non-integral charges and non-integral baryonic numbers are avoided;
2. there is no place in the four classes given in table 3 for the representations $\overline{10}$ ($N = 1$) and 27. (This was also the case in the schemes proposed in refs. 2 and 3.
3. the trions T and Θ are all possible triplets with charges 0, ±1 such that $D > 0$. ($D > 0$ goes with $N = 1$, $D < 0$ with $N = -1$. This correlation between the signs of D and of N is related to the asymmetry existing between positive and negative charges in the baryon decuplet which contains one particle with charge +2 while all other particles have charges 0, ±1.)

The occurrence in our model of the third quantum number D besides I_3 and Y suggests the introduction of a simple group of rank three to describe a possible higher symmetry involving all trions and their combinations. Such groups correspond to the three Lie algebras A_3 (group SU_4), $B_3(SO_7)$ and $C_3(Sp_6)$. These algebras all contain $A_2(SU_3)$ as a subalgebra. Hereafter we examine the C_3 case as the simplest example. The small differences shown by A_3 and B_3 are mentioned afterwards. The lowest representations of C_3 are given in table 4 with their contents in A_2 representations [4].

Z is the third additive quantum number which is obtained besides Y and I_3 from the Abelian subalgebra of C_3. In our model it is related to D and N by

$$D = \tfrac{3}{2}(N-Z) .$$

Any representation of C_3 can be obtained from products of representations 6 (octahedrons). From the preceding considerations the T-trions and the Θ-trions are to be classified in this representation 6, mesons in the product

$$6_1 \times 6_{-1} = 1_0 + 14'_0 + 21_0$$
$$(1) + (8) + (1+8)$$

and baryons in

$$6_1 \times 6_1 \times 6_{-1} = 6_1 + 6_1 + 6_1 + 14_1 + 56_1 + 64_1 + 64_1 .$$
$$(1) + (10) + (8) + (8)$$

The subscript added to the dimension of the representation is the corresponding baryonic number N. The brackets below the representations give the SU_3 submultiplets with $D = 0$ contained in them.

The A_3 case can be treated in complete analogy with C_3 because A_3 has also a representation 6 with the $A_2(SU_3)$ contents $3 + \bar{3}$. But A_3 has a lower dimensional representation (the representation 4 of SU_4) which moreover cannot be obtained by products of the representation 6. This makes it less attractive than C_3 for our model with its six basic particles.

As to the algebra B_3, it has A_3 as a subalgebra. Its lowest representation of dimension 7 decomposes in $3 + \bar{3} + 1$, thus implying the introduction of a seventh fundamental particle in the basis.

The authors are indebted to Dr. J. Prentki for very useful critical remarks.

References

1) M. Gell-Mann, California Institute of Technology Synchrotron Laboratory report CTSL-20 (1961): Phys. Rev. 125 (1962) 1067;
Y. Ne'eman, Nuclear Phys. 26 (1961) 222.
2) M. Gell-Mann, Physics Letters 8 (1964) 214.
3) G. Zweig, preprint CERN (1964). An SU_3 model for strong interaction symmetry and its breaking.
4) G. Loupias, M. Sirugue and J. C. Trotin, preprint Marseilles (1963). About simple Lie groups of rank 3

* * * * *

REPRINT 3

SPIN AND UNITARY-SPIN INDEPENDENCE IN A PARAQUARK MODEL OF BARYONS AND MESONS

O. W. Greenberg*
Institute for Advanced Study, Princeton, New Jersey
(Received 27 October 1964)

Wigner's supermultiplet theory,[1] transplanted independently by Gürsey, Pais, and Radicati,[2] and by Sakita,[2] from nuclear-structure physics to particle-structure physics, has aroused a good deal of interest recently. In the nuclear supermultiplet theory, the approximate independence of both spin and isospin of those forces relevant to the energies of certain low-lying bound states (nuclei) makes it useful to classify the states according to irreducible representations of SU(4). Parallel to this, in the particle supermultiplet theory, the possible independence of both spin and unitary spin of those forces relevant to the masses of certain low-lying bound states (particles) makes it interesting to classify the states according to irreducible representations of SU(6). Three results associated with this SU(6) classification indicate its usefulness: (1) The best known baryons (in particular, the spin-$\frac{1}{2}^+$ baryon octet and the spin-$\frac{3}{2}^+$ baryon decuplet) are grouped into a supermultiplet containing 56 particles.

V540 1-5

The pseudoscalar 0^- octet, vector 1^- octet, and vector 1^- singlet of mesons are grouped into a supermultiplet containing 35 particles. (2) Rather accurate mass formulas have been written down (partly on heuristic grounds) for the supermultiplets.[2,3] (3) In the approximation where the spin and unitary-spin independence of the forces relevant to the $\underline{56}$ is broken only by electromagnetic coupling, the magnetic moments of all the baryons in the $\underline{56}$ have been calculated up to a single common factor.[4] This calculation predicts the ratio $\beta = \mu_n/\mu_p = -\frac{2}{3}$, which agrees with the experimental value to within 3%.

Analogy with the Wigner supermultiplet theory leads us to adopt an atomic model in which all of the baryons and mesons are composite objects made up of basic particles. We assume that the basic forces are independent of unitary spin, but are in general spin dependent, and that the approximate symmetry group of the theory is $\mathcal{P}'\otimes SU(3)$, where $\mathcal{P}'$ is the covering group of the Poincaré group. However, for low-lying bound states, in particular when all orbital angular momenta are zero, all orbit-orbit and spin-orbit forces vanish so that there will be an additional degeneracy which will allow SU(6) invariance for these particular states, provided the spin-spin forces are not too large.[5] The desired supermultiplets, the $\underline{56}$ for the baryons and the $\underline{35}$ for the mesons, contain, respectively, the symmetric direct product of three SU(6) multiplets, and the antisymmetric direct product of an SU(6) and an SU(6)* multiplet. These assignments suggest that the basic particles are quarks.[6-9] For the mesons the $\underline{35}$ can be achieved by a state containing a fermion and an antifermion in s states; however, for the baryons the assignment of three fermions to the $\underline{56}$ is not possible if all three fermions are in s states.[10] We will return to this problem later, but for the moment assume that we can arrange to construct both the $\underline{35}$ and the $\underline{56}$ with all particles in s states.

The notion that an atomic model underlies the SU(6) invariance gives some hints for the derivation of mass formulas. In analogy with atomic and nuclear physics we suggest that the terms violating the exact SU(6) symmetry, for those states where the symmetry is relevant, arise either from one-body or two-body forces. A particularly simple assumption is that all the SU(6)-violating terms come from the $J=I=Y=0$ member of the (35-dimensional) adjoint representation of SU(6). With this assumption, the one-body force gives for the mass operator

$$\mathfrak{M}^{(1)} = \sum_i M_0 V_0(r_i) + \sum_i [T_3{}^3(i) - T_6{}^6(i)] V_1(r_i),$$

where $T_i{}^j$ is a tensor operator which transforms in the same way as the adjoint representation. The two-body contribution gives

$$\mathfrak{M}^{(2)} = \tfrac{1}{2} \sum_{i\neq j} \sum_{\lambda} [(T_3{}^3 + T_6{}^6)_i \times (T_3{}^3 + T_6{}^6)_j]^{(\lambda)} V_2{}^{(\lambda)}(|r_i - r_j|),$$

where λ distinguishes the different contributions which can occur from the two-body operator in the brackets. These contributions are $M_{(1)}{}^{(1)}$, $M_{(35)}{}^{(8)}$, $M_{(405)}{}^{(1)}$, $M_{(405)}{}^{(8)}$, and $M_{(405)}{}^{(27)}$, using the notation of Bég and Singh.[3] Note that with this assumption, only the representations $\underline{1}$, $\underline{35}$, and $\underline{405}$ can contribute to $M^{(2)}$, because these are the only symmetric real representations contained in $\underline{35}\otimes\underline{35}$. For the $\underline{56}$, the contributions from $M_{(1)}{}^{(1)}$ and $M_{(35)}{}^{(8)}$ can be absorbed in $\mathfrak{M}^{(1)}$. Contributions from $M_{(405)}{}^{(1)}$ and $M_{(405)}{}^{(8)}$, together with the one-body operator, already suffice to give the mass formula which has been suggested for the $\underline{56}$:

$$M = M_0 + \alpha Y + \beta[I(I+1) - \tfrac{1}{4}Y^2] + \gamma J(J+1).$$

The magnetic-moment calculation,[4] as already pointed out by the authors, can be obtained by assuming that the entire magnetic moments of the baryons in the $\underline{56}$ are produced by the intrinsic magnetic moments of the quarks,[11] and that the quark moments are proportional to their Dirac moments, $Q\hbar/2Mc$, Q = quark charge, M = quark mass. If the free quark moments equal their Dirac moments, then one can resolve the incompatibility of assumptions (I)-(IV) discussed by Bég, Lee, and Pais[4] by saying that quarks, rather than nucleons, have minimal electromagnetic coupling, and that the radiative corrections (in empty space) to the quark moments are small (as is the case for the electron and muon), or proportional to their Dirac moments. However, if the quarks bound in nucleons have Dirac moments, then $M = m_p/2.79 = 336$ MeV,[12] so that one must look for a mechanism (perhaps acting only in strongly bound states) which enhances quark magnetic moments in proportion to their Dirac moments.

Now we return to the question of placing three spin-$\frac{1}{2}$ quarks in s states in the baryon $\underline{56}$.

V540 2-5

This can be done if the quarks are parafermions of order $p=3$. This suggestion is the main new idea of this article.[13] For parafermions of order 3, one has the Green Ansatz for the creation and annihilation operators,

$$a_\lambda^{\dagger}=\sum_{\alpha=1}^{3} a_\lambda^{(\alpha)\dagger}, \quad a_\lambda=\sum_{\alpha=1}^{3} a_\lambda^{(\alpha)},$$

where the $a^{(\alpha)}$ and $a^{(\beta)\dagger}$ satisfy the anticommutation rules for the same α,

$$[a_\lambda^{(\alpha)},a_\mu^{(\alpha)\dagger}]_+=\delta_{\lambda,\mu}, \quad [a_\lambda^{(\alpha)\dagger},a_\mu^{(\alpha)\dagger}]_+=0,$$

and commute for different α and β,

$$[a_\lambda^{(\alpha)},a_\mu^{(\beta)\dagger}]_-=0, \quad \alpha\neq\beta;$$

$$[a_\lambda^{(\alpha)\dagger},a_\mu^{(\beta)\dagger}]_-=0, \quad \alpha\neq\beta.$$

Here λ stands for the single-particle quantum numbers; for example, momentum, spin, I_z, and Y. Let

$$f_{\lambda\mu\nu}^{\dagger}\equiv[[a_\lambda^{\dagger},a_\mu^{\dagger}]_+,a_\nu^{\dagger}]_+$$

$$=4\sum_{\substack{\alpha,\beta,\gamma=1\\ \alpha\neq\beta\neq\gamma\neq\alpha}}^{3} a_\lambda^{(\alpha)\dagger}a_\mu^{(\beta)\dagger}a_\nu^{(\gamma)\dagger}$$

Then the state $f_{\lambda\mu\nu}^{\dagger}\Phi_0$ is symmetric under all permutations of λ, μ, and ν.[14] This composite state is a fermion,[15] since $[f_{\lambda\mu\nu}^{\dagger},a_\sigma^{\dagger}]_+=0$, which implies $[f_{\lambda\mu\nu}^{\dagger},f_{\sigma\tau\eta}^{\dagger}]_+=0$.

The comparison of superselection sectors for paraquarks due to their para nature with the charge and baryon-number superselection sectors is given in Table I.

Table I. Comparison of para. charge, and baryon-number superselection sectors for $p=3$ para-Fermi quarks.

State[a]	Para superselection sector	Q	B
$a^{\dagger}\Phi_0$	para-Fermi	$\frac{2}{3}, -\frac{1}{3}$	$\frac{1}{3}$
$[a^{\dagger},a^{\dagger}]_+\Phi_0$	para-Bose	$\frac{4}{3}, \frac{1}{3}, -\frac{2}{3}$	$\frac{2}{3}$
$[a^{\dagger},b^{\dagger}]_+\Phi_0$	para-Bose	1, 0, −1	0
$[a^{\dagger},a^{\dagger}]_-\Phi_0$	Bose	$\frac{4}{3}, \frac{1}{3}, -\frac{2}{3}$	$\frac{2}{3}$
$[a^{\dagger},b^{\dagger}]_-\Phi_0$	Bose	1, 0, −1	0
$[[a^{\dagger},a^{\dagger}]_+,a^{\dagger}]_+\Phi_0$	Fermi	2, 1, 0, −1	1
$[[a^{\dagger},a^{\dagger}]_+,b^{\dagger}]_+\Phi_0$	Fermi	5/3, $\frac{2}{3}, -\frac{1}{3}, -\frac{4}{3}$	$\frac{1}{3}$

[a] $a^{\dagger}$ is the creation operator for a quark, $b^{\dagger}$ for an antiquark.

The suggestion that quarks are parafermions (and, in a field theory, the quanta of para-Fermi fields) is allowed by the selection rules which follow from locality.[13] Relevant[16] local interactions (in the sense of spacelike commutativity of the interaction Hamiltonian density) can be constructed with these fields; for example, the Yukawa interaction

$$H_I=g[[\overline{\Psi},\Psi]_+-\langle[\overline{\Psi},\Psi]_+\rangle_0,\varphi]_+,$$

or the Fermi interaction

$$H_I=G\{[[\overline{\Psi},\Psi]_-,[\overline{\Psi},\Psi]_-]_+-\langle\text{same}\rangle_0\},$$

where Ψ and φ are, respectively, para-Fermi and para-Bose of order 3. The paraquark suggestion does not fall under the quantum-mechanical theorem[17] that particles with anomalous permutation properties cannot be produced from initial states ($\mathfrak{F}^{\times}$) with at most one such particle because, in this theorem, it was assumed that the only superselection rules were those generated by charge, baryon number, and lepton number, while in parafield theories there are additional superselection rules.[13,18] The question of the compatibility of parafield theory with intuitive notions concerning the behavior of quantum systems when separated into subsystems has been raised.[19] This question deserves serious attention; however, we do not consider it here.

After this brief defense of the possibility that quarks are para-Fermi, we proceed to the classification of baryon states in the paraquark model. The baryon wave functions must be symmetric under permutations. We present in Table II states in which the wave functions[5] are sums of products of space wave functions and spin-unitary-spin wave functions. All the quarks are in the lowest radial state for a given l. The Young diagrams for both the space and spin-unitary-spin wave functions are the same; the numbers listed give the number of boxes in successive rows. Even if the SU(6) classification is useful only for the lowest $\underline{56}$ with configuration s^3, the (SU(3),J) classification given in column 5 should be useful for higher states. We have continued the table up to the p^3 configuration in order to obtain states with $J=\frac{9}{2}$, since there is some experimental evidence for such states.[20] However, we postpone assigning the known baryons to multiplets. The fact that only the $\underline{1}$, $\underline{8}$, and $\underline{10}$ SU(3) mul-

Table II. Low-lying states in paraquark model of baryons.[a]

Orbitals configuration	L	Parity	Young diagram	(SU(3), J) decomposition	Total multiplicity	Total no. of I multiplets
s^3 (pure)	0	+	(3)	$(\underline{8}, J=1/2)$ $(\underline{10}, J=3/2)$	56	8
s^2p^1 (spurious)	1	−	(3)	$(\underline{8}, J=1/2, 3/2)$ $(\underline{10}, J=1/2, 3/2, 5/2)$	168	20
s^2p^1 (pure)	1	−	(2, 1)	$(\underline{1}, J=1/2, 3/2)$ $(\underline{8}, J=1/2, 3/2, 5/2)$ $(\underline{10}, J=1/2, 3/2)$ $(\underline{8}, J=1/2, 3/2)$	210	30
s^1p^2, s^2d^1 (mixed)	2	+	(3)	$(\underline{8}, J=3/2, 5/2)$ $(\underline{10}, J=1/2, 3/2, 5/2, 7/2)$	280	24
s^1p^2, s^2d^1 (mixed)	2	+	(2, 1)	$(\underline{1}, J=3/2, 5/2)$ $(\underline{8}, J=1/2, 3/2, 5/2, 7/2)$ $(\underline{10}, J=3/2, 5/2)$ $(\underline{8}, J=3/2, 5/2)$	350	34
s^1p^2, s^2d^1 (mixed)	1	+	(2, 1)	$(\underline{1}, J=1/2, 3/2)$ $(\underline{8}, J=1/2, 3/2, 5/2)$ $(\underline{10}, J=1/2, 3/2)$ $(\underline{8}, J=1/2, 3/2)$	210	30
s^1p^2 (pure)	1	+	(1, 1, 1)	$(\underline{8}, J=1/2, 3/2)$ $(\underline{1}, J=1/2, 3/2, 5/2)$	60	11
s^1p^2, s^2d^1 (mixed)	0	+	(3)	$(\underline{8}, J=1/2)$ $(\underline{10}, J=3/2)$	56	8
s^1p^2, s^2d^1 (mixed)	0	+	(2, 1)	$(\underline{1}, J=1/2)$ $(\underline{8}, J=3/2)$ $(\underline{10}, J=1/2)$ $(\underline{8}, J=1/2)$	70	13
$p^3, s^1p^1d^1, s^2f^1$ (mixed)	3	−	(3)	$(\underline{8}, J=5/2, 7/2)$ $(\underline{10}, J=3/2, 5/2, 7/2, 9/2)$	392	24
$p^3, s^1p^1d^1$ (mixed)	2	−	(2, 1)	$(\underline{1}, J=3/2, 5/2)$ $(\underline{8}, J=1/2, 3/2, 5/2, 7/2)$ $(\underline{10}, J=3/2, 5/2)$ $(\underline{8}, J=3/2, 5/2)$	350	34
$p^3, s^1p^1d^1, s^2f^1$ (mixed)	1	−	(3)	$(\underline{8}, J=1/2, 3/2)$ $(\underline{10}, J=1/2, 3/2, 5/2)$	168	20
$p^3, s^1p^1d^1$ (mixed)	1	−	(2, 1)	$(\underline{1}, J=1/2, 3/2)$ $(\underline{8}, J=1/2, 3/2, 5/2)$ $(\underline{10}, J=1/2, 3/2)$ $(\underline{8}, J=1/2, 3/2)$	210	30
$p^3, s^1p^1d^1$ (mixed)	0	−	(1, 1, 1)	$(\underline{8}, J=1/2)$ $(\underline{1}, J=3/2)$	20	5
				Totals:	2600	291

[a]See reference 23.

tiplets occur is common to any three-quark model. The table can be constructed using only elementary facts[21] known to nuclear physicists. A useful check[22] on the construction of the table is the observation that if the s- and p-orbital states are considered equivalent, then these four states transform as the fundamental representation of an "orbital" SU(4) group. When this last group is combined with SU(6), one reaches SU(24), whose three-particle symmetric representation has dimension 2600.[23]

If this model is correct, then it should be possible to produce real paraquarks in high-energy interactions. The superselection rules for production of paraquarks from normal matter are the same as for Fermi quarks (see Table I); for example, $b+m \rightarrow 3q$, but $b+m \not\rightarrow 2q$

or q, where b, m, q stand for baryon, meson, quark. However, the threshold behavior of $b+m \to 3q$ for paraquarks would reflect the s-state wave functions and would differ from the threshold behavior for Fermi quarks.

In Coulomb scattering from normal matter, the lowest order cross section for para particles is the same as for normal particles of the same charge, so para particles should be detected as easily as normal particles.

We thank Professor J. Robert Oppenheimer for his warm hospitality at the Institute for Advanced Study. We have benefited from the atmosphere in the physics community here. We thank, in particular, A. J. Dragt, P. G. O. Freund, B. W. Lee, and S. MacDowell for helpful discussions.

---

*Alfred P. Sloan Foundation Fellow on leave from the University of Maryland, College Park, Maryland.

[1]E. P. Wigner, Phys. Rev. 51, 106 (1937); E. P. Wigner and E. Feenberg, Rept. Progr. Phys. 8, 274 (1941).

[2]F. Gürsey and L. A. Radicati, Phys. Rev. Letters 13, 173 (1964); A. Pais, Phys. Rev. Letters 13, 175 (1964); F. Gürsey, A. Pais, and L. A. Radicati, Phys. Rev. Letters 13, 299 (1964); B. Sakita, Phys. Rev. (to be published).

[3]T. K. Kuo and T. Yao, Phys. Rev. Letters 13, 415 (1964); M. A. B. Bég and V. Singh, Phys. Rev. Letters 13, 418 (1964).

[4]M. A. B. Bég, B. W. Lee, and A. Pais, Phys. Rev. Letters 13, 514 (1964); B. Sakita, to be published.

[5]We have no theoretical justification for the use of a nonrelativistic classification of forces and states.

[6]M. Gell-Mann, Phys. Letters 8, 214 (1964); G. Zweig, to be published.

[7]B. Sakita, reference 2.

[8]P. G. O. Freund and B. W. Lee (private communication) have constructed models of baryons using Fermi quarks.

[9]It is amusing that one reaches the concrete notion of atomic structure after a lengthy detour through the special unitary groups.

[10]This was already pointed out by Sakita,[2] who suggested for this reason the use of the antisymmetric 20-dimensional representation for the baryons. However, this suggestion has two defects: First, the 20 no longer accommodates the decuplet; and secondly, the SU(6)-invariant electromagnetic coupling to the 20 leads to the wrong value of β.[4]

[11]This will be the case if the quarks are all in s states.

[12]Quarks having this mass would already have been detected. See W. Blum et al., Phys. Rev. Letters 13, 353a (1964); V. Hagopian et al., Phys. Rev. Letters 13, 280 (1964); and references in these articles.

[13]All statements made here concerning para particles are straightforward consequences of results contained in O. W. Greenberg and A. M. L. Messiah, to be published. The "absence of para particles" in the title of this article refers to the presently known particles.

[14]Permutations of these indices are related to permutations of the particles in the state for one-dimensional representations of the permutation group, but not in general.[13]

[15]We can also construct the meson 35 using a particle-antiparticle pair of order 3 para-Fermi quarks in s states. Let

$$b_{\lambda\mu}^{\dagger} = [a_{\lambda}^{\dagger}, a_{\mu}^{\dagger}]_{-} = 2 \sum_{\alpha \neq \beta = 1}^{3} a_{\lambda}^{(\alpha)\dagger} a_{\mu}^{(\beta)\dagger}.$$

Then the state $b_{\lambda\mu}^{\dagger}\Phi_0$ is antisymmetric under permutation of λ and μ, and this composite state is a boson since $[b_{\lambda\mu}^{\dagger}, a_{\nu}^{\dagger}]_{-} = 0$, which implies $[b_{\lambda\mu}^{\dagger}, b_{\nu\sigma}^{\dagger}]_{-} = 0$. This construction works for all para orders, including $p=1$, the Fermi case. So the mesons constructed with parafermions are the same as those constructed with fermions; for this reason we will not consider the mesons further in this article.

[16]By "relevant," we mean that these interactions lead to connected Feynman graphs with only the desired 56 (or 35) in the initial and final states.

[17]A. M. L. Messiah and O. W. Greenberg, Phys. Rev. 136, B248 (1964).

[18]We expect that when this theorem[17] is amended to include the parafield superselection rules, the absolute selection rule for production of paraquarks from $\mathfrak{F}^{\times}$ will allow production, from ordinary states, of both symmetric and antisymmetric paraquark states, provided these states occur in different superselection sectors.

[19]C. N. Yang, private communication.

[20]A. H. Rosenfeld et al., Rev. Mod. Phys. (to be published).

[21]A. de-Shalit and I. Talmi, Nuclear Shell Theory (Academic Press, Inc., New York, 1963).

[22]We thank P. G. O. Freund and B. W. Lee for pointing this out.

[23]Because Table II lists shell-model states, some spurious states are present due to incorrect treatment of the center-of-mass motion. Only the configuration s^2p^1, with Young diagram (3), is purely spurious; for the other configurations we have indicated the higher shell-model states which must be mixed in to produce proper internal states. (Harmonic oscillator wave functions were used.) We plan to do more detailed calculations with more specific assumptions about the forces to try to estimate where the various SU(3) multiplets should lie. Perhaps other orbitals, such as the second radial s state, should be considered. Empirical information will be helpful in guiding such calculations. See J. P. Elliott and T. H. R. Skyrme, Proc. Roy. Soc. (London) A232, 561 (1955), and E. Baranger and C. W. Lee, Nucl. Phys. 22, 157 (1961), for discussions of spurious states.

REPRINT 4

Reprinted from THE PHYSICAL REVIEW, Vol. 139, No. 4B, B1006–B1010, 23 August 1965
Printed in U. S. A.

Three-Triplet Model with Double $SU(3)$ Symmetry*

M. Y. HAN
Department of Physics, Syracuse University, Syracuse, New York

AND

Y. NAMBU
The Enrico Fermi Institute for Nuclear Studies, and the Department of Physics, The University of Chicago, Chicago, Illinois

(Received 12 April 1965)

With a view to avoiding some of the kinematical and dynamical difficulties involved in the single-triplet quark model, a model for the low-lying baryons and mesons based on three triplets with integral charges is proposed, somewhat similar to the two-triplet model introduced earlier by one of us (Y. N.). It is shown that in a $U(3)$ scheme of triplets with integral charges, one is naturally led to three triplets located symmetrically about the origin of I_3-Y diagram under the constraint that the Nishijima–Gell-Mann relation remains intact. A double $SU(3)$ symmetry scheme is proposed in which the large mass splittings between different representations are ascribed to one of the $SU(3)$, while the other $SU(3)$ is the usual one for the mass splittings within a representation of the first $SU(3)$.

I. INTRODUCTION

ALTHOUGH the $SU(6)$ symmetry strongly indicates that the baryon is essentially a three-body system built from some basic triplet field or fields, the quark model[1] is not entirely satisfactory from a realistic point of view, because (a) the electric charges are not integral, (b) three quarks in s states do not form the symmetric $SU(6)$ representation assigned to the baryons, and (c) a simple dynamical mechanism is lacking for realizing only zero-triality states as the low-lying levels.

These difficulties may be avoided if we introduce more than one basic triplet. Recently one of us (Y. N.) has attempted a two-triplet model[2] where the members of the triplets t_1 and t_2 had the charge assignment $(1,0,0)$ and $(0,-1,-1)$, as had been proposed earlier by Bacry *et al.*[3] The baryon would be represented by the combination $t_1t_1t_2$, whereas the mesons would correspond to some combination $\sim at_1\bar{t}_1'+bt_2\bar{t}_2'$. The triplets are assumed to have masses large compared to the baryon mass, which would mean that baryons and mesons have very large binding energies. A dynamical mechanism for this is provided by a neutral field coupled strongly to the "charm number"[4] C, which is 1 for t_1 and -2 for t_2, and therefore $C=0$ for baryons and mesons. In analogy with electrostatic energy, we can argue that the potential energy due to the charm field would be lowest when the system is "neutral," namely, $C=0$. Thus all other unwanted configurations with $C\neq 0$, which include among others triplet, sextet, etc. representations, would have high masses, and hence would not be easily observed.

There have been proposed two different ways in which to introduce basic triplet or triplets with integral charges. One approach essentially involves a modification of the Nishijima–Gell-Mann relation by way of introducing an additional quantum number, the triality quantum number,[5] and this has led to considerations of higher symmetry schemes based on rank-three Lie groups.[6] On the other hand, Okubo *et al.*[7] have recently shown that the minimal group required for this purpose is actually the group $U(3)$.[8] It is shown that a triplet scheme may be defined in $U(3)$ such that the triplet always possesses integral values of charge and hypercharge and satisfies the Nishijima–Gell-Mann relation without a modification. The $U(3)$ triplet considered by Okubo *et al.* is of Sakata type; i.e., it consists of an isodoublet and an isosinglet. Actually, the $U(3)$ scheme is much more appealing than those of the rank-three Lie groups on two accounts: firstly, the Nishijima–Gell-Mann relation is satisfied universally by triplets as by octets and decuplets, and secondly as far as the hitherto realized representations are concerned, $U(3)$ is equivalent to $SU(3)$.[9]

In what follows, we show that the $U(3)$ scheme, when fully utilized as described below, naturally and uniquely

* Work supported in part by the U. S. Atomic Energy Commission under the Contract No. AT(30-1)-3399 and No. AT(11-1)-264.

[1] M. Gell-Mann, Phys. Letters **8**, 214 (1964); G. Zweig, CERN (to be published).

[2] Y. Nambu, *Proceedings of the Second Coral Gables Conference on Symmetry Principles at High Energy* (W. H. Freeman and Company, San Francisco, 1965).

[3] H. Bacry, J. Nuyts, and L. van Hove, Phys. Letters **9**, 279 (1964).

[4] This name was originally used in connection with the $SU(4)$ symmetry. B. J. Bjørken and S. L. Glashow, Phys. Letters **11**, 255 (1964); A. Salam, Dubna Conference Report, 1964 (unpublished).

[5] G. E. Baird and L. C. Biedenharn, *Proceedings of the First Coral Gables Conference on Symmetry Principles at High Energy* (W. H. Freeman and Company, San Francisco, 1964); C. R. Hagen and A. J. Macfarlane, Phys. Rev. **135**, B432 (1964) and J. Math. Phys. **5**, 1335 (1964).

[6] For example, see I. S. Gerstein and M. L. Whippmann, Phys. Rev. **137**, B1522 (1965). Earlier references are given in this paper.

[7] S. Okubo, C. Ryan, and R. E. Marshak, Nuovo Cimento **34**, 759 (1964).

[8] The use of $U(3)$ in this connection has also been remarked by I. S. Gerstein and K. T. Mahanthappa, Phys. Rev. Letters **12**, 570, 656(E) (1964).

[9] S. Okubo, Phys. Letters **4**, 14 (1963).

leads to a set of three basic triplets with integral charges, namely an I-triplet (isodoublet and isosinglet), a U-triplet (U-spin doublet and U-spin singlet) and a V-triplet (V-spin doublet and V-spin singlet).[10] These triplets arise from three different ways of defining charge Q, hypercharge Y, and a displaced isospin I_3 in the $U(3)$ group as opposed to the $SU(3)$, in such a way that the charge and hypercharge have integral values, while keeping the Nishijima–Gell-Mann relation intact, and they differ from each other in their quantum-number assignments as well as in their transformation properties under the Weyl reflections.[11] This is described in Sec. II. In Sec. III, a double $SU(3)$ symmetry scheme is proposed based on the three-triplet model in which the large mass splittings between different representations are ascribed to one of the $SU(3)$, and the other $SU(3)$ is, as usual, responsible for the mass splittings within a representation. The low-lying baryon and meson states may be taken as singlets with respect to one of the $SU(3)$. The extended symmetry group with respect to the $SU(6)$ symmetry is briefly discussed.

II. THREE TRIPLETS

We shall denote the infinitesimal generators of $U(3)$ by $A_\nu{}^\mu$ which satisfies the following commutation relations:

$$[A_\beta{}^\alpha, A_\nu{}^\mu] = \delta_\beta{}^\mu A_\nu{}^\alpha - \delta_\nu{}^\alpha A_\beta{}^\mu, \tag{1}$$

where all indices take on the values 1, 2, and 3. The corresponding infinitesimal generators $B_\nu{}^\mu$ of $SU(3)$ are then given by

$$B_\nu{}^\mu = A_\nu{}^\mu - \tfrac{1}{3}\delta_\nu{}^\mu A_\lambda{}^\lambda \tag{2}$$

which satisfy the following equations:

$$[B_\beta{}^\alpha, B_\nu{}^\mu] = \delta_\beta{}^\mu B_\nu{}^\alpha - \delta_\nu{}^\alpha B_\beta{}^\mu \tag{3}$$

and

$$B_\lambda{}^\lambda = 0. \tag{4}$$

Furthermore, the unitary restriction gives

$$(A_\nu{}^\mu)^\dagger = A_\mu{}^\nu, \quad (B_\nu{}^\mu)^\dagger = B_\mu{}^\nu. \tag{5}$$

Let us now briefly summarize the relevant results of Okubo *et al.* In the $SU(3)$ scheme, the charge Q, the hypercharge Y and the third component of isospin I_3 are identified as follows[12]:

$$Q = -B_1{}^1, \tag{6a}$$

$$Y = B_3{}^3 = -B_1{}^1 - B_2{}^2 \quad [\text{by the relation (4)}], \tag{6b}$$

$$I_3 = \tfrac{1}{2}(B_2{}^2 - B_1{}^1). \tag{6c}$$

In the $U(3)$ scheme, the corresponding quantities $\tilde{Q}$, $\tilde{Y}$, and $\tilde{I}_3$ are defined as follows:

$$\tilde{Q} = -A_1{}^1 = Q - \tfrac{1}{3}\tau, \tag{7a}$$

$$\tilde{Y} = -A_1{}^1 - A_2{}^2 = Y - \tfrac{2}{3}\tau, \tag{7b}$$

$$\tilde{I}_3 = \tfrac{1}{2}(A_2{}^2 - A_1{}^1) = I_3, \tag{7c}$$

where

$$\tau = A_1{}^1 + A_2{}^2 + A_3{}^3. \tag{8}$$

With these definitions, the Nishijima–Gell-Mann relation is seen to be equally satisfied by the $U(3)$ and $SU(3)$ theories, i.e.,

$$Q = I_3 + \tfrac{1}{2}Y \tag{9}$$

and

$$\tilde{Q} = \tilde{I}_3 + \tfrac{1}{2}\tilde{Y}, \tag{10}$$

respectively. Since the generators $A_1{}^1$, $A_2{}^2$, and $A_3{}^3$ possess integral eigenvalues in any representation,[13] the identifications of $\tilde{Q}$ and $\tilde{Y}$ to be the charge and the hypercharge, respectively, in $U(3)$ theory shall always lead to integral values for the charge and the hypercharge. In particular, in the three-dimensional representation, the $U(3)$ triplet has the eigenvalues

$$\tilde{Q} = \begin{bmatrix} 1 & 0 & 0 \\ 0 & 0 & 0 \\ 0 & 0 & 0 \end{bmatrix}, \quad \tilde{I}_3 = \begin{bmatrix} \frac{1}{2} & 0 & 0 \\ 0 & -\frac{1}{2} & 0 \\ 0 & 0 & 0 \end{bmatrix}, \quad \tilde{Y} = \begin{bmatrix} 1 & 0 & 0 \\ 0 & 1 & 0 \\ 0 & 0 & 0 \end{bmatrix}. \tag{11}$$

This triplet corresponds to the Sakata triplet which we call an I triplet for short.

We can now generalize the above constructions of the $U(3)$ triplet in the following way. Comparing (6b) and (7b), we see that a particular choice has been made for $\tilde{Y}$. Had we defined $\tilde{Y}$ to be $A_3{}^3$, it would still have integral eigenvalues but the relation (10) would have been violated. This is because $B_\lambda{}^\lambda = 0$ in $SU(3)$ but $A_\lambda{}^\lambda \neq 0$ in general in $U(3)$ and thus some care is needed in defining corresponding quantities in $U(3)$. Making use of (4), the definition in (6) can be written more generally as

$$Q = -B_1{}^1 = B_2{}^2 + B_3{}^3, \tag{12a}$$

$$Y = B_3{}^3 = -B_1{}^1 - B_2{}^2, \tag{12b}$$

$$I_3 = \tfrac{1}{2}(B_2{}^2 - B_1{}^1) = \tfrac{1}{2}(2B_2{}^2 + B_3{}^3) = -\tfrac{1}{2}(2B_1{}^1 + B_3{}^3). \tag{12c}$$

As in (7), replacing $B_\nu{}^\mu$'s in (12) by corresponding $A_\nu{}^\mu$'s, we list all possible candidates for the corresponding quantities in $U(3)$ which are now however not equivalent to each other [they are equivalent, of course, when reduced to $SU(3)$], i.e.,

$$\tilde{Q}: \quad -A_1{}^1, \quad A_2{}^2 + A_3{}^3, \tag{13a}$$

$$\tilde{Y}: \quad A_3{}^3, \quad -A_1{}^1 - A_2{}^2, \tag{13b}$$

$$\tilde{I}_3: \quad \tfrac{1}{2}(A_2{}^2 - A_1{}^1), \quad \tfrac{1}{2}(2A_2{}^2 + A_3{}^3), \quad -\tfrac{1}{2}(2A_1{}^1 + A_3{}^3). \tag{13c}$$

[10] C. A. Levinson, H. J. Lipkin, and S. Meshkov, Nuovo Cimento **23**, 236 (1961); Phys. Letters **1**, 44 (1962) and Phys. Rev. Letters **10**, 361 (1963).

[11] A. J. Macfarlane, E. C. G. Sudarshan, and C. Dullemond, Nuovo Cimento **30**, 845 (1963).

[12] We use the sign convention of S. P. Rosen, J. Math. Phys. **5**, 289 (1964).

[13] For a derivation of this result, see Eq. (7) of Ref. 7.

To start with, the alternative choices in (13) provide twelve inequivalent ways in which to choose a set of three quantities $\tilde{Q}$, $\tilde{Y}$ and $\tilde{I}_3$ for the $U(3)$ scheme. In every choice $\tilde{Q}$ and $\tilde{Y}$ will have integral eigenvalues, but as can be easily checked the Nishijima–Gell-Mann relation will not be valid for all of them. In fact, there are only three cases for which it is valid and we are thus naturally led to three inequivalent triplets in the $U(3)$ scheme; they are defined by the following three choices:

$$t_I:\ \tilde{Q}=-A_1{}^1,\qquad \tilde{Y}=-A_1{}^1-A_2{}^2,\qquad \tilde{I}_3=\tfrac{1}{2}(A_2{}^2-A_1{}^1),\tag{14a}$$

$$t_U:\ \tilde{Q}=A_2{}^2+A_3{}^3,\quad \tilde{Y}=A_3{}^3,\qquad \tilde{I}_3=\tfrac{1}{2}(2A_2{}^2+A_3{}^3),\tag{14b}$$

$$t_V:\ \tilde{Q}=-A_1{}^1,\qquad \tilde{Y}=A_3{}^3,\qquad \tilde{I}_3=-\tfrac{1}{2}(2A_1{}^1+A_3{}^3).\tag{14c}$$

Now the first one, t_I, for which

$$\tilde{Y}=-A_1{}^1-A_2{}^2,\tag{15}$$

$$\tilde{I}_3=\tfrac{1}{2}(A_2{}^2-A_1{}^1)=\tfrac{1}{2}(B_2{}^2-B_1{}^1)=I_3\tag{16}$$

corresponds to the I triplet mentioned above.

The structure of the remaining triplets t_U and t_V can be brought to much more transparent and symmetric forms in terms of the U-spin and V-spin subalgebras.[10] As in the case of relations (9) and (10) for $SU(3)$ and $U(3)$, we define the U and V spin of $U(3)$ in exactly the same forms as in $SU(3)$ except that all quantities are tilded quantities. From the $SU(3)$ definitions,[12] we then have

$$\tilde{Y}_U=-\tilde{Q}=-A_2{}^2-A_3{}^3,\tag{17}$$

$$\tilde{U}_3=\tilde{Y}-\tfrac{1}{2}\tilde{Q}=\tfrac{1}{2}(A_3{}^3-A_2{}^2)=\tfrac{1}{2}(B_3{}^3-B_2{}^2)=U_3\tag{18}$$

for (14b), and

$$\tilde{Y}_V=\tilde{Q}-\tilde{Y}=-A_3{}^3-A_1{}^1,\tag{19}$$

$$\tilde{V}_3=-\tfrac{1}{2}(\tilde{Y}+\tilde{Q})=\tfrac{1}{2}(A_1{}^1-A_3{}^3)=\tfrac{1}{2}(B_1{}^1-B_3{}^3)=V_3\tag{20}$$

for (14c). They correspond, therefore, to a U triplet and a V triplet, respectively, and hence the notations t_I, t_U, and t_V. With respect to the $SU(3)$ triplet (quark), these $U(3)$ triplets have their respective "hypercharges" (i.e., Y, Y_U, and Y_V) shifted by the amount of $\frac{2}{3}$ and as such they have quite different transformation properties under the Weyl reflections W_1, W_2, and W_3[11] which are reflections about the axis $I_3=0$, $U_3=0$, and $V_3=0$, respectively. Whereas the $SU(3)$ triplet is invariant under all three Weyl reflections, the $U(3)$ triplets are not. They transform according to

$$W_1:\quad t_I\to t_I,\quad t_U\leftrightarrow t_V;\tag{21a}$$

$$W_2:\quad t_U\to t_U,\quad t_I\leftrightarrow t_V;\tag{21b}$$

$$W_3:\quad t_V\to t_V,\quad t_I\leftrightarrow t_U.\tag{21c}$$

Figure 1 and Table I(a) list the quantum numbers $\tilde{I}_3$ and $\tilde{Y}$ for the single triplet (quark) model; a possible assignment implied by the two-triplet model[2] is shown in Fig. 2 and Table I(b); the corresponding quantum numbers for the three-triplet model are given in Fig. 3 and Table I(c).

TABLE I. Quantum-number assignments for (a) the quark model, (b) the two-triplet model, and (c) the three-triplet model.

(a)

	quark		
$\tilde{I}_3$	$\frac{1}{2}$	$-\frac{1}{2}$	0
$\tilde{Y}$	$\frac{1}{3}$	$\frac{1}{3}$	$-\frac{2}{3}$
$\tilde{Q}$	$\frac{2}{3}$	$-\frac{1}{3}$	$-\frac{1}{3}$

(b)

	t_1			t_2		
$\tilde{I}_3$	$\frac{1}{2}$	$-\frac{1}{2}$	0	$\frac{1}{2}$	$-\frac{1}{2}$	0
$\tilde{Y}$	1	1	0	−1	−1	−2
$\tilde{Q}$	1	0	0	0	−1	−1

(c)

	$t_1(t_I)$			$t_2(t_U)$			$t_3(t_V)$		
$\tilde{I}_3$	$\frac{1}{2}$	$-\frac{1}{2}$	0	0	−1	$-\frac{1}{2}$	1	0	$\frac{1}{2}$
$\tilde{Y}$	1	1	0	0	0	−1	0	0	−1
$\tilde{Q}$	1	0	0	0	−1	−1	1	0	0

III. DOUBLE $SU(3)$ SYMMETRY

Let us call the three triplets $t_1(=t_I)$, $t_2(=t_U)$, and $t_3(=t_V)$. Each triplet may be characterized in general by the average values, $\bar{I}_3$ and $\bar{Y}$, of $\tilde{I}_3$ and $\tilde{Y}$ for its three members. This specifies the location of the center of the triplet in the $\tilde{I}_3-\tilde{Y}$ diagram. Since $\bar{A}_1{}^1=\bar{A}_2{}^2=\bar{A}_3{}^3=\bar{\tau}/3=\tau/3$, Eq. (14) gives for the three definitions of

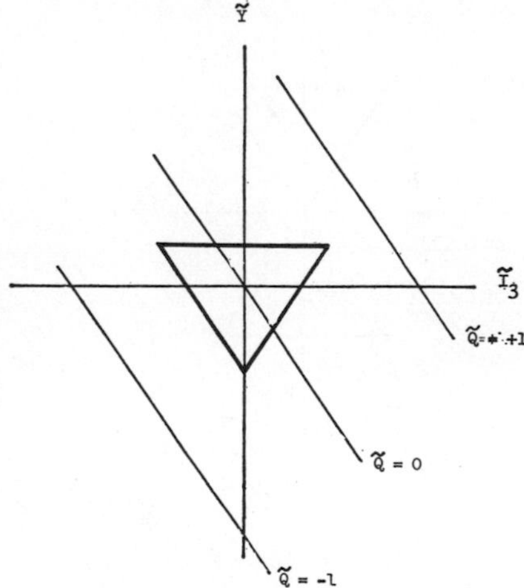

FIG. 1. The single-triplet (quark) model.

$\tilde{I}_3$ and $\tilde{Y}$,

$$\tilde{I}_3=0,\ \tfrac{1}{2}\tau,\ -\tfrac{1}{2}\tau,\qquad \tilde{Y}=-\tfrac{2}{3}\tau,\ \tfrac{1}{3}\tau,\ \tfrac{1}{3}\tau, \tag{22}$$

respectively, where $\tau=-1$ for all the triplets. We may define new quantities I_3, Y and $Q=I_3+\frac{1}{2}Y$ by the relations:

$$\tilde{I}_3=\bar{I}_3+I_3,\qquad \tilde{Y}=\bar{Y}+Y,\qquad \tilde{Q}=\bar{I}_3+\tfrac{1}{2}\bar{Y}+I_3+\tfrac{1}{2}Y=\bar{Q}+Q. \tag{23}$$

It is clear that I_3 and Y play the role of $SU(3)$ generators within each triplet. The charm number C defined in the two-triplet model[2] is then

$$\tfrac{1}{3}C=\bar{Q}=\bar{I}_3+\tfrac{1}{2}\bar{Y}. \tag{24}$$

Now it is interesting to note that according to Eq. (22) and Fig. 3, the centers of the three triplets form an antitriplet, equivalent to an antiquark, symmetrically located around the origin. Let us suppose that the nine members of the three triplets $t_{1\alpha}$, $t_{2\alpha}$, $t_{3\alpha}$, $\alpha=1, 2, 3$ be combined into a single multiplet $T=\{t_{i\alpha}\}$, $i=1, 2, 3$. We can then imagine two distinct sets of $SU(3)$ operations on T. One is the $SU(3)$ acting on the index α for each triplet, while the other $SU(3)$ acts on the index i, which mixes corresponding members of different triplets. T is then a representation $(3,3^*)$ of this group $G\equiv SU(3)'\times SU(3)''$.[14] The quantum numbers of $SU(3)'$ and $SU(3)''$ are identified as $I_3'=I_3$, $Y'=Y$, $I_3''=\bar{I}_3$ and $Y''=\bar{Y}$ in Eq. (22), so that

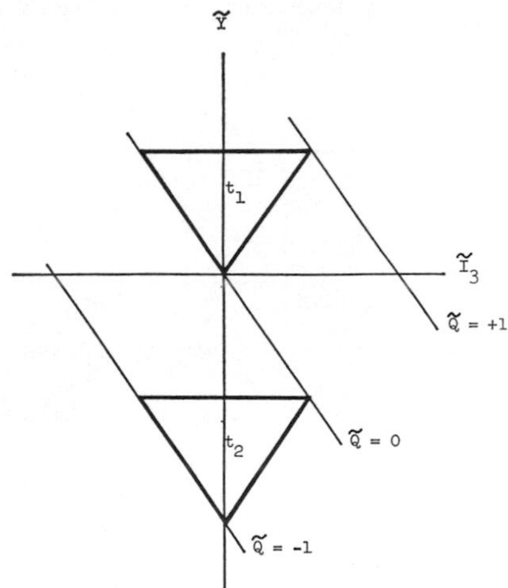

FIG. 2. The two-triplet model.

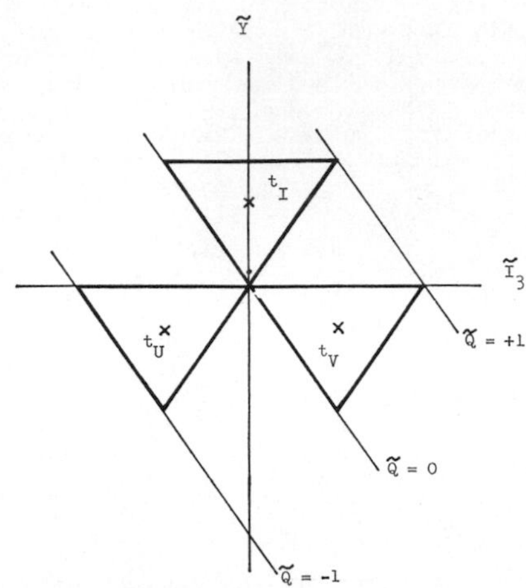

FIG. 3. The three-triplet model.

$$\tilde{I}_3=I_3'+I_3'',\quad \tilde{Y}=Y'+Y'',\qquad \tilde{Q}=I_3'+I_3''+\tfrac{1}{2}Y'+\tfrac{1}{2}Y'',\qquad \tfrac{1}{3}C=I_3''+\tfrac{1}{2}Y''. \tag{25}$$

A general representation of G may be characterized by four numbers p', q', p'', q'' so that $D(p',q',p'',q'')\sim D(p',q')\times D(p'',q'')$, where $D(p,q)$ is a representation of $SU(3)$. However, in our scheme where the nonet T is the fundamental field, we do not get all the possible representations of G. This can be illustrated by means of the triality numbers[5] $t'=p'-q'\bmod(3)$, $t''=p''-q''\bmod(3)$. The nonet T has $t'=1$, $t''=-1$. All representations constructed out of T and T^* then satisfy $t'=-t''$.

Let us next consider the meson and baryon states $\sim TT^*$ and $\sim TTT$. The $SU(3)'\times SU(3)''$ contents of these 81- and 729-plets are

$$\begin{aligned}(3,3^*)\times(3^*,3)&=(8,1)+(1,1)+(1,8)+(8,8),\\ (3,3^*)\times(3,3^*)\times(3,3^*)&=(1,1)+2(8,1)+2(1,8)\\ &\quad+(1,10^*)+(10,1)+2(8,10^*)+2(10,8)\\ &\quad+4(8,8)+(10,10^*).\end{aligned} \tag{26}$$

It is an attractive possibility to postulate at this point that the energy levels are classified according to $SU(3)''$. The masses will then depend on the Casimir operators of $SU(3)''$. For example, a simple linear form will be

$$m=m_0+m_2C_2''+m_3C_3'', \tag{27}$$

[14] Such a nonet provides a natural basis for the symmetry of $SU(9)$. However, we will not consider it here.

where C_2'', C_3'' are the eigenvalues of quadratic and cubic Casimir operators of $SU(3)''$. In particular, we may assume that the main mass splitting comes from C_2''. Since this increases with the dimensionality of representation, the lowest mass levels will be $SU(3)''$ singlets. This selects the low-lying meson and baryon states to be (8,1), (1,1) and (8,1), (1,1), (10,1), respectively. In general, all low-lying states will have triality zero, $t'=t''=0$.

As for the baryon number assignment to the triplets, the simplest possibility would be to assign an equal baryon number, i.e., $B=\frac{1}{3}$, to them. In this case the triplets themselves would be essentially stable, and their nine members would behave like an octet plus a singlet of "heavy baryons" as may be seen from Fig. 3. Another simple possibility may be $B=\frac{1}{3}+Y''$, namely $B=(1,0,0)$ for (t_1,t_2,t_3). We expect a mass splitting depending on B or Y'', which may be the origin of the Okubo–Gell-Mann mass formula.

The advantage of the three-triplet model is that the $SU(6)$ symmetry can be easily realized with s-state triplets. The extended symmetry group becomes now $SU(6)'\times SU(3)''$. Since an $SU(3)''$ singlet is antisymmetric, the over-all Pauli principle requires the baryon states to be the symmetric $SU(6)$ 56-plet. Other $SU(6)$ representations such as the 70, will be obtained by bringing in either the orbital angular momentum or the "ρ spin" of the Dirac spinor triplets.

As in the two-triplet model mentioned in the Introduction, the mass formula of the type (27) may be derived dynamically. Instead of the charm number field, we introduce now eight gauge vector fields which behave as (1,8), namely as an octet in $SU(3)''$, but as singlets in $SU(3)'$. Since their coupling to the individual triplets is proportional to λ_i'' [the generators of $SU(3)''$], the interaction energy arising from the exchange of these vector fields will yield the first and second terms of Eq. (27). If these mesons obey again a similar type of mass formula, they will be expected to be massive compared to the ordinary mesons. However, it is not clear whether the resulting short-range character of the interaction can be readily reconciled with the postulated largeness of the interaction energy.

We may characterize the hierarchy of interactions and their symmetries implied by the above model as follows. First, the *superstrong* interactions responsible for forming baryons and mesons have the symmetry $SU(3)''$, and causes large mass splittings between different representations. The scale of mass involved would be comparable or large compared to the baryon mass, namely $\gtrsim 1$ BeV. The lowest states, i.e., $SU(3)''$ singlet states, would split according to $SU(3)'$, which would be the $SU(3)$ group observed among the known baryons and mesons, with their *strong* interactions. The scale of mass splitting would then be $\lesssim 1$ BeV.

When we go to the massive $SU(3)''$ nonsinglet states, there may very well be coupling between the two $SU(3)$ groups similar to the $L\cdot S$ coupling. The levels should be classified in terms of the three sets of Casimir operators formed out of λ_i', λ_i'', and $\lambda_i=\lambda_i'+\lambda_i''$, respectively. The splitting due to the coupling would naturally be intermediate between the above two splittings, namely ~ 1 BeV. Because of this coupling, the separate conservation of the two $SU(3)$ spins, I_3' and Y' on the one hand, and I_3'' and Y'' on the other, would be destroyed, and only the sums $I_3=I_3'+I_3''$ and $Y=Y'+Y''$ would be conserved under *strong* interactions. This in turn would mean that all the massive states are in general highly unstable, and decay strongly to the low-lying states. (In the two-triplet model, we considered only weak decays of $C\neq 0$ states. But strong decays are also a possibility as is contemplated here.)

We have discussed here a possible model of baryons and mesons based on three triplets. How can we distinguish this and other different models mentioned already? Certainly different models predict considerably different structure of massive states. These states are characterized by the triality for the quark model, by the charm number for the two-triplet model and by the $SU(3)''$ representation for the present three-triplet model. If we restrict ourselves to the low-lying states only, however, it seems difficult to distinguish them without making more detailed dynamical assumptions.

ACKNOWLEDGMENTS

One of us (M. Y. H.) wishes to thank Professor E. C. G. Sudarshan and Professor A. J. Macfarlane for their encouragement and useful discussions and Professor L. O'Raifeartaigh and J. Kuriyan for helpful comments.

Physics Vol. 2, No. 2, pp. 95-105, 1965. Physics Publishing Co. Printed in Great Britain.

IS A NON-RELATIVISTIC APPROXIMATION POSSIBLE FOR THE INTERNAL DYNAMICS OF "ELEMENTARY" PARTICLES? *

G. MORPURGO

Istituto di Fisica dell'Universita di Genova
Sezione di Genova dell'Istituto Nazionale di Fisica Nucleare, Genova, Italy

(*Received* 28 *April* 1965)

Abstract

It is pointed out that, contrary to what it is usually implied, the internal dynamics in a compound model of an "elementary" particle is not necessarily relativistic. If the force which binds the constituent objects has a finite range and is not too singular, the relativistic character of the internal motion only depends on the range of such force and on the mass of the constituent particles, not on the depth of the potential well. For instance, for a quark antiquark model of the octet bosons with a quark mass of 5 GeV and a range of the binding force $(5m_\pi)^{-1}$, *one has* $(p/M)^2 = 1/40$, *a non-relativistic situation quite similar to that occurring in nuclei.*

Starting from this observation it is pointed out that several features of the SU_3 *and* SU_6 *dynamics can be understood by writing a non-relativistic Hamiltonian for quarks, in a way similar to that which is used in writing an Hamiltonian for a nucleus. More precisely: (1) one can understand why the Gell Mann-Okubo* SU_3 *mass formula for baryons works much better than its perturbative derivation would imply; (2) one can obtain the -3/2 ratio between the magnetic moments of proton and neutron, due to* SU_6, *by a very simple calculation, which, at the same time exhibits how peculiar is the situation for the absolute values of the magnetic moments; some interesting aspects of the situation, though implied in the conventional derivation, are masked there under the algebra; (3) the point of view taken in this paper leads to the conclusion that* SU_6 *should possibly be valid only at non-relativistic energies of the interacting particles.*

1. Introduction

THE PURPOSE of the present note, which we hope to expand in future, is to draw attention to a circumstance which has been considered almost obvious since the work of Fermi and Yang [1] but which is, in our opinion, not evident at all.

* Paper presented at the Frascati meeting of the INFN on high energy physics - April 12, 1965.

The question is whether, assuming a compound model for elementary particles, the motion of the constituent particles is a relativistic one, or a non-relativistic one like e.g. in positronium or in a nucleus.

It has almost always considered obvious or implied that the motion is a relativistic one, indeed an extremely relativistic one. The reason for this belief can probably be traced back to two circumstances. The first is that Fermi and Yang used, for their construction of the pion as a $N\,N$ system, a potential well where the range of the well was assumed equal to the *nucleon* Compton wavelength M_N^{-1}. Doing so the motion of the $N\,\bar{N}$ system is necessarily relativistic simply because of the indeterminacy principle; indeed, the indeterminacy in the momentum must be of the order M_N, so that we have that the order of magnitude of $(\Delta p/M_N)^2$ is ~ 1, that is the motion is fully relativistic. The second circumstance has been that with a long range force the average value of the kinetic energy has the same order of magnitude as the average value of the potential energy (virial theorem); so that since the potential energy has to be of the order of the rest energy of the particles which are bound, the kinetic energy has the same order of magnitude and the problem is clearly fully relativistic.

Now assume for a moment that the range of the force giving the attraction between a nucleon and an anti-nucleon to produce the pion is not M_N^{-1} but $(2m_\pi)^{-1}$, that corresponding to two pion masses; that is we assume for a moment a strongly attractive potential well with range $(2m_\pi)^{-1}$. It should be emphasized that this assumption is here made only to exemplify what we have in mind and may be in this case in contrast with the experimental facts on nucleon-antinucleon scattering and annihilation. In this case the indeterminacy in momentum is $\Delta p \simeq 2m_\pi$ and the average kinetic energy is of the order of $(2m_\pi)^2/M$. The ratio between kinetic energy and nucleon rest energy is $(2m_\pi)^2/M_N^2 \sim 1/12$, a reasonably non-relativistic situation.

In other words we can have a situation in which the potential well which binds the nucleon and antinucleon is so deep as to cancel the masses of the particles which are bound; and has also a range much larger than the Compton wave length of the constituent particles. The relativistic or non-relativistic character of the situation for the ground state does not depend on the depth of the potential; it *only* depends on the range of the potential well and the mass of the constituent particles.

We have so far considered the Fermi-Yang model of the pion, but in reality these ideas were originated thinking of the quark structure of particles [2,3,4]. Think of the pion as a quark-antiquark compound and assume that quarks are real particles (not only mathematical structures) and that their mass is rather large, say $M = 5$ GeV; we do not know of course the exact value. The interaction between quarks can be transmitted by quark-antiquark compounds; to get attraction it can be transmitted e.g. by a particle of the vector octet. The range is therefore $\sim (5m_\pi)^{-1}$ and the kinetic energy T of the quark-antiquark compound is $(5m_\pi)^2/M$. With $M = 5$ GeV the ratio T/M is $\sim 1/40$, a clearly non-relativistic situation quite similar to that which occurs in nuclei.

If this is so a number of apparently mysterious facts can be, at least qualitatively, explained.

We first consider a "simple" SU_3 theory [5,6] and next discuss SU_6.

The first point which becomes clear is that if particles are composed of quarks, a description in which the number of quarks and antiquarks contained in a given particle is fixed is a very good description, in the same sense in which a description of a nucleus with a wave function with a fixed number of nucleons is a very good description. It is true that a nucleon-antinucleon pair may be present in a nucleus in addition to the nucleons which it contains, but in practice a good description of a nucleus is obtained neglecting such virtual pairs and also neglecting virtual pions. One might object that in our case the situation is not so clear because, even if it is true that the motion of quarks inside a particle is non-relativistic, the quarks find themselves in a very deep potential well, so deep as to cancel, practically, their rest energy, while this is not the case, of course, for nuclei. But this difference should not affect the conclusion stated above.

Consider in fact a very simple model of binding for quarks, a model which has only the purpose of illustrating the above point. Assume that quarks are bound through the intermediary of a neutral vector meson field, whose mass is chosen so as to give the requested long range (say 5 m_π as stated above) and whose coupling constant g is also chosen so as to give the required depth for the potential well which binds the quarks.

Then, as is well known [7], the interaction of our quark system plus meson field can be transformed to all orders in g so as to give rise to an instantaneous Yukawa interaction plus other terms, in a way entirely similar to that in which one obtains the Coulomb interaction in electrodynamics. In other words:

$$H'_{\mathrm{transf}} = \frac{g^2}{4\pi}\int J_0(x)\,\frac{\exp - \mu|x - x'|}{|x - x'|}\,J_0(x')\,d^3x\,d^3x' +$$

$$+ \text{ terms proportional to } \mathbf{J}(x).$$

Here $J_0(x)$ and $\mathbf{J}(x)$ are the time and the space components of the quark current

$$J_\mu(x) = \sum_{1}^{3}{}'_i\ \bar{\psi}_i(x)\gamma_\mu\psi_i(x)$$

Now the conclusion stated above, that it is a good approximation to deal only with a fixed number of quarks, arises from the fact that the matrix elements of the kind $< q/H'/q, \bar{q}, q >$ are of the order p/M where p is the momentum of the initial or of one of the final quarks. If p is the momentum of the initial quarks, this is small as we have said above. If it is the momentum of one of the final quarks this may be large, but then the transition becomes off the energy shell by an amount M and is therefore improbable [8].

2. Discussion of the Gell-Mann Okubo formula

A second point which perhaps can be better understood, if the quarks move non-relativistically, is why the Gell-Mann Okubo [9] mass formula has a validity which appears to go much beyond first order perturbation theory.

Consider the baryon decuplet or octet and write an hamiltonian for a three quark system which consists of a unitary invariant part H_0 plus a part, H_1, which is assumed, as usual, to transform like the $T_3{}^3$ component of a unitary tensor. H_0 will be e.g. of the form

$$H_0 = 2M + M' + T_1 + T_2 + T_3 + V(12) + V(13) + V(23) \tag{1}$$

where $2M + M'$ is the rest energy of the quarks (two of them have the same mass M and the third a different mass M' as discussed in more detail later); the T_i's are the kinetic energies of the quarks (with the same mass) [10] and the $V(ik)$ are the potential energies, written under the assumption of two body forces; this assumption is however irrelevant and all that has to be assumed of the hamiltonian $H_0(1)$ and of the potential energy in (1) is that it is a *symmetric* function of the quark coordinates and spins, independent of the unitary spin operators or containing them only through the Casimir invariants. On the other hand the part H_1 of the hamiltonian will be symmetric in the space, spin and unitary spin coordinates and have a linear dependence on the $\lambda_i^{(8)}$ [11]. We can write

$$H_1 = H_1^{(T)} + H_1^{(U)}$$

where $H_1^{(T)}$ is the kinetic and rest-mass term contribution to the part of the hamiltonian transforming as $\lambda_i^{(8)}$ and $H_1^{(U)}$ is the potential energy contribution. For instance if there are only two body forces we can write for $H_1^{(U)}$

$$H_1^{(U)} = U(12)(\lambda_1^{(8)} + \lambda_2^{(8)}) + U(13)(\lambda_1^{(8)} + \lambda_3^{(8)}) + U(23)(\lambda_2^{(8)} + \lambda_3^{(8)}) \quad (2)$$

while $H_1^{(T)}$ is of course given by:

$$H_1^{(T)} = \frac{1}{3}(M - M')\sum_{i}^{3}\lambda_i^{(8)} + \sum_{i}^{3}\left(\frac{p_i^2}{2M} - \frac{p_i^2}{2M'}\right)\lambda_i^{(8)} \quad (3)$$

where M is the common mass of quarks of kind 1 and 2 (p, n) and M' is the mass of the quarks of kind 3 (Λ).

Let us now remark that the major contribution to the mass splitting both in the baryon decuplet and in the baryon octet may well arise from the first term in $H_1^{(T)}$, that which describes the difference in mass between the third quark and the other two; that this mass difference can be responsible for the largest part of the splitting has been already pointed out by Zweig [4]. A measure of $M - M'$ is given by the difference in mass $(M(\Sigma) + M(\Lambda)/2) - M(n) = 1154 - 938 \approx 216$ MeV; or equivalently by the difference $M(\Xi) - (M(\Sigma) + M(\Lambda)/2) \approx 175$ MeV. That is we can take $M - M'$ in the first term of (3) as having an order of magnitude around 200 MeV. To this strong perturbation, which, however, *commutes with the remaining hamiltonian, and, therefore, can be treated exactly*, a minor perturbation has to be added which is, for instance, responsible of the difference in mass between Λ and Σ; $(M(\Sigma) - M(\Lambda))/2$ is ~ 40 MeV, so this should be the order of magnitude of this second perturbation. It is therefore not very strange that the first order calculation with this perturbation gives accurate results.

Now one would be tempted to identify this second perturbation with the second term of $H_1^{(T)}$. Indeed if this were the case one would understand why also this second perturbation is linear in the $\lambda_i^{(8)}$.

However the second (kinetic) term of (3) appears to be too small; it has in fact in order of magnitude $(M - M') \times \langle p^2/M^2 \rangle$ and for a non-relativistic motion of the quarks this cannot be much larger than ~ 5 or 10 MeV.

Therefore this "40 MeV" perturbation has probably to be found in the potential energy, although the question arises of why this perturbation should be simply linear in the $\lambda_i^{(8)}$ [12].

In any case assuming the "40 MeV" perturbation to be due to a potential energy linear in the $\lambda_i^{(8)}$ such as that given by equation (2), the effect of this perturbation on the masses of the baryons can be simply calculated in a way entirely similar to that in which one calculates the binding energies of the nuclei.

For instance the expectation value of $H_1^{(U)}$ in the decuplet states can be immediately calculated as follows: call χ_i $(i = 1 \dots 10)$ the 10 wave functions of the decuplet states. The χ_i are symmetric in the unitary spin variables and therefore can be written as the product of a completely antisymmetric space and spin part times the symmetric unitary spin functions which we shall call W_i $(i = 1 \dots 10)$. That is

$$\chi_i = f(1, 2, 3)W_i$$

where the antisymmetric $f(123)$ is the same for all the values of i. We therefore have

$$< \chi_i|H_1^{(U)}|\chi_i > = < f(123)W_i|U(12)(\lambda_1^{(8)} + \lambda_2^{(8)}) + U(13)(\lambda_1^{(8)} + \lambda_3^{(8)}) + + U(23)(\lambda_2^{(8)} + \lambda_3^{(8)})|f(123)W_i > \tag{4}$$

Now due to the factorized form of χ_i each of the addends in (4) separates into a space and spin matrix element and a unitary spin one. Due to the antisymmetry of $f(123)$ we have

$$< f(123)|U(12)|f(123) > = < f(123)|U(13)|f(123) > = = < f(123)|U(23)|f(123) > = U/6$$

Therefore, as expected

$$< \chi_i|H_1^{(U)}|\chi_i > = \frac{\bar{U}}{3} < W_i|\lambda_1^{(8)} + \lambda_2^{(8)} + \lambda_3^{(8)}|W_i > = \bar{U}\, Y_i$$

where Y_i is the hypercharge of the i-th decuplet particle. We can therefore write the mass formula for the decuplet as

$$M_i = M_0 + (M - M')Y_i + \bar{U}\, Y_i$$

where, as we repeat, the dominant term proportional to $(M - M')$ is exact and only the last "40 MeV" term is to be regarded as calculated perturbatively (or variationally). A similar calculation of $H_1^{(U)}$ can be performed of course for the baryon octet although there it is more complicated due to the fact that the space and spin part of the wave function is not antisymmetrical but transforms according to the 2 dimensional representation of the permutation group of three objects.

As far as the meson octets are concerned entirely similar considerations hold. Thinking of the mesons as a quark-antiquark compound we have of course to assume that there exist a strongly attractive unitary symmetric quark-antiquark force, perturbed again primarily by a perturbation due to the mass difference among quarks and, secondarily, by another perturbation linear in the $\lambda_i^{(8)}$. Two remarks are appropriate here:

(1) It can appear strange that there are attractive forces both between quarks, and among quarks and antiquarks. For instance if the forces were only due to the neutral vector meson which was considered previously they would be attractive between quark and antiquark but repulsive between two quarks. Note however that the quark-quark force has a strength different from the quark-antiquark one. For instance assuming that the quark mass is 5 GeV, the binding between quark and an antiquark has an order of magnitude of ~ 9.5 GeV, while the binding

between two quarks has an order of magnitude of $(15 - 1)/3 \sim 4.7$ GeV. Therefore, roughly, the quark-antiquark binding is twice as strong as the quark-quark one. This might explain, by the way, the absence of particles built with two quarks; they would have a mass of the order of the quark mass. Of course the question remains of the non-existence of particles built with 4 or 5 quarks.

(2) In a scheme like the one presented here it is difficult to understand the fact that the formula for the meson masses is quadratic. This is not, however, typical of a non-relativistic approach like this. The explanations given so far for the fact that the meson mass formulas must be quadratic are indeed not convincing [13].

3. Remarks on SU_6

If the internal structure of particles is non-relativistic, no particular difficulty arises in the problem of formulating SU_6 invariance. It is sufficient to assume that, in first approximation, our quark hamiltonian is independent of the spin; this requirement can be imposed easily on a non-relativistic system, as is well known. If we look at the SU_6 symmetry [14] from this point of view it is clear that SU_6 is an approximate symmetry violated possibly by non-relativistic effects and certainly by relativistic ones; exactly as the Wigner supermultiplet SU_4 symmetry in nuclei is an approximate symmetry violated by tensor, spin orbit and spin-spin effects. The only problem becomes that of finding the kind of tensor, spin-orbit or spin-spin terms which do violate SU_6 symmetry. If the effects which these SU_6 violating terms produce in the wave function of a proton or of a neutron are not too large, SU_6 should be successful, while if the opposite is true SU_6 should not be useful; which is the case is not yet entirely clear.

To consider a definite case we shall calculate [15] the ratio between the magnetic moment of proton and neutron by means of SU_6 in the representation *56*; this calculation becomes identical to the calculation of the ratio of the magnetic moments of He^3 and H^3 in a situation where:

(1) The space part of the wave function of these peculiar "He^3" and "H^3" nuclei built with quarks is antisymmetrical and has zero orbital angular momentum [16].

(2) The quarks have Bohr magnetic moments proportional to their charges, namely proportional to $2/3(e\hbar/2Mc)$ for the p quark, $-1/3(e\hbar/2Mc)$ for the n quark.

The calculation is straightforward. We call p, n, and Λ the three quarks (of course Λ does not intervene in this calculation) and note that the unitary spin part of the wave function for the proton and the neutron are, respectively

$$"p" = p_1(p_2n_3 - p_3n_2)$$

and

$$"n" = n_1(n_2p_3 - n_3p_2)$$

Calling $f(1, 2, 3)$ the space and spin part of the wave function, we now assume [16] that the *space* part of the wave function $X(r_1, r_2, r_3)$ is rotationally invariant ($L = 0$), depends only on the relative coordinates and is antisymmetrical; that is we assume that it is:

$$f(123) = X(r_1, r_2, r_3)\alpha_1(\alpha_2\beta_3 - \alpha_3\beta_2)$$

where $X(r_1, r_2, r_3)$ is antisymmetrical and where the spin part is dictated by the requirement of having a spin 1/2. This is the only point at which SU_6 intervenes; indeed, assuming that the octet and decuplet particles belong to the same *56* representation of SU_6 the space part of the wave function of all the decuplet and octet particles must be the same; but due to the Pauli principle, the space part of the decuplet, as we have already stated, must be antisymmetric, and this must be also the case for the octet space part; it seems appropriate to remark however that our assumption of antisymmetry of $X(r_1, r_2, r_3)$ is in fact weaker than to assume the validity of SU_6; it might well be that the shape of $X(r_1, r_2, r_3)$ for the octet particles is different from that for the decuplet particles (while SU_6 requires of course the same $X(r_1, r_2, r_3)$ for both) and still the results on the ratio between magnetic moments do hold provided that $X(r_1, r_2, r_3)$ is antisymmetric.

To proceed let us write the complete wave functions for proton and neutron

$$'p' = N\underline{\underline{A}}\,X(r_1, r_2, r_3)\alpha_1(\alpha_2\beta_3 - \alpha_3\beta_2)p_1(p_2n_3 - p_3n_2)$$

$$"n" = N\underline{\underline{A}}\,X(r_1, r_2, r_3)\alpha_1(\alpha_2\beta_3 - \alpha_3\beta_2)n_1(n_2p_3 - n_3p_2)$$

where N is a normalization factor and $\underline{\underline{A}}$ is an antisymmetrization operator. Because $X(r_1,r_2,r_3)$ is already antisymmetrical the spin and unitary spin part must be symmetrical. Assuming X to be normalized we obtain:

$$"p" = X(r_1, r_2, r_3)1/\sqrt{18}\{2[\alpha_1p_1\alpha_2p_2\beta_3n_3 + \alpha_1p_1\alpha_3p_3\beta_2n_2 + \alpha_2p_2\alpha_3p_3\beta_1n_1] -$$

$$- [\alpha_1p_1\alpha_2n_2\beta_3p_3 + \alpha_1p_1\beta_2p_2\alpha_3n_3 + \alpha_2p_2\alpha_1n_1\beta_3p_3 + \alpha_2p_2\beta_1p_1\alpha_3n_3 +$$

$$+ \alpha_3p_3\alpha_1n_1\beta_2p_2 + \alpha_3p_3\beta_1p_1\alpha_2n_2]\}$$

and for "n" a similar wave function where simply each p is replaced by an n and each n with a p.

The expectation value of the spin magnetic moment operator (there is no orbital part because $L = 0$)

$$\boldsymbol{\mu} = \frac{e\hbar}{2Mc}\left(\frac{2}{3}\,\boldsymbol{\sigma}_p - \frac{1}{3}\,\boldsymbol{\sigma}_n\right) \tag{5}$$

(where σ_p and σ_n are the proton quark and neutron quark spins) is:

$$< \mu_z >_{"p"} = \frac{1}{18}\left[4 \times 3\times\left(\frac{5}{3}\right) + 6 \times \left(-\frac{1}{3}\right)\right]\frac{e\hbar}{2Mc} = \frac{e\hbar}{2Mc}$$

$$< \mu_z >_{"p"} = \frac{1}{18}\left[4 \times 3 \times\left(-\frac{4}{3}\right) + 6 \times \left(\frac{2}{3}\right)\right]\frac{e\hbar}{2Mc} = -\frac{2}{3}\,\frac{e\hbar}{2Mc}$$

One can see that the famous relation [15] $< \mu >_{"p"} / < \mu >_{"n"} = - 3/2$ is obtained [17].

A few comments on the problem of reconciling SU_6 and Lorentz invariance, to which a great deal of attention has been devoted recently [18] and which indirectly stimulated the present paper appear appropriate at this point. It can first be said that in spite of the huge amount of work no satisfactory solution to this problem has appeared. Indeed it has not proven possible to construct a Lie group G having as subgroups both the Lorentz group and the SU_6 group, without introducing at least 32 generators having an obscure physical meaning. Or stated differently, it does not appear possible, and in a sense it has been proven that is impossible [19], to construct a relativistic invariant Lagrangian for a system of interacting particles (containing only quantities having a physical meaning) which is also invariant under the transformations of the SU_6 group.

Now one might ask: what is the relevance of the above conclusion for the point of view developed in the present paper? The answer is simply: no relevance at all. We don't require and we do not think that the quark Lagrangian is exactly invariant under a group G such as that mentioned above. We simply require that the interactions are such that this SU_6 invariance possibly holds in the non-relativistic limit.

Of course since reactions among particles, composed of quarks, take place also at relativistic velocities we must finally be able to construct a relativistic Lagrangian of interacting quarks; but we repeat: of this Lagrangian we should only require that be possibly invariant with respect to SU_6, in the non-relativistic limit, not that it is exactly SU_6 invariant.

If this is so a conjecture can be made: *that SU_6 is possibly a good symmetry for non-relativistic phenomena but fails to be such when particles, and hence the quarks which they contain, collide at relativistic velocities* [20].

To make an analogy let us fix our attention for a moment on a positronium atom. The energy levels of positronium are determined to a good accuracy by the Balmer formula. The spin orbit interaction or spin-spin interactions can be neglected to a good approximation. However if we want to treat reactions in which a fast positronium atom intervenes (consider for instance production of positronium by a high energy photon in the field of a nucleus) two things become necessary:

(1) A relativistic description of the positronium state; or in other words: how does the positronium wave function transform under a Lorentz transformation; this is a purely kinematic problem.

(2) A relativistic description of the interaction of the electrons in the positronium with other particles; in particular the spin orbit terms become important; this is a dynamical problem.

The problem of a particle composed of massive quarks is according to the point of view suggested in the present paper exactly similar to that of positronium; the problem is not that of constructing a Lagrangian which is simultaneously relativistically and SU_6 invariant. What apparently we have learnt instead is that in the non-relativistic limit the dynamics and the interactions become simple and this holds in particular, as we have seen, for the internal dynamics. Relativistically they presumably are more complicated; how much more complicated is a question which we must leave for the future.

4. Final Remarks

Three further remarks seem appropriate at this point.

(1) One might object that if the potential well representing the interaction among two quarks

has a relatively long range, as assumed in this paper, the density of levels in this well might be too high as compared to the density of observed particles or resonances. This is not so, however; for instance, considering the mesons, taking a potential well with a range of $(5\ m_\pi)^{-1}$ and assuming an infinite potential well the distance among the first two S states is $27(5\ m_\pi)^2/M \cong 20\ m_\pi$ where the mass M of a quark has been taken again to be 5 GeV. Of course there are also p, d, etc. levels, but on the whole the distance among two states does not seem too small, considering also the fact that in some states the forces may well be repulsive [2].

(2) An objection which might be raised against SU_6 or, more particularly, against the representation *56* for the baryons, is that it looks strange that the space part for the baryons is completely antisymmetrical; indeed the kinetic energy in antisymmetrical states is larger than in symmetrical states and it might appear strange that the baryon octet, which does constitute the ground state for three quarks, is a spatially antisymmetrical state. We have already expressed our point of view on the SU_6 classification and noted that its validity (even non-relativistically) is not yet established. However this particular objection appears to us inconsistent because the problem here is entirely different from that in ordinary nuclear physics. Here the kinetic energy is only a very small perturbation with respect to the very large potential energy. Essentially what one has to minimize is the potential energy and it may well be that the forces holding together the quarks are of exchange character and attractive in spatially antisymmetric states.

(3) Finally, if the present ideas are valid, the quarks should exist; they should not be only mathematical entities. It has obviously no meaning to write an hamiltonian, that is an energy, for mathematical entities. So one should finally discover the quarks. Which are the most appropriate conditions for this should be investigated [22]. We hope to come back to this point in the future [23].

References

1. E. FERMI and C.N. YANG, *Phys. Rev.* 76, 1739 (1948).

2. M. GELL MANN, *Physics Letters* 8, 214 (1964).

3. T.D. LEE, F. GURSEY and M. NAUENBERG, *Phys. Rev.* 135, B467 (1964).

4. G. ZWEIG-CERN preprint 8419/th 412, Feb. 1964.

5. M. GELL MANN, *Phys. Rev.* 125, 1067 (1962).

   Y. NEEMAN, *Nuclear Physics* 26, 222 (1961).

6. For a recent survey of the situation compare A. SALAM: Proc. of the Dubna 1964 Conference on high energy physics (to be published).

7. Compare e.g. Y. FUJII, *Progr. Theor. Physics* 21, 232 (1959).

8. It must be pointed out, however, that a virtual $q\ \bar{q}$ system can be produced in a strongly bound state. In this case its mass is not of the order M (the quark mass), but of the order of a few pion masses; the argument which we have just given should therefore not be taken

as indicating for instance that a virtual process like $\pi \to \pi + \rho$ is weak or unimportant; in other words if we have a $q\,\bar{q}$ system representing a pion it certainly can be accompanied for part of the time by a ρ; or, if we have a qqq system, say a nucleon, it certainly can be accompanied for part of the time by a $q\,\bar{q}'$ system representing a pion. However in the same sense in which a rather accurate description of nuclei is possible without taking the exchange currents into account, that is in terms of the nucleon coordinates only, a description of the nucleons might be possible where only the quark coordinates intervene.

9. Compare ref. [5] and S. OKUBO, *Progr. Theor. Physics* 27, 949 (1962).

10. $T_1 + T_2 + T_3 = \sum_{i=1}^{3} p_i{}^2/2\mu; \quad \mu = 3MM'/(2M' + M)$.

11. The matrix $\lambda^{(8)}$ will be taken, in this paper simply as $(^1 1_{-2})$.

12. That this question is a real question, different from that of why once the perturbation is taken as being linear in the $\lambda_i{}^{(8)}$ its second order effects are negligible, can be appreciated if we consider for a moment the problem of the Coulomb deviations from charge independence in ordinary nuclear physics. The terms which produce these deviations have the form

$$(*)\quad \frac{1}{2}\sum_i (M_n - M_p)\tau_i{}^{(3)} + \sum_i \left(\frac{p_i{}^2}{2M_p} - \frac{p_i{}^2}{2M_n}\right)\tau_i{}^{(3)} + \sum_{i>J}\frac{e^2}{r_{iJ}}\,\frac{\tau_i{}^{(3)} + \tau_J{}^{(3)} + \tau_i{}^{(3)}\tau_J{}^{(3)}}{4}$$

The first two terms in (*) are the terms analogous to these of $H_1{}^{(T)}$ in our case; in particular the second term is usually negligible just for the same reasons mentioned above; the third term in (*) (that arising from the Coulomb repulsion among protons) contains, as one can see, both terms linear in the $\tau_i{}^{(3)}$ and terms bilinear in the $\tau_i{}^{(3)}$ with the same strength. Why the terms quadratic of the kind $\lambda_i{}^{(8)} \times \lambda_J{}^{(8)}$ are absent in the "40 MeV" perturbation in our case or why, if present, they contribute practically nothing to the binding energies is the question which we have posed, but which we must leave unanswered in this paper.

13. OKUBO and RYAN (*Nuovo Cimento* 34, 776 (1964)) base their explanation on the fact that, if one writes $M^2 = P_\mu P^\mu$ and decomposes P_μ as $P_\mu{}^{(0)} + P_\mu{}^{(8)}$ the terms of first order in $P_\mu{}^{(8)}$ are quadratic in the masses; this argument appears to us inconsistent because it might be equally well be used to show that the mass formulas must be of order $2n$ in the masses; one would have simply to write $M^{2n} = (P_\mu P^\mu)^n$ and proceed in the same way as Okubo and Ryan do.

On the other hand the explanation given in reference (3) is based on the assumption of a zero order approximation in which all the bosons have zero mass.

14. F. GURSEY and L.A. RADICATI, *Phys. Rev. Letters* 13, 173 (1964).

B. SAKITA, *Phys. Rev.* 136, B1756 (1964).

See also A. PAIS, *Phys. Rev. Letters* 13, 175 (1964).

15. M.A. BEG, B.W. LEE and A. PAIS, *Phys. Rev. Letters* 13, 514 (1964).

16. Contrary to what it might appear at first sight, there is nothing which prevents the construction of a wave function $X(r_1, r_2, r_3)$ totally antisymmetric with respect to r_1, r_2, r_3 depending only on the relative coordinates and rotationally invariant (that is with zero orbital angular momentum).

If we write $\mathbf{r} = \mathbf{r}_1 - \mathbf{r}_2$ and $\boldsymbol{\rho} = \mathbf{r}_3 - (\mathbf{r}_1 + \mathbf{r}_2)/2$ the expression $X(r_1, r_2, r_3) = A(\mathbf{r}\cdot\boldsymbol{\rho}|\mathbf{r}|$ or the expression $A(\mathbf{r}\cdot\boldsymbol{\rho})|\mathbf{r}|^4$ where A means antisymmetrization with respect to 1,2,3 is an example.

Note however that for instance $A(\mathbf{r} \times \mathbf{p})$ or $A(\mathbf{r} \times \mathbf{p})|\mathbf{r}|^2$ do vanish identically. I am very grateful to Dr. C. Becchi for a remark on this point which has been essential for avoiding a mistake.

17. While the ratio μ_p/μ_n is obtained correctly, the absolute values of the magnetic moments constitute a mystery. To obtain the correct absolute values one should assume that e/M (where M is the quark mass) is equal to 2.79 e/M_p where M_p is the proton mass; in other words the g factor of the p quark should be (4/3) 2.79 M/M_p; this is entirely mysterious.

    Note also that, as far as the ratio among the magnetic moments is concerned, all values of the p and n quark charge in the ratio 2 : -1 lead to the -3/2 result; in other words, as far as this particular result is concerned the charges themselves need not be fractional. This observation may be of interest if two different triplets are assumed to exist with integral charge (compare H. BACRY, J.NUYTS and L.VAN HOVE, *Physics Letters*, **9**, 279 (1964).

    Note finally a third, more conventional, but nevertheless important and related question: can really the exchange currents (compare footnote (8)) be neglected in the calculation of the magnetic moments?

18. The paper by R. DELBOURGO, A.SALAM and J. STRATHDEE (*Proc. Roy. Soc.* **A284**, 146 (1965)) contains much of the relevant bibliography; compare also W. RUHL, *CERN* preprints 10058/Th 505 and 65/70/5/Th 514.

19. W.D. MCGLINN, *Phys. Rev. Letters* **12**, 467 (1964).

    W. RUHL, *CERN* preprint 9830/Th 492.

    C. BECCHI (to be published).

20. If this is so one might take some two reactions capable of furnishing a test of SU_6 (we have not yet thought in detail which might be the most appropriate) and explore their behaviour with increasing energy. Assuming that at low energy (here low energy means low with respect to the masses of the intervening particles, *not* with respect to the mass of the quarks) the SU_6 predictions are satisfied, larger and larger deviations should occur with increasing energy. It should, however, be observed that at low energy the problem arises of the different Q values or masses, so that it may be really difficult to find an energy region where the predictions of SU_6 are satisfied.

21. Of course the excited states become more and more relativistic.

22. The present evidence (or better lack of evidence) for quarks has been discussed by M. SCHWARTZ in the Proceedings of the Galilec meeting in Pisa, September 1964 (to be published).

23. *Note added in proof.* (a) it may be of interest to point out that indirect tests of the present model are provided:
    (1) by the radiative decay rates of vector mesons (C. BECCHI and G. MORPURGO, *Phys. Rev.*, in course of publication);
    (2) by the vanishing of the E2 amplitude in the $N_{33}^* \to N + \gamma$ transition (C. BECCHI and G. MORPURGO, *Physics Letters*, in course of publication).
    (b) A preprint by Y. Nambu, received while the present paper was in the press (Dynamical symmetries and fundamental fields - EFINS-65-6), contains some ideas similar to those of the first section of the present paper.

REPRINT 6

Reprinted from THE PHYSICAL REVIEW, Vol. 150, No. 4, 1177–1180, 28 October 1966
Printed in U. S. A.

Saturation in Triplet Models of Hadrons

O. W. GREENBERG*
The Rockefeller University, New York, New York
AND
DANIEL ZWANZIGER†
Courant Institute of Mathematical Sciences, New York University, New York, New York
(Received 27 May 1966)

Triplet models of hadrons are studied according to the criterion of saturation, namely, that the lowest-lying baryons contain exactly three triplets. Two main types of saturation are discussed: Pauli saturation, which depends on antisymmetrization of wave functions, and Coulomb saturation, which relies on the scheme of forces among the particles. The quark, quark-plus-singlet-core, two-triplet, three-triplet, and paraquark models are surveyed, and, using the saturation mechanisms discussed in the text, all of the models are made to satisfy the saturation criterion with the sole notable exception of the quark model, which fails.

1. INTRODUCTION

THE suggestion[1] that one or more fundamental unitary triplets can provide an explanation for the observed regularities of low-lying hadronic states received support from the $SU(6)$ classification[2,3] of these states. Since most of the successes[2–6] of this classification can be understood simply in terms of models in which the hadrons are composites of nonrelativistic triplets, it seems worthwhile to explore the consequences of the existence of triplets as real objects. In this direction, Thirring,[7] and Lipkin and Scheck[8] have found results, in agreement with experiment, which go beyond $SU(6)$ and appear to depend on the existence of real triplets.

There are three striking facts which provide criteria for such models: (1) a strong form of saturation whereby $N\equiv|n_t-n_{\bar{t}}|=0$, 3, only, for low-lying single-centered systems, where n_t ($n_{\bar{t}}$) is the number of triplet (antitriplet) particles[9]; (2) the lowest-lying baryons occur in the symmetric **56** of $SU(6)$ rather than in an antisymmetric $SU(6)$ configuration[10]; (3) the $SU(6)$ prediction of $-\frac{3}{2}$ for the ratio of the proton and neutron magnetic moments[6] is accurate to within 3%.

In the present article, we assume a nonrelativistic composite picture for the hadrons, and ignore the serious open dynamical problems connected with composite models of hadrons, such as the compatibility of strong binding with nonrelativistic triplet motion[11] and the coexistence of triplet and hadronic cloud structure. The question of saturation depends on the dominant $SU(6)$-invariant effects rather than on the weaker $SU(6)$-violating ones, and therefore we assume that the basic objects belong to low-dimensional irreducible representations of $SU(6)$, in particular to **6**, **6***, and **1**, and that the forces between the basic objects are $SU(6)$-invariant. There are only two different $SU(6)$-invariant forces between a pair of objects which are each in the **6**; these forces can be taken to be one, $V(21)$, which acts only between an $SU(6)$ symmetric pair in the **21**, and a second, $V(15)$, which acts only between an $SU(6)$ antisymmetric pair in the **15**. Similarly, for three-body forces between triples of objects, each in the **6**, there are four invariant forces, $V(56)$, $V(70)$, $V(70)'$, and $V(20)$, acting between triples in the associated representations, etc.

These forces are of exchange character, so that the theorem[12] that the nodeless wave function has the lowest energy is not relevant. To see this, consider a

* Alfred P. Sloan Foundation Fellow, on leave of absence from the Department of Physics and Astronomy, University of Maryland, College Park, Maryland.

† Work performed under a Ford Foundation grant.

[1] M. Gell-Mann, Phys. Letters **8**, 214 (1964); G. Zweig, CERN Reports 8182/TH. 401 and 8419/TH. 412, 1964 (unpublished).

[2] F. Gürsey and L. A. Radicati, Phys. Rev. Letters **13**, 173 (1964).

[3] B. Sakita, Phys. Rev. **136**, B1756 (1964).

[4] A. Pais, Rev. Mod. Phys. **38**, 215 (1966); F. J. Dyson, *Symmetry Groups in Nuclear and Particle Physics* (W. A. Benjamin, Inc., New York, 1966); R. H. Dalitz, in *Proceedings of the Oxford International Conference on Elementary Particles, 1966* (Rutherford High Energy Laboratory, Harwell, England, 1966), and in *High Energy Physics*, edited by C. DeWitt and M. Jacob (Gordon and Breach, Science Publishers, Inc. New York, 1965), contain reviews, reprints, and bibliographies.

[5] F. Gürsey, A. Pais, and L. A. Radicati, Phys. Rev. Letters **13**, 299 (1964).

[6] M. A. B. Bég, B. W. Lee, and A. Pais, Phys. Rev. Letters **13**, 514 (1964); B. Sakita, *ibid.* **13**, 643 (1964).

[7] W. Thirring, Phys. Letters **16**, 335 (1965).

[8] H. J. Lipkin and F. Scheck, Phys. Rev. Letters **16**, 71 (1966).

[9] This saturation is similar to that in molecular physics, where fixed numbers of atoms combine to form molecules. This should be contrasted with the kind of saturation which occurs in solid or liquid bulk matter or in nuclear matter in which the binding energy per particle is roughly constant. No "quark matter" analogous to nuclear matter seems to exist.

[10] The antisymmetric $SU(6)$ states would be analogous to the ground states of the lightest nuclei. See discussion of type 1b.

[11] O. W. Greenberg, Phys. Rev. **147**, 1077 (1966), discusses this problem for S states in a potential.

[12] The relevant theorem [R. Courant and D. Hilbert, *Methods of Mathematical Physics* (Interscience Publishers, Inc., New York, 1953), p. 452] applies in the case of a self-adjoint Schrödinger equation with a local potential: If the bound-state wave functions are ordered according to increasing energy, then the nodes of the nth wave function divide configuration space into no more than n disjoint regions. In particular, the lowest wave function is nodeless, and therefore all the others, which must be orthogonal to it, have nodes. Note that it is not necessary that a wave function which divides space into n regions lie higher than one which divides space into fewer than n regions. In addition, the Pauli principle might exclude the nodeless solution. However, for the special case of the one-dimensional Sturm-Liouville problem, the nth eigenfunction divides the fundamental domain into precisely n parts by means of its nodal points (see p. 454).

TABLE I. Types of saturation.

Pauli saturation	
1. internal	a-absolute b-known quantum numbers
2. orbital	a-with a core b-without a core
3. accidental	
Coulomb saturation	
4. generalized charge	a-additive quantum number b-nonadditive quantum number
5. hard core	
6. accidental	

pair of particles interacting via a space exchange potential which is repulsive in even space states and attractive in odd ones. Here any bound states which occur will have at least one node.

2. TYPES OF SATURATION

Now we discuss some mechanisms of saturation. They fall into two categories which we call "Pauli saturation" and "Coulomb saturation." Pauli saturation is the mechanism which operates when a given set of states is filled by the maximum number of Fermi or para-Fermi particles which can enter. Coulomb saturation operates when the number at which saturation occurs is determined by the scheme of forces among the particles, rather than by the permutation symmetry of the state. Table I lists the types of saturation which we will describe. These types are not disjoint.

Type 1: Internal saturation occurs when states labeled by internal quantum numbers are filled. Type 1a: A direct way to achieve saturation at three is to introduce a new three-valued internal quantum number[13] so that there are three sets of triplets, or altogether, nine fundamental particles. If the triplets are fermions, then requiring an antisymmetric three-particle wave function in the new quantum number leads to a symmetric wave function in the other quantum numbers, and for a symmetric three-particle S state the **56** follows. For the known hadron states, this threefold degenerate quark model is qualitatively the same as the order-three para-Fermi quark model,[14] as can be seen from Green's ansatz. However, these two models differ in the number of different quarks: The paraquark model has only three. Type 1b: Filling of states labeled by known internal quantum numbers is the familiar type which operates in atomic and nuclear physics, for example, the two-electron $SU(2)$ singlet for the atom, or the four-nucleon $SU(4)$ singlet for the α particle. The analog of these for $SU(6)$ would be a six-particle singlet. Type 2a: Orbital saturation occurs at $2l+1$ for fermions in an orbital l shell around a core. Type 2b: Without a core, the l shell saturates at $2l+2$, since the wave function for n particles depends on only $n-1$ independent relative coordinates, and the coordinates of one of the particles may be used kinematically to play the role of a core. Simple examples are: for symmetric S waves, 1; for antisymmetric P waves, $\mathbf{r}_{12}$, $\mathbf{r}_{12}\times\mathbf{r}_{13}$, $\mathbf{r}_{12}\times\mathbf{r}_{13}\cdot\mathbf{r}_{14}$, for 2, 3, and 4 particles, respectively. We took particle 1 as the core particle; however, these last three functions are totally antisymmetric under all permutations of particles because of the linear dependence of the relative coordinates. Here, as well as later in this article, we omit a function of the scalar products which is symmetric under particle permutations and which decreases exponentially for large magnitude of any relative coordinate vector. Because of this factor, the pairs are not in pure relative l waves, so our analysis applies only to the dominant terms. Note that $\mathbf{r}_{12}\times\mathbf{r}_{23}\cdot\mathbf{r}_{31}$ vanishes identically, so that there is no $L=0$ antisymmetric state of three particles in the same P shell. Type 3: Pauli-accidental saturation occurs when the antisymmetric wave functions are formed with particles in different principal quantum states. For example, n fermions can be put into S states with principal quantum numbers $1S$, $2S$, $\cdots$, nS.[15] Some potentials might lead to saturation in such a state, but we call this case accidental because detailed study of the relevant bound-state equation is needed to decide whether saturation occurs.

Type 4: In Coulomb saturation by a generalized charge, there are forces depending on discrete quantum numbers whose eigenvalues characterize, *a priori*, the lowest lying compound systems. Type 4a: The additive case includes Coulomb forces: a particle with charge Ze will not bind strongly more than Z particles with charge $-e$, regardless of their statistics. For some two-triplet models of baryons,[16] "charm" replaces charge and the zero-charm states are the saturated systems. Type 4b: A nonadditive quantum number can also characterize saturation, for example, the Casimir operator C_2 in a three-triplet model.[13] Type 5: Simple geometry shows that finite-range hard-core potentials lead to saturation. For example, if a particle of type A attracts particles of type B via a finite-range potential and the B particles repel each other with a hard-core potential, then there is an upper limit to the number of B particles which can be bound to A. Type 6: We include in the Coulomb-

[13] Y. Nambu, in *Preludes in Theoretical Physics*, edited by A. De-Shalit, H. Feshbach, and L. Van Hove (North-Holland Publishing Company, Amsterdam, 1966), pp. 133–142; M. Y. Han and Y. Nambu, Phys. Rev. **139**, B1006 (1965); N. N. Bogolyubov *et al.*, Dubna Reports D1968, D2015, D2141, 1965 (unpublished), cited in A. Pais, Ref. 4.

[14] O. W. Greenberg, Phys. Rev. Letters **13**, 598 (1964).

[15] It can be shown, provided the potential is regular at the origin, that baryons constructed in this way in the quark model have a wave function at the origin which is of degree 6, $(\mathbf{r}_{12}^2-\mathbf{r}_{23}^2)\times(\mathbf{r}_{23}^2-\mathbf{r}_{31}^2)(\mathbf{r}_{31}^2-\mathbf{r}_{12}^2)$, or greater.

[16] Y. Nambu, in *Symmetry Principles at High Energy*, edited by B. Kurşunoğlu, A. Perlmutter, and I. Sakmar (W. H. Freeman and Company, San Francisco, 1965), pp. 274–283; Y. Nambu, Ref. 13; H. Bacry, J. Nuyts, and L. Van Hove, Phys. Letters **9**, 279 (1964); **12**, 285 (1965); Nuovo Cimento **35**, 510 (1965); L. Van Hove, Progr. Theoret. Phys. (Kyoto) Suppl., p. 14 (1965).

accidental category those systems with forces which lead to saturation, but for which the number at which saturation occurs cannot be found *a priori*. An example of this category is obtained if in the discussion of type 5 above we replace the AB and BB potentials by attractive and repulsive Yukawa potentials, respectively. The Pauli and Coulomb mechanisms can combine to produce saturation; for example, the neutrality of atoms is due to Coulomb saturation, while chemical inertness of the (neutral) rare gases is due to Pauli saturation.

We remind the reader that the problem of saturation is removed if no triplets are present and the fundamental symmetry of particles is $SU(3)/Z_3$. However, it is not clear how to account for the successes of $SU(6)$ with this group.

3. SURVEY OF MODELS

We will now apply simple symmetry and energy agruments to a number of models and see if they saturate via one of the mechanisms described above.

A. Quark Model

The quark model[1,17,18] is the most economical, and the easiest to study. Among the three quark states, the symmetric **56** representation will be lowest if the two-body potential is attractive in the **21** state and repulsive in the **15**. The Pauli principle requires an antisymmetric space wave function. The lowest available orbital shell is the P shell which saturates with four particles rather than three, and which does not have an antisymmetric $L=0$ three-particle wave function. (See discussion of type 2b above.) There is an antisymmetric $L=1$ three-particle P-shell wave function, but $L=1$ will upset the proton/neutron magnetic-moment ratio, and the $L=1$ coupled to the $S=\frac{1}{2}, \frac{3}{2}$ of the **56** no longer produces a true **56**.[19] Accidental saturation could occur as under the discussion of type 3 above.

From the standpoint of energy, consider the phenomenological mass formula

$$M(N)=NM_q+\tfrac{1}{2}N(N-1)U, \quad 1\leq N\leq 4,$$

where M_q is the quark mass, and U includes the effect of two-body potentials as well as kinetic-energy changes due to binding. From $M(3)<M(1)$, we find $U<-\frac{2}{3}M_q$, and $M(4)<0$, so saturation occurs at 4 rather than 3.[20]

Thus both symmetry and energy arguments indicate that the quark model fails.[21]

Further restrictions are obtained by applying the saturation requirement to the mesons which in the quark model are $q\bar{q}$ bound states in the **35** representation. For example, the $qq\bar{q}$ system in the **120** representation has three attractive pairs since both $q\bar{q}$ pairs are in the **35** and the qq pair is in the symmetric **21**. Such a state would lie too low unless the potentials are chosen properly: for example, a repulsive $qq\bar{q}$ three-body force, or a qq hard core which prevents the $q\bar{q}$ force from forming two bonds.

B. Quark-plus-Singlet-Core Model

The model with one triplet and an $SU(6)$ singlet core[22,23] avoids some difficulties of the quark model. There is an antisymmetric three-particle $L=0$ state, whose wave function is $\mathbf{r}_1\times\mathbf{r}_2\cdot\mathbf{r}_3$ (where $\mathbf{r}_j$ is the distance of particle j to the core), which saturates the P shell. (See discussion of type 2a above.) One can make this state lie lowest and make more complicated single-centered systems unbound if the forces between quarks (q) and cores (c) are: attractive in the P wave for $c-q$, attractive in **21** and repulsive in **15** for $q-q$, and repulsive for $c-c$. Thus it allows saturation.[24]

C. Two-Triplet Model

The two-triplet model[13,16] can be made to saturate using type 4a. Let the triplets[25] be t_1 and t_2 with masses M_1 and M_2, and charms C_1 and C_2. Coulomb-like forces among them give the mass formula

$$M\{\alpha_i\}=\sum_i M_{\alpha_i}+\sum_{i>j} C_{\alpha_i}C_{\alpha_j}V=\sum_i m_{\alpha_i}+\tfrac{1}{2}C^2V, \quad \alpha_i=1, 2,$$

where the effective mass $m_\alpha=M_\alpha-C_\alpha{}^2V$ and the total charm $C=\sum_i C_{\alpha_i}$. If $m_\alpha\ll V$ then "neutral" systems with $C=0$ will lie lowest, and for these systems

---

[17] Y. Nambu in Ref. 16; T. S. Kuo and L. M. Radicati, Phys. Rev. **139**, B746 (1965); L. A. Radicati, Cargèse Lectures, 1965 (to be published); G. Morpurgo, Physics **2**, 95 (1965); R. H. Dalitz in Ref. 4; and A. N. Mitra, Phys. Rev. **142**, 1119 (1966).

[18] K. Kinoshita and Y. Kinoshita, Progr. Theoret. Phys. (Kyoto) **35**, 330 (1966) have also studied saturation in the quark model and have found similar conclusions.

[19] These objects apply to the model of A. N. Mitra, Ref. 18.

[20] This conclusion no longer holds if one uses the formula

$$M(N)=NM_q+\tfrac{1}{2}N(N-1)U_2+\tfrac{1}{6}N(N-1)(N-2)U_3, \quad 1\leq N\leq 4,$$

which may crudely account for the effects of three-body potentials. Now saturation can occur at three, provided $U_2<-\frac{2}{3}M_q$ and $U_3>\frac{1}{2}M_q$; i.e., attractive two-body forces to bind three quarks into baryons and repulsive three-body forces to effect saturation at three. Kuo and Radicati, Ref. 17, introduce instead three-body forces, attractive in the **56**, which bind three quarks into baryons but lead to four-quark states that are much more tightly bound. In particular, their V_3, Eq. (14), p. B748, has the value $6V$ ($V<0$) for the symmetric and antisymmetric three-quark states and $24V$ for the corresponding four-quark states. Thus their model does not saturate at three.

[21] We are not convinced by the arguments for saturation given in G. Morpurgo, Phys. Letters **20**, 684 (1966).

[22] F. Gürsey, T. D. Lee, and M. Nauenburg, Phys. Rev. **135**, B467 (1964), Appendix IV, model II. Only a neutral core and fractionally charged quarks will give the observed magnetic-moment ratio, as shown by M. A. B. Bég and A. Pais, Phys. Rev. **137**, B1514 (1965).

[23] P. G. O. Freund and B. W. Lee, Phys. Rev. Letters **13**, 592 (1964). The singlet core in this model is the internally saturated 6-particle S-shell antisymmetric $SU(6)$ singlet. It is arbitrary to assume, as in this model, that the next shell should saturate via orbital (P-shell) saturation, and have a totally symmetric $SU(6)$ wave function.

[24] However the core-core interaction would upset the results of Ref. 8.

[25] Here we follow Nambu, Ref. 13. In the model of Van Hove, Ref. 16, $\bar{\theta}\sim t_1$, $T\sim t_2$, and supercharge$\sim-$charm.

$M=\sum_i m_{\alpha_i}$. We expect more complicated systems to be multiple-centered, in analogy with collections of neutral atoms. The assignment $C_1=2$, $C_2=-1$ leads to $(t_1t_2t_2)$ for the lowest baryons. Let $\mathbf{r}_1$ and $\mathbf{r}_2$ be the distances of the t_2's from the t_1. For the **56**, the Pauli principle requires antisymmetry in $\mathbf{r}_1$ and $\mathbf{r}_2$. However, there is no antisymmetric S state with both t_2's in the same orbital shell relative to t_1. The lowest degree antisymmetric wave function with the t_2's in the same orbital shell is $\mathbf{r}_1\times\mathbf{r}_2$, which has $L=1$. However, the antisymmetrized $1S$, $2S$ wave function $\mathbf{r}_1^2-\mathbf{r}_2^2$ has the same degree, and if the forces are attractive (repulsive) for a pair in the **21** (**15**) the **56** can be the lowest three-particle state. An analogous situation occurs in orthohelium for which the electron spin state is symmetric: the lowest state is the $1S$, $2S$ with $1S$, $2P$ nearby, and the $2P$, $2P$ state, analogous to $\mathbf{r}_1\times\mathbf{r}_2$ above, lies much higher. Thus this model can saturate properly.[26]

D. Paraquark and Three-Triplet Models

The order three-paraquark[14] and three-triplet[13] models yield the same baryon states; in particular, both models require a symmetric three-particle joint orbital and $SU(6)$ wave function (see discussion of type 1a above). Paraquarks must have fractional charge, and among the three-paraquark states only the symmetric one is an effective fermion. If the Green components of the paraquark model are taken to be independent fields and are Klein transformed, then, as far as the known hadrons are concerned, the paraquark model can be considered a special case of the three-triplet model. Using the (three-valued) $SU(3)''$ degree of freedom, one can make pairs of particles in the antisymmetric $SU(3)''$ state attract and pairs in the symmetric one repel,[13] so that saturation will occur at three and the orbital-$SU(6)$ wave function will be symmetric.[27] By proper choice of such forces, more complicated single-centered systems can be made unbound.

The states produced by low orbital excitation in the paraquark model have been tabulated[14]; these same states are also relevant for orbital excitation in the three-Fermi-triplet model.[28]

In the model of Han and Nambu,[13] an octet of gauge fields couples to the $SU(3)''$ generators $\frac{1}{2}\lambda_\mu''$ of the triplets and leads to the mass formula

$$M(N)=NM_t+\tfrac{1}{4}g^2\sum_{\mu=1}^{8}\sum_{\substack{i,j=1\\ i<j}}^{N}\lambda_\mu''^{(i)}\lambda_\mu''^{(j)}$$
$$=Nm_t+\tfrac{1}{2}g^2C_2,$$

where $m_t=M_t-\frac{1}{2}g^2C_{20}$ ($C_{20}=\frac{4}{3}$) is the effective mass, and

$$C_2=\tfrac{1}{4}\sum_{\mu=1}^{8}\Big[\sum_{n=1}^{N}\lambda_\mu''^{(n)}\Big]^2$$

is the quadratic Casimir operator for $SU(3)''$. If $m_t\ll g^2$, the lowest-lying states will be those for which $C_2=0$ [i.e., the singlets of $SU(3)''$, all of which have $SU(3)$ triality 0], which here play the role of "neutral" systems. Note, however, that C_2 is not an additive quantum number. Thus this model makes essential use of saturation mechanism 4b.

In conclusion, although we have shown how several models can be made to satisfy the saturation criteria, it remains a challenge to show how, if at all, these criteria can be satisfied in the quark model.[29]

ACKNOWLEDGMENTS

We are happy to thank Professor M. A. B. Bég, Professor A. Martin, Professor S. Meshkov, Professor A. Pais, Professor M. Ruderman, and Professor L. Van Hove for helpful conversations. One of us (OWG) thanks Professor A. Pais for his hospitality at the Rockefeller University. One of us (DZ) is grateful for the hospitality extended to him at the Courant Institute for Mathematical Sciences.

[26] The proton/neutron magnetic-moment ratio is not determined uniquely here; however, the experimental value can be gotten with a reasonable value of the free parameter. See Van Hove, Ref. 16.

[27] This can be done directly in the paraquark model.

[28] Dalitz, Ref. 4, suggested that a universal short-range repulsion between baryons might result from overlapping wave functions in the paraquark model. In view of the fact that the Pauli principle alone does not suffice for saturation in nuclei, it is not clear that overlapping wave functions, without suitable dynamics, will give such a repulsion. Proper choice of forces in the models which saturate, i.e., core-core repulsion, t_2-t_2 repulsion, or repulsion in $SU(3)''$ symmetric pairs, will give such a repulsion.

[29] S. Meshkov and H. Lipkin have independently studied saturation in triplet models [S. Meshkov (private communication)].

REPRINT 7

NONRELATIVISTIC QUARK MODEL*

L. I. Schiff
Institute of Theoretical Physics, Department of Physics, Stanford University, Stanford, California
(Received 1 August 1966)

Several recent papers[1] have shown that experimental observations on hadron rest masses, scattering cross sections, and annihilation processes are in remarkably good agreement with a simple additive quark model in which the quarks and antiquarks interact with each other nonrelativistically.[2] However, the difficult question immediately arises as to why quarks are not easily knocked out of nucleons and observed by themselves. It is apparent that a selection principle that restricts the baryon number to integer values would accomplish this if properly applied. What is needed is not only that the over-all baryon number be an integer, but that the baryon number for each mutually interacting cluster of quarks be an integer. At the same time, the quarks should be able to move freely within each interacting cluster, without being greatly inhibited by the selection principle.

The present paper proposes a phenomenological model for such a selection principle in terms of many-particle interactions between quarks. We write the potential energy of a cluster consisting of n quarks and m antiquarks that are within interaction range of each other in the form

$$V=V_0\sum_{s=0}^{n}\sum_{t=0}^{m}a(s,t)\nu_s\nu_t,$$

$$V_0>0,\quad a(s,t)=a(t,s),\quad a(0,0)=0, \tag{1}$$

where ν_s is the number of ways in which s quarks can be chosen from the n that are present:

$$\nu_s=n!/(n-s)!s! \tag{2}$$

For example, with $n=3$ and $m=2$, Eqs. (1) and (2) give

$$V=V_0[5a(1,0)+4a(2,0)+6a(1,1)+a(3,0)$$
$$+9a(2,1)+2a(3,1)+3a(2,2)+a(3,2)].$$

It is, of course, possible to choose the interaction coefficients $a(s,t)$ so that only those clusters for which the baryon number $\frac{1}{3}(n-m)$ is a positive or negative integer or zero are energetically favored; however, the coefficients then become unrealistically large for the larger values of s or t.

We therefore assume that all coefficients that correspond to interactions of more than three particles are zero. Our approach consists in generalizing a two-particle interaction for which the particles have zero potential energy when close together and potential energy V_0 otherwise. Such an interaction is of the type (1) for $n=2$, $m=0$ if we take $a(1,0)=\frac{1}{2}$, $a(2,0)=-1$. We choose the coefficients such that the following clusters have zero potential energy and all others have positive potential energy:

$$n=3,m=0;\quad n=1,m=1;\quad n=0,m=3. \tag{3}$$

With $a(1,0)$ arbitrarily chosen equal to unity, the other coefficients are easily seen to satisfy the relations

$$-2<a(2,0)<-\tfrac{4}{3},\quad a(1,1)=-2,$$
$$a(3,0)=-3[1+a(2,0)],\quad a(2,1)>1-a(2,0).$$

A reasonable set of values is

$$a(1,0)=1,\quad a(2,0)=-\tfrac{3}{2},\quad a(1,1)=-2,$$
$$a(3,0)=\tfrac{3}{2},\quad a(2,1)=3. \tag{4}$$

It is interesting to note that the unlike-particle interactions $a(1,1)$ and $a(2,1)$ are stronger than the corresponding like-particle interactions $a(2,0)$ and $a(3,0)$.

Several comments can be made on the foregoing model. (a) With V_0 chosen to be large, clusters that have nonintegral baryon numbers, as well as single quarks, will be difficult to produce. At the same time, particles in the allowed clusters (3) can move nonrelativistically with zero potential energy and be assigned rest masses unrelated to V_0. It is then reasonable to assume that the quark rest mass is roughly equal to one-third of a baryon mass or one-half of a meson mass (these are of the same order of magnitude). (b) V_0 can be thought of as the rest energy of a quark excited state rather than that of the ground state of the quark which is a constituent of hadrons. (c) Each coefficient in the potential energy (1) is characterized by a range, but the ranges associated with the last four coefficients in (4) need not all be the same. It seems likely that crossover of quarks from one hadron to another during a collision will be facilitated by making the pair-interaction ranges slightly greater than the three-particle ranges and adjusting the strength accordingly. (d) The model can be used for explicit calculations of hadron processes by assuming particular forms for the space dependences of the two- and three-particle interactions, so that they lead to the potential energy given by (1) and (4). (e) There must be an additional potential energy that is much weaker than (1) and of longer range, which is responsible for the bulk of the interactions between hadrons.

It is a pleasure to express appreciation for the hospitality of the Institute of Geophysics and Planetary Physics, University of California, San Diego, where this work was performed.

---

*Work supported in part by the U. S. Air Force through Air Force Office of Scientific Research Contract No. AF 49(638)-1389.

[1]E. M. Levin and L. L. Frankfurt, Zh. Eksperim. i Teor. Fiz.—Pis'ma Redakt. 2, 105 (1965) [translation: JETP Letters 2, 65 (1965)]; H. J. Lipkin and F. Scheck, Phys. Rev. Letters 16, 71 (1966); J. J. Kokkedee and L. Van Hove, Nuovo Cimento 42, 711 (1966); H. R. Rubinstein and H. Stern, Phys. Letters 21, 447 (1966); H. R. Rubinstein, Phys. Rev. Letters 17, 41 (1966).

[2]G. Morpurgo, Physics 2, 95 (1965).

SOVIET PHYSICS USPEKHI VOLUME 8, NUMBER 5 MARCH-APRIL, 1966

539.12

QUARKS: ASTROPHYSICAL AND PHYSICOCHEMICAL ASPECTS

YA. B. ZEL'DOVICH, L. B. OKUN', and S. B. PIKEL'NER

Usp. Fiz. Nauk 87, 113-124 (September, 1965)

1. INTRODUCTION

THE preceding issue of Uspekhi contained a series of predictions about directions of development and about problems of elementary particle physics. In connection with this discussion it is worth mentioning another possible direction for investigation which has developed recently, along with studies using accelerators and cosmic rays.

We refer to attempts to find new rare types of stable particles in nature. Thus, in studying elementary particles one can use, in addition to the traditional methods (but of course not in place of them) physicochemical methods of enrichment and investigation. We shall discuss various aspects of this approach.

There has recently been discussion of the possible existence of new types of particles that are heavier than the proton and have fractional charge. The classification of the known strongly interacting particles (SU_3 or SU_6 symmetry) leads naturally to the assumption that there exist three particles (quarks) with charges $+(2/3)e$, $-(1/3)e$, $-(1/3)e$ [1,2] (cf. the popular summary [48]).

There is still also the possibility that new types of particles with integral charge exist, both within the framework of the SU_3 symmetry,*[3,8] and also without any connection to the SU_3 symmetry.[9]

Among the quarks, these particles with fractional charge, there is one, the lightest, that should be stable not only in vacuum but, because of its fractional charge, also stable in contact with ordinary matter (nuclei, electrons). The particles with integral charge may be unstable, but there may be selection rules that cause these particles to be stable. These selection rules may be connected with the conservation of a new quantum number that is like the charge—the supercharge.† Under strict conservation of supercharge the creation and annihilation may also be selection rules because the particles have unusual combinations of the usual quantum numbers. In this case their numbers should not be conserved absolutely, but, as for the quarks, modulo some number. For example, baryons with integer spin can be created in pairs in nucleon collisions (conservation modulo 2). We note that the quarks are conserved modulo 3, i.e., in reactions only 3,6,9, etc., quarks can be created or destroyed; for example, 7 quarks cannot convert completely into ordinary matter—there still remains one free quark.

2. FORMATION OF QUARKS BY HIGH ENERGY PARTICLES

High energy experiments have so far not led to the discovery of new stable particles and have shown that the masses of such particles cannot be small. Experiments at accelerators [10-15] have detected no quarks up to masses of 3-5 GeV and above a cross section for creation of 10^{-34}—10^{-32} cm^2.

A cosmic-ray experiment [21] at a height of 2.5 km gives an upper limit for the flux of relativistic quarks with charge $(1/3)e$ of $I_{1/3} < 1.6 \times 10^{-8}$ cm^{-2} sec^{-1} sr^{-1} (a sea level experiment [22] gives the flux limit 20×10^{-8} cm^{-2} sec^{-1} sr^{-1}). If we assume that the slowing down of quarks in the atmosphere is approximately the same as for nucleons, and that the cross section for creating them is ~ 0.01 mb, the upper limits given show that $m_q > 7$ GeV. In this estimate we have used the integral spectrum of the primary cosmic radiation

$$N(E) = 0.9 E^{-1.5} \mathrm{cm}^{-2}\,\mathrm{sec}^{-1}\,\mathrm{sr}^{-1}, \qquad (1)$$

where E is in GeV.

Searches for longlived particles with integral charge at the accelerators at Brookhaven and CERN [16-20] have given a negative result up to a mass of 4 GeV, and have shown that if such particles are formed their numbers are approximately three orders smaller than the number of antiprotons.

Aside from a search for new stable particles in experiments on collisions at high energies, there is another procedure—a search for particles that were formed long ago and have assumed the temperature of their surroundings. If one assumes that quarks can be created by the primary cosmic ray nucleons with E > 300 GeV, then, for the parameters cited above, during 5×10^9 years there should have been 10^{11} cm^{-2} created in the atmosphere, and this is approximately 10^8 quarks per gram of absorbing layer of atmosphere. The quarks diffuse from the upper to the lower layers of the atmosphere, there

*Schemes that combine the particle classification according to SU_3 or SU_6 with the assumption of the existence of fundamental particles with integral, instead of fractional, charges, are more complicated than the quark scheme, and contain more fundamental particles.

†By the supercharge we mean three times the average charge of an SU_3 supermultiplet. If SU_3 triplets with integral charge (like the p,n,Λ) exist, their supercharge is 1. For the quarks the supercharge is zero.

serve as nuclei for condensation of drops, fall with precipitation onto the earth's surface, and are mixed into the oceans. We then get approximately 10^5 quarks per gram of water. But if the precipitation is collected in outdoor reservoirs which are then allowed to evaporate, the concentration may be 1-2 orders of magnitude higher.

Because of the absence of mixing, the concentration of quarks formed by cosmic rays may be of the order of 10^9 per gram in meteorites. But the size of the meteorite must be very large (~ 30 cm) to retain the quarks at the time they are created.

Under special circumstances the concentration of cosmic rays may be much higher than average. On the sun, at the time of chromospheric flares, many cosmic rays are produced, albeit of relatively low energy. Much more powerful sources are the variable stars like Taurus τ which are in the process of gravitational collapse: in these stars there is strong convection which results in varying magnetic fields and acceleration of particles. Thus the stars are the source of the "real cosmic rays." This is indicated by the anomalously large content of Li and certain other elements that are fragments of heavier nuclei. There are stars with an anomalously high content of He^3 which, according to [33], is formed from He^4 by cosmic rays. The increased deuterium and Li content of the earth is also related to the period of formation of the solar system, when the sun was a star like Taurus τ and irradiated the planetary matter. This energy spectrum is not known, but if it were sufficiently hard, quarks would have been formed along with the Li.

The most powerful sources of cosmic rays, superstars or quasars,[24] also must produce quarks. Finally quarks may be produced in small-scale explosions occurring in galactic cores. But the relatively short duration of the explosion process and the small mass of gas leads one to think that the main contribution in the galaxy comes from ordinary cosmic rays.

3. CREATION AND BURNUP OF QUARKS IN THE INITIAL PERIOD OF EXPANSION OF THE METAGALAXY

If the hypothetically stable particles (not quarks) possess some particular strictly conserved quantum number, like the baryonic charge, their minimum concentration is a universal constant like the total baryonic charge of our portion of the universe, and can in principle be arbitrary. If, however, these particles are conserved modulo some base, their concentration will depend on their history, i.e., on the earlier physical condition of the material and on the processes that lead to the annihilation of the particles. For example, let us consider annihilation of quarks.

Since quarks are heavier than nucleons we can have the process

$$q_1 + q_1 \to q_3 + q_{-1} \qquad (2)$$

followed by $q_1 + q_{-1} \to n\,q_0$. Here the subscript indicates the number of quarks contained in the particle, the minus sign denoting the antiparticle. Thus q_1 denotes single quarks, q_2 pairs of quarks coupled by the strong interaction, q_3 ordinary baryons made up of three quarks, and q_0 mesons. Because of reaction (2), annihilation of the quarks can occur in a series of pair collisions instead of via the much rarer triple collisions.

The process (2) does not consider the possibility of the existence of a q_2. But including q_2 does not alter the conclusion about the role of pair collisions. If $m_2 > m_1 + m_3$, the reaction $q_2 \to q_3 + q_{-1}$ goes; but if $m_2 < m_1 - m_3$, the free quarks are unstable: $q_1 \to q_3 + q_{-2}$. In this case the particles with fractional charge that can exist in nature are the diquarks. If, finally, m_2 lies in an interval that guarantees the simultaneous stability of q_2 and q_1, both types of particles are annihilated in all variants with double collisions. One can treat $q_4, q_5, \ldots$, similarly with the same conclusions.

From the point of view of possible creation and burnup of quarks, the most important period is the initial expansion of the metagalaxy, if this expansion proceeded from a singular state. We must start from some definite cosmological hypothesis. Here we shall assume that the Friedmann model of a homogeneous isotropic universe (cf., for example, the survey[25]) is applicable with sufficient accuracy up to $t \lesssim 10^{-7}$ sec. Deviations from homogeneity and isotropy, which may be significant at an early stage,[26,27] can of course significantly change the results. The choice between open and closed models is entirely unimportant at the early stage. On the other hand the Friedmann theory leaves free the values of the thermodynamic parameters, the specific entropy and specific leptonic charge of unit rest mass of the matter.

Let us assume following Gamow [28] that in the singular state at infinite density the specific entropy was large ("hot model").* Then in the early stages of the expansion the densities of quanta and of all types of particle-anti-particle pairs greatly exceeded the excess density of baryons, corresponding to a charge asymmetry in our vicinity, which we extrapolate to the whole universe. For $t \to 0$, $\rho \to \infty$, $T \to \infty$. Fixing the quark mass m, one can easily find the relative equilibrium concentration of quarks for $T \ll m$:† this concentration is $n \sim e^{-m/T}$.

*This hypothesis has also been supported recently by Hoyle and Tuler.[**]

†We work in units with $h = c = k = 1$. In these units, mass, energy and temperature have the same dimensions, and can be in degrees, MeV, proton masses. etc.

There are no conditions at the present time under which a significant number of quarks would be in equilibrium. We must therefore determine the moment when, in the course of the expansion, the actual quark concentration ceased following the equilibrium behavior (the moment of "quenching" of the equilibrium). The analogous problem was solved earlier for the freezing in of antinucleons.[29]

From the equations of general relativity for the Friedmann solution and from thermodynamics

$$\varrho = ahT^4 = \frac{3}{32\pi G t^2}, \qquad s = \frac{4ahT^3}{3\varrho_b}; \tag{3}$$

here $a = 4\sigma/c = \pi^2/15$, where σ is the Stefan-Boltzmann constant, ρ_b the density of rest mass of excess baryons, s the specific entropy per unit of this mass, h a dimensionless number that takes account of the presence of other particles, that are in equilibrium with the radiation at the given temperature ($h = 1$ for single quanta, $h = 2.75$ for quanta and e^+, e^- pairs when $T > m_e c^2$).

With muons and neutrinos included, $h \sim 9$. Formula (3) applies to the initial stages, when $\rho_b \ll \rho$. We denote by n the concentration of quarks relative to the concentration of excess baryons $N = \rho_b/M$, where M is the baryon mass. The equilibrium concentration when $T \ll m$ is

$$n_{eq} \approx \left(\frac{2}{N}\right)^{2/3} \frac{mT}{2\pi} e^{-\frac{m-M/3}{T}}. \tag{4}$$

This equation reminds one of the Saha equation, but for a system of three particles. The kinetic equation has the form

$$\frac{dn}{dt} \approx v\sigma_2 N (n_{eq}^2 - n^2), \tag{5}$$

where v is the mean velocity, σ_2 the cross section for collision of two quarks, antiquarks or diquarks, leading to a reduction of the number of such particles by unity. The factor N appears because the quark concentration expressed in cm^{-3} is $C_q = nN$. It is clear that C_q changes both because of reactions and because of the general expansion, whereas n changes only because of reaction. The time for establishing equilibrium is $\tau \approx (v\sigma_2 N n_{eq})^{-1}$.

In order to determine the moment of "quenching", we must compare the time τ with the characteristic time for change of n_{eq} because of the expansion, described by formula (3). This characteristic time t_1 is gotten from the condition

$$t_1^{-1} = \frac{d \ln n_{eq}}{dt} \approx \frac{m}{T}\frac{1}{2t} = \frac{1}{2\theta t}, \tag{6}$$

where we use (4) and $T \sim t^{-1/2}$ from (3). The quantity $\theta = T/m$. (We neglect the change in the factor multiplying the exponential in (4).)

The whole period of expansion can be divided into two stages. In the first $t < t_1$ and $n \approx n_{eq}$. In the second stage $t > t_1$, $n > n_{eq}$ and one can neglect the creation of new quarks. At the time t_0 separating the two stages, one can approximately set $n \approx 2n_{eq}(t)$. Integration of the equation

$$\frac{dn}{dt} = -v\sigma_2 N n^2 \tag{7}$$

from t_0 gives for the relative concentration after "quenching" the expression

$$\frac{1}{n(\infty)} = \int_{t_0}^{\infty} v\sigma_2 N\, dt \approx 2\sigma_2 v N_0 t_0. \tag{8}$$

The last result is obtained if we use the relation $N = N_0(t_0/t)^{3/2}$ (cf. (3)) and $\sigma_2 v = \text{const}$. Using t_0 from (3), we rewrite (8) in the form

$$n(\infty) = \sqrt{\frac{32\pi a}{3}} \frac{\sqrt{G}}{\sigma_2 v T_0 h_0^{1/2}} \frac{h_0 T_0^3}{N_0} = \sqrt{\frac{32\pi a}{3}} \frac{\sqrt{G}}{\sigma_2 v T_0} \left(\frac{h^2}{h_0}\right)^{1/2} \frac{T^3}{N}, \tag{9}$$

where T is the temperature of the radiation remaining at the present time (the expansion is assumed to be isentropic) while N is the average nucleon density at the present time. The value $h \approx 3$ refers to the time when only quanta and the two kinds of neutrino pairs were left, ν_e, $\bar{\nu}_e$, ν_μ, $\bar{\nu}_\mu$; $h_0 \approx 9$.

In units of the nucleon mass M we may take $\sigma_2 v \approx M^{-2}$, $T_0 \approx M$ (cf. below), $G = 0.6 \times 10^{-38} M^{-2}$. It then follows that

$$n(\infty) \approx 6 \cdot 10^{-19} \left(\frac{T^3}{M}\right). \tag{10}$$

Basically the low concentration of quarks is a consequence of the smallness of the gravitational forces. To give a dimensionless characteristic of the gravitational interaction, we must write $GM^2/\hbar c$ (M is the nucleon mass), by analogy with $e^2/\hbar c$, the fine structure constant. It is qualitatively easy to understand why the weakness of the gravitational interaction results in a low concentration: the rate of expansion in the initial stages must be chosen so that the kinetic energy of expansion overcame the gravitational attraction and enabled the material to go over from the value $\rho = \infty$ to the present value $\bar{\rho} = 10^{-30}$. The weakness of gravitation means a slow expansion and produces the conditions for the death of quarks.

On the other hand, the higher the temperature and entropy, the more different particles (quanta, e^+, e^- pairs, etc) appear per nucleon; in a more dilute system the quarks collide and die more infrequently, and the concentration of quarks per nucleon is higher.

The value of T^3/N taken per nucleon is now known with a very large uncertainty. If $T \approx 1°$, while $N \approx 2 \times 10^{-7}$ cm^{-3}, which corresponds to the lower limit of the density including some galaxies (cf.[30] with reduction to the Hubble constant $H = 100$ km/sec-Mps), then $T^3/N \approx 10^9$. This corresponds to a hot model of the universe. Direct measurements of the metagalactic background radio emission lead to the conclusion that $T < 3°$K.* But the

*The latest information, obtained by measuring radio noise at 7 cm, favors the value $T \sim 4$ °K.[47]

value $T^3/N \approx 1$ does not contradict the observations. Such a small entropy corresponds to a model with initially cold matter consisting of free quarks and nucleons.* Thus, depending on the value of T^3/N, one can have a quark concentration after the primary expansion of 10^{-9}—10^{-18}. It should be emphasized that these numbers are rough estimates. In particular they may change drastically if we include inhomogeneity and anisotropy.

Let us now fix the values of T_0 and t_0, which are determined from the equation

$$(v\sigma_2 N n_{eq})^{-1} = 2\theta t \qquad (11)$$

or

$$\theta e^{-\frac{1}{\theta}} \approx \sqrt{\frac{32\pi a}{3}} \frac{G^{1/2} s^{1/3}}{v\sigma_2 m} \left(\frac{h}{h_0}\right)^{1/3} \approx 5 \cdot 10^{-16}, \qquad (12)$$

if $s \approx 10^9$. From this it follows that $\theta \approx 1/30$. If the quark mass is $m \approx 10$ GeV, the freezing temperature $T_0 \sim 300$ MeV, and the time of the freeze $t_0 \approx G^{-1/2} T_0^{-2} \approx 10^{-5}$ sec. From (8) and (10) it follows that the value of T and consequently also of $n(\infty)$ are weakly dependent on the quark mass m. The point is that although the equilibrium concentration n_{eq} depends exponentially on m and T, the reaction rate itself depends on n_{eq}. Thus the time t_0 turns out always to correspond to a definite n, which depends on m only algebraically.

The whole process of freezing is completed at a temperature above 100 MeV, so that Coulomb barriers and Coulomb attraction of the quarks to nucleons play no part in the estimate of $v\sigma_2$, characterizing the cross section for the reaction between two quarks. Under these conditions nuclei do not exist.

4. CONSERVATION OF QUARKS DURING THE EVOLUTION OF THE GALAXY

Earlier we estimated the burnup of quarks during the first microseconds of the Friedmann expansion Now let us consider how the quark content must change during the process of further evolution of matter. This problem is of such great interest because an improvement of the upper limit for the quark content could give some limitations on the choice of cosmological models.

According to the present cosmological pictures, the primary gas developed condensations which, gradually coalescing, gave the first galaxies. The gas in the galaxies changed into stars, of which the more massive ones went through their evolution rapidly, ejected part of the gas, enriched in heavy elements, into interstellar space. In our Galaxy more than 98% of the gas has already been converted into stars. In the stars the process of burnup of the quarks in pair collisions has continued. But now the Coulomb interaction between quarks and nuclei and between the quarks themselves begins to be important.

For a Maxwell distribution the number of reactions per cm^3 per sec is (cf., for example,[32])

$$C_1 C_2 F_{12} = C_{12} C_1 C_2 \left(\frac{Z_1 Z_2}{A_{12}}\right)^{1/3} T^{-2/3} e^{-3\left(\frac{\pi^2}{2} \alpha^2 Z_1^2 Z_2^2 \frac{m_{12}}{T}\right)^{1/3}}, \qquad (13)$$

where m_{12} is the reduced mass of the particles, A_{12} is the same quantity in fractions of the proton mass, $\alpha = 1/137$, $C_{1,2}$ are the particle concentrations, C_{12} is a constant for the particular reaction. If we take as the reaction cross section parameter that for deuterium and express T in ergs, $C_{12} \approx 2 \times 10^{-20}$. From equations of the type of (7) and from (13) we find the concentration of the remaining quarks

$$C(t) \approx \frac{2}{F_{qq}(t)}, \qquad (14)$$

if, of course, the initial concentration was higher.

For quarks with $Z = +2/3$ and $A \approx 5$ the concentration after 10^9 years for $T = 10^6$ °K will be $C_q \leq 10^{15}\,cm^{-3}$, which amounts to 10^{-9} of the hydrogen concentration in the Sun's layers at this temperature. At higher temperatures the consumption of quarks increases markedly. For $T = 10^7$ °K, $C_q \lesssim 10^6\,cm^{-3}$, i.e., 10^{-18} per gram in the corresponding layers.

For quarks with $Z = -1/3$, it follows from (13) that burnup occurs much faster. But these quarks can combine with nuclei to form a stable system. The charge of the quark-proton system is $+(2/3)e$ and the burnup of the quarks should now occur at approximately the same rate as for the case treated above. But at temperatures where annihilation is possible, the quarks will first be detached from the protons and joined to He or heavier nuclei. The burnup will already be unimportant in this case because of the large values of Z and A. We make a quantitative estimate.

The binding energy of a quark to a nucleus is $Q = 2.76\, Z_n^2 A$ keV, where Z_n is the charge number of the nucleus and A is the reduced mass of the system in units of the proton mass. According to the Saha formula, the relative concentration of free and bound quarks is

$$\frac{C_q}{C_{qn}} = \frac{1}{C_n}\left(\frac{A m_n T}{2\pi}\right)^{3/2} e^{-Q/T}.$$

At $T = 10^6$ °K the concentration of quarks attached to protons is 10^9 times as great as that of the free quarks. But equilibrium is reached after 10^{-4}—10^{-5} sec, so that even with a small fraction of free quarks, after $t \sim 10^5$ sec they all go over to the heavier nuclei, in this case He. At higher temperatures the quarks will separate from the He but will attach to heavier elements. In all cases the time for

*It was already pointed out in[45] that in theories in which the baryons are regarded as composites, at sufficiently high density one cannot regard the gas as consisting of the experimentally known particles (p,N,Λ, Σ, Ξ). One must instead speak of a gas of the "really" elementary particles, the p,N,Λ of the Sakata model, or the quarks, according to the present view.

going over to the heavier nuclei is much less than the burnup time.

At $T = 10^7$°K the fraction of quarks attaching to He is 10^9 times greater than that of the free quarks. Using the concentrations of C, N, and O one can estimate that the time for all the quarks to go over to these nuclei is less than 10^7 sec. Detachment from these nuclei requires a very high temperature. For example, for $T = 5 \times 10^7$°K, which exceeds the temperature in the interior of stars of the main sequence, the fraction of free quarks as compared with the quarks attached to O is 10^{-100}. Thus, transfer to heavier nuclei such as Fe practically does not occur; the fractions of Fe and O atoms having quarks are the same, but the Fe content is small compared to the O. If during explosion the temperature is raised above 10^9, the quarks go over to the Fe.

Summarizing, we may say that quarks with $Z = +\frac{2}{3}$ impinging on a star are largely annihilated; the concentration stays less than 10^{-18} per gram. Only those are left that stayed on the surface all the time. This is possible in stars having no convective zone, but since in the early and late stages almost all stars are convective, retention is improbable. Quarks with $Z = -\frac{1}{3}$, falling into a star, attach to the elements C, N, O and heavier ones. One should therefore look for spectra of atoms and molecules with C, N, O, and heavier atoms, whose nuclei contain quarks. The atomic spectra should differ from the usual ones because of the change in the nuclear charge (the isotope shift is small) while the molecular spectra will be different because of the change in the vibration-rotation parameters of the system.

We now consider the quarks which do not remain in stars. They should either be free ($Z = +\frac{2}{3}$) or attached to hydrogen ($Z = -\frac{1}{3}$). We should mention that in the interstellar gas quarks and quark nuclei should attach to dust particles because of the presence of the charge. Thus their lines may also not be present in the spectrum of instellar gas. Besides, the present methods of investigating the instellar medium cannot in general give information about elements with low concentration.

We now estimate the probability that during the process of formation of the galaxy and the building up of stars no quarks entered the stars. In each process of star formation about half the condensing gas is converted into stars of low mass, which evolve slowly. The other half is converted into massive stars which go through their cycle rapidly and finally eject about half their mass into the interstellar space. The remainder collapses or forms a superdense star. Let us assume that $\frac{1}{4}$ of the mass converted initially into stars is again ejected into the interstellar gas and mixes with the residue of the primary gas, after which star formation proceeds once more (cf., for example, the survey [33]). Such a gradual emission of gas is indicated by the gradual change in the chemical composition of stars and clusters with changes in their spatial and kinematic characteristics. Suppose that the fraction α of all the remaining gas is converted into stars in one cycle. This quantity is unknown; it may be of the order of 0.1—0.3, but its precise value is irrelevant. After n cycles, $(1 - \frac{3}{4}\alpha)^n$ of the gas remains, of which the fraction $a = [1 - \alpha/1 - (3\alpha/4)]^n$ did not pass through the star stage. At the present time 2% of the initial mass of the Galaxy is left in the form of gas. Thus $n\alpha \approx 5$ and $a \approx 0.25$—0.20 over the wide range of values of α from 0.1 to 0.3. Despite its naiveté, the computation shows that the gas in interstellar space should contain a considerable admixture of the original gas, and consequently the percentage content of quarks in the interstellar gas should be 10—20% of the initial value. As already pointed out, however, to detect them there is hardly possible.

The best conditions for experimental detection occur on planets like the earth. The solar system apparently was formed during the process of contraction of a nebula whose central part became the sun. The planets, in particular the inner ones, were formed mainly from dust.[34,35] Thus the fraction of quarks in them should be reasonable. During the period of formation of the earth, the temperature of the main mass of the sun must have been low, since this was still during the stage of compression. The physical conditions during this period have not been carefully studied; it is difficult to judge the probability of mixing with deep layers and annihilation of quarks, if they have positive charge. The negative quarks would have gone into He nuclei or heavier elements. It is more probable, however, that there was no significant burnup, since $T \sim 10^6$ deg was attained only at the very center of the condensing sun, while the envelope was mainly convective. In addition the gas around the earth was rarefied, and did not completely draw away the dust out of which the Earth was formed. Thus, if the quarks are negative they should be sought in hydrogen or heavier elements, and their content in these should be comparable to the initial value; if they are positive, their content can be either large or small, depending on the conditions of convection on the sun during the period of formation of the earth.

We should mention that the farther a planet is from the sun, the higher the probability that quarks are retained in it. Meteorites that are the products of decay of comets are of great interest from this point of view. According to present notions, comets are retained on the periphery of the solar system, go over under the influence of perturbations into orbits closer to the sun, after which they gradually disintegrate.[36] Meteorites from such comets in all probability were not in the depths of the Sun during the period of formation of the solar system.

Since the annihilation of positive quarks occurs

under the same conditions as the burning of deuterium, the deuterium content should serve as a check. However, its paucity on Earth is explained, as already mentioned, by the activity of the sun during the period of condensation, when many of the cosmic rays were formed.

5. POSSIBLE WAYS OF SEARCHING FOR NEW PARTICLES

In searching for new particles one should consider the possibility of enriching or depleting samples by taking advantage of their physico-chemical properties.* Let us therefore consider some of the physico-chemical properties of the quarks and the hypothetical stable particles with integer charge, and discuss possible ways of searching for these particles.

Particles with integral charge $Z = +1 (i^+)$ do not differ physico-chemically from the hydrogen isotopes. They are concentrated during the production of heavy water. Mass spectrometric investigation of heavy water samples gives a relative concentration $C < 10^{-10}$ based on hydrogen in the original water (before separation).[37,38] There is an important possibility of lowering this limit by several factors of ten. Optical spectroscopic methods for detecting such "hydrogen" under terrestrial conditions are not as good as the mass spectroscopic method. Optical searches extraterrestrially, using the isotope shift, are also very difficult, since the isotope shift is usually very much smaller than the line width. The example of the search for deuterium in the sun's spectrum shows that the sensitivity is no better than 10^{-3} of the content of the main isotope.[39] The molecular spectrum of hydrides depends strongly on the masses of the atoms, but is is observed only within a narrow interval of spectral classes, limited above by molecular dissociation and below by the low luminous intensity of stars.

The particles with integral charge $Z = -1 (i^-)$, in particular, the antiparticles of the preceding ones, are created by energetic cosmic rays in the atmosphere, attach to nuclei in the atmosphere, jump from the protons to heavier nuclei, as in the case of μ^--mesic atoms. It is natural to look for them among the isotopes of carbon (N, i^-), nitrogen (O, i^-) and oxygen (F, i^-). Such atoms are formed as the result of reactions like $O + p, i^- \rightarrow F, i^- + \gamma$. Their binding energy of such nuclei is of the order of several MeV.

The $q^{+2/3}$ or $q^{-1/3}$ quark (depending on which one is the lighter) and the corresponding antiquark are stable and can accumulate in the earth. Atoms containing the quarks have an uncompensated electric charge and behave like ions. Solvation of the ions in polar solutions practically excludes the possibility of evaporation from water of the quarks or of molecules containing quarks. One can cite the example of the Li^+, Na^+, F^+ and Cl^+ ions. All these ions have a noble gas structure, and their solubility in water is small. But the charge on the ions gives an energy of solvation of the order of 1.5 eV, which makes it impossible to drive them out of solution. For quarks the energy of solvation is lower in the ratio Z or Z^2, i.e. it is of order 0.5—1 eV for $Z = 2/3$ and 0.2—0.5 eV for $Z = -1/3$. At 100°C the corresponding value of $e^{-Q/T}$ is $10^{-14} - 10^{-17}$ in the first case and 10^{-3}—10^{-7} in the second. The nonvolatility of the quarks must be considered in mass-spectroscopic searches for them; their concentration in vapors is substantially less than in liquids. Upon distillation of the water the sample is purified of quarks. The experiments of Kohlrausch on the electrical conductivity of pure water[40] apparently give a relative concentration of quarks less than 10^{-9}. Because of our earlier remarks, this estimate is even worse for ordinary water.

Ions containing quarks should be adsorbed from nonpolar materials (petroleums, oils) onto the surface of minerals containing petroleum, or onto filters or the glass and metallic walls of vessels containing oil. Loss of quarks during purification of oil should be considered in interpreting the Millikan experiment, which indicates a relative concentration below 10^{-15}.

The technique of accurate determination of very small periodic forces, which has been successfully developed by V. B. Braginskiĭ,[41] has been proposed by him for use in detecting single fractional charges in samples weighing 10^{-4} g, placed in a periodic electric field. This corresponds to a sensitivity of 10^{-19}.

The optical spectra of atoms containing quarks should be very characteristic. The L_α lines for $(q^{+2/3}e^-)$ and $(q^{-1/3}pe^-)$ atoms fall in the near ultraviolet $\lambda = 2750$ Å. The Hubble red shift for distant galaxies and quasars shifts this line to a convenient region for observation. Atoms of C, N, O, and Fe, which have a quark attached to their nuclei, should have spectra altogether different from the usual spectra of these elements, since all the screening parameters of the electron shells are changed. Calculation of the spectra of such atoms represents a definite quantum mechanical problem. After the calculations have been made, one must make a serious search for these lines and also for the $\lambda = 2750$ Å line and molecular lines for unusual masses* in the spectra of various cosmic objects, entirely independently of all estimates of quark concentrations, which at present pretend to be reliable.

*In principle it is impossible, for example, to exclude the possibility of biological concentration of quarks by some organisms.

*For the analogous proposals for positronium and antipositronium cf.[42,43]

6. CONCLUSION

One of the main questions arising in connection with the possible existence of new stable particles, and quarks in particular, is why these particles have so far not been seen by us in nature. As the above arguments show, this is not at all surprising. In the process of the primary Friedmann expansion quarks were consumed extensively and changed into nucleons; their concentration becomes of order 10^{-9}—10^{-18} per nucleon, even if the quarks and nucleons had the same initial concentrations. If the positively charged quarks are lightest, and consequently stable, their burnup continues in the interior of stars. The negatively charged quarks are "conserved," attaching themselves to nuclei. Thus the fact that quarks have so far not been seen can be regarded as an argument that the positive quarks are the stable ones. One should however remember that in the process of evolution part of the matter does not go through the stage of being part of a star, and preserves the quark concentration which was left after the initial stage of the Friedmann expansion.

In searching for thermalized quarks under terrestrial conditions one should take account of their physico-chemical peculiarities, such as solvation in water solutions and precipitation on the walls in nonpolar solvents. Under laboratory conditions the best methods for searching for quarks are to measure the elementary charges on macroscopic bodies and to use mass spectrometry. The latter method is especially effective in looking for new particles with integral charge. Optical spectroscopy can be used for quarks in extraterrestrial objects.

[1] M. Gell-Mann, Phys. Letters 8, 214 (1964).

[2] G. Zweig, preprint CERN 8182 TH/401, 1964.

[3] Gürsey, Lee, and Nauenberg, Phys. Rev. **B135**, 467 (1964).

[4] P. Franzini and J. Lee-Franzini, Phys. Rev. Letters 12, 602 (1964).

[5] M. Gell-Mann, Physics 1, 63 (1964).

[6] T. D. Lee, Nuovo Cimento 35, 933 (1965).

[7] L. B. Okun', Ya. F (U.S.S.R.) 1, 297 (1965), Soviet JNP 1, 211 (1965).

[8] Ya. B. Zel'dovich, JETP Letters 1, No. 4 (1965), transl. 1, 103 (1965).

[9] L. B. Okun', JETP 11, 1773 (1964) [sic !].

[10] R. Adair, Coral Gables Conf. on Symmetry Principles, W. H. Freeman, 1964, p. 36.

[11] Leipuner, Chu, Larsen, and Adair, Phys. Rev. Letters 12, 423 (1964)

[12] D. R. O. Morrison, Phys. Letters 9, 199 (1964).

[13] H. H. Bingham et al., Phys. Letters 9, 201 (1964).

[14] V. Hagopian et al., Phys. Rev. Letters 13, 280 (1964).

[15] W. Blum et al., Phys. Rev. Letters 13, 353a (1964).

[16] P. Franzini et al., Phys. Rev. Letters 14, 196 (1965).

[17] L. Gilly et al, Proc Rochester Conf. 1960, p. 808.

[18] VonDardel, Mermod, Weber, and Winter, Proc. Rochester Conf. 1960, p. 836.

[19] V. T. Cocconi et al, Phys. Rev. Letters 5, 19 (1960).

[20] W. F. Baker et al., Phys. Rev. Letters 7, 101 (1961).

[21] Bowen, Lise, Kalbach and Mortara, Phys. Rev. Letters 13, 728 (1964).

[22] Sunyar, Schwarzschild and Connors, Phys. Rev. **136**, B1157 (1964).

[23] Jugaku, Sargent and Greenstein, Astrophys. J. **134**, 783 (1961).

[24] Burbidge, Burbidge, Fowler and Hoyle, Revs. Modern Phys. 29, 547 (1957); D. Layzer, Phys. Rev. Letters 15, (1965). Ginzburg, Ozernoĭ and Syrovatskiĭ, DAN SSSR **154**, 557 (1963) Soviet Phys. Doklady 9, 3 (1964); Ginzburg, Ozernoĭ and Syrovat-skiĭ, Quasistellar Sources and Gravitational Collapse, Univ. of Chicago, 1965, p. 937.

[25] Ya. B. Zel'dovich, UFN 80, 357 (1963), Soviet Phys. Uspekhi 6, 475 (1964).

[26] W. H. McCrea, Z. Astrophys. 18, 98 (1939).

[27] A. L. Zel'manov, Reports on the Sixth Conference on Problems of Cosmogony, Moscow, Academy of Sciences, USSR, 1959.

[28] G. Gamow, Phys. Rev. **70**, 572 (1946).

[29] Ya. B. Zel'dovich, Advances in Astron. and Astrophys. 3, p. 241, Academic Press, 1965.

[30] Turtle, Pugh, Kenderdine and Pauliny-Toth, Monthly Not. **124**, 297 (1962).

[31] C. W. Allen, Astrophysical Quantities, University of London, Athlone Press, 1955, p. 298; E. Ohm, Bell System Tech. J. **40**, 1065 (1961); De Grasse, Hogg, Ohm and Scovil, J. Appl. Phys. 30, 2013 (1959).

[32] M. Schwarzschild, Structure and Evolution of the Stars, Princeton, 1958.

[33] S. A. Kaplan and S. B. Pikel'ner, Mezhzvezdnaya sreda (The Interstellar Medium) Moscow, Fizmatgiz, 1963.

[34] O. Yu. Shmidt, Chetyre lektsii o teorii proiskhozhdeniya Zemli (Four Lectures on the Origin of the Earth), Moscow, 1950.

[35] H. C. Urey, The Planets, USA, 1952.

[36] J. H. Oort, BAN 11, No. 408, 91 (1960).

[37] Sherr, Smith and Bleakney, Phys. Rev. **54**, 388 (1938).

[38] Kukavadze, Memelova and Suvorov, preprint ITEP, 1965.

[39] A. B. Severnyĭ, Astron. Zh. 34, 328 (1957), Soviet Astron. AJ 1, 324 (1957).

[40] H. Remy, Treatise on Inorganic Chemistry, N.Y., Elsevier, 1956, vol. 1, p. 49.

[41] V. B. Braginskiĭ, UFN **86**, 433 (1965), Soviet Phys. Uspekhi 8, 513 (1965); PTÉ No. 3, 130 (1964).

[42] S. Mohorovicic, Astron. Nachr. 259, 94 (1934).

[43] N. A. Vlasov, Astron. Zh. 41, 893 (1964).
[44] F. Hoyle and A. Tuler, Nature 224, 1000 (1965).
[45] Ya. B. Zel'dovich, JETP 37, 569 (1959), Soviet Phys.-JETP 10, 403 (1960)
[46] Ya. B. Zel'dovich, JETP Letters 1, No. 4, 1 (1965), transl. 1, 103 (1965).
[47] Scientific American 213, No. 1, p. 44, July, 1965, editorial comment.
[48] Ya. B. Zel'dovich, UFN 86, 303 (1965), Soviet Phys. Uspekhi 8, 489 (1965).

Translated by M. Hamermesh

VOLUME 18, NUMBER 15 PHYSICAL REVIEW LETTERS 10 APRIL 1967

SEARCH FOR QUARKS

J. J. de Swart*
Department of Physics, University of Pittsburgh, Pittsburgh, Pennsylvania
(Received 16 March 1967)

The quark is probably unstable with respect to strong interactions. It is possible that the stable particle with nonintegral charge has a charge $|Q| > \frac{2}{3}$.

Two objections[1] heard quite often against the realistic quark model[2] are the following: (1) Despite the large efforts of the experimentalists,[3] the quarks are not found yet. (2) It is very difficult to find a mechanism[4] which will explain the low-lying triality-zero ($t = 0$) states, such as the mesons ($q\bar{q}$) and the baryons (qqq), and which prevents other quark and antiquark combinations with $t \neq 0$ (nonintegral charge) to be low lying.

We would like to point out[5] [part (a)] that there do exist perhaps relatively low-lying $t \neq 0$ states which have masses lower than the quark mass M. The stable state with $t \neq 0$ can have a charge larger than $\frac{2}{3}$, for example $\frac{4}{3}$, 5/3, 7/3, or 8/3 [part (b)]. All the other $t \neq 0$ particles can perhaps decay quite rapidly into this state [part (c)]. This could perhaps[6] account for the fact that particles with nonintegral charge have not been found yet. The experimentalists, therefore, should not only look for $|Q| = \frac{1}{3}$ and $\frac{2}{3}$ charged states, but also search for particles with the charges $|Q| = \frac{4}{3}$, 5/3, 7/3, and 8/3, or perhaps even larger charges.

(a) The existence of $t \neq 0$ particles with mass lower than the quark mass M will be made plausible with a solution of the saturation problem as proposed[7] by Schiff. This is only a qualitative argument and could very well be quantitatively wrong or just plain wrong. Our conclusion is, however, independent of this specific model.

Assuming attractive two-body forces and repulsive three-body forces one can give rough expressions for the masses of the ($nq, m\bar{q}$) combinations. These are the following:

$$M(q) = M, \quad M(q\bar{q}) = 2M - \bar{V}_2,$$
$$M(2q) = 2M - V_2, \quad M(2q\bar{q}) = 3M - V_2 - 2\bar{V}_2 + \bar{V}_3,$$
$$M(3q) = 3M - 3V_2 + V_3,$$
$$M(3q\bar{q}) = 4M - 3V_2 - 3\bar{V}_2 + V_3 + 3\bar{V}_3,$$
$$M(4q) = 4M - 6V_2 + 4V_3,$$

where M is the average quark mass; $-V_2$, $-\bar{V}_2$, V_3, and $\bar{V}_3$ are the expectation values of the two-body qq and $q\bar{q}$ potential and of the three-body qqq and $qq\bar{q}$ potential. If we assume the potential strengths to be such that

$$V_2 = 2M(1 - \tfrac{1}{2}\epsilon), \quad \bar{V}_2 = 2M,$$
$$V_3 = 3M(1 - \epsilon), \quad \bar{V}_3 = 3M(1 + \tfrac{1}{3}(\eta - \epsilon))$$

then $M(q) = M$, $M(3q) = M(q\bar{q}) = 0$, $M(2q) = \epsilon M$, $M(4q) = 4M(1 - \frac{3}{2}\epsilon)$, $M(2q\bar{q}) = \eta M$, and $M(3q\bar{q}) = 4M[1 + \frac{3}{4}(\eta - c)]$. If $0 < c < \frac{2}{3}$ and $\eta > 0$, then we obtain very-low-lying mesons and baryons and all the other masses are positive. One notices that $M(2q) < M$ always, $M(4q) < M$ if $\frac{1}{2} < \epsilon < \frac{2}{3}$, and $M(2q\bar{q}) < M$ if $\eta < 1$. There are therefore several possibilities for states to exist with $t \neq 0$ and a mass substantially lower than the quark mass. In such a case the quarks will be unstable with respect to strong interactions. It is very hard to guess what will be the stable state with $t \neq 0$. Possible[8] candidates are $q = (q)$, $D = (2q)$, $Q = (4q)$, $T = (2q\bar{q})$, and $F = (3q\bar{q})$. If these particles have a sufficiently lower mass than the quark, there will exist the strong decays $q \to \bar{D}$, or $\bar{F}$ + baryon; $q \to Q$ + antibaryon; and $q \to T$ + meson.

(b) What will be the charge of the stable $t \neq 0$ particle? This will depend on the detailed nature of the forces, which we unfortunately do not know. But we can say some general things. Assume that the two-quark combination D has the lowest mass. From the fact that the baryons belong to the irreducible representation (I.R.) {56} with $L^P = 0^+$ of SU(6)⊗O(3), one concludes that the qq forces are the strongest in the totally symmetric spin-unitary spin configuration. One would therefore expect D to belong to the I.R. {21} with $L^P = 1^-$ of SU(6) ⊗ O(3). This I.R. contains a $S = 1$ particle belonging to the I.R. {6} of SU(3) and a $S = 0$ particle belonging to the I.R. {3*}. If the I.R. {6} is the lowest (qq) state, then the stable one of these will probably have[9] $B = Y = \frac{2}{3}$, $I = I_3 = 1$, and therefore $Q = \frac{4}{3}$. The spin-parity J^P ($\vec{J} = \vec{L} + \vec{S}$) could be 0^-, 1^-, or 2^-. Of course it was just an assumption that D was the lowest $t \neq 0$ state. It could very well be any of the particles

q, D, Q, T, or F. The charge of the stable $t \neq 0$ particle could therefore be $|Q| = \frac{1}{3}$, $\frac{2}{3}$, $\frac{4}{3}$, 5/3, 7/3, or 8/3.

(c) What will be the lifetime of the particles belonging to the same supermultiplet as the stable particle? The mass differences between the isomultiplets with different strangeness are perhaps large enough for strong decay with the emission of a K meson, or if this is energetically impossible, for a relatively fast weak decay with the emission of π mesons. Within the same isomultiplet the mass differences are of electromagnetic origin and supposedly smaller than between different isomultiplets. If one assumes for the electromagnetic mass differences ΔM that $\Delta M/M$ is roughly a constant (M is the average mass of the particles) for all the isomultiplets, then from the $\frac{1}{2}^+$ baryon octet[10] we get $\Delta M/M \simeq (0.2\text{-}0.5)\%$, and from the 0^- meson octet $\Delta M/M \simeq (0.8\text{-}3.0)\%$.

The lifetime for decay of a spin-$\frac{1}{2}$ particle with weak interactions similar to the neutron[11] is

$$\tau = \frac{60\pi^3}{G_V^{\;2} + 3G_A^{\;2}} \frac{1}{E_m^{\;5}} = \frac{2340}{E_m^{\;5}} \text{ sec},$$

where E_m is the maximum energy available for the electron in MeV. If we take $\Delta M/M = 1\%$, then

$$\tau = 0.02/M^5 \text{ sec},$$

where M is the mass of the particle in GeV/c^2. We will adopt this as an estimate for the lifetime even if the spin is not $\frac{1}{2}$. For $M = 10$ GeV/c^2, we get then $\tau \simeq 10^{-6}$ to 10^{-7} sec. This is sufficiently short that in most production or cosmic-ray experiments looking for charges $|Q| = \frac{1}{3}$ or $\frac{2}{3}$ these members of the multiplets should not have been seen.

We would like to acknowledge helpful and stimulating discussions with Professor L. Wolfenstein and Professor S. Okubo. Further we would like to thank Dr. R. C. Lamb and Dr. D. D. Yovanovitch for an enlightning discussion about the experiments and Mr. E. Stokke for his much appreciated moral support.

---

*National Science Foundation Senior Foreign Scientist Fellow. On leave from the University of Nijmegen, Nijmegen, The Netherlands.

[1]S. Gasiorowicz, Elementary Particle Physics (John Wiley & Sons, Inc., New York, 1966), p. 278.

[2]This is the model that takes the existence of the quarks seriously. See, e.g., R. H. Dalitz, in Proceedings of the Thirteenth International Conference on High Energy Physics, Berkeley, California, 1966 (to be published).

[3]More references to the experimental literature can be found in R. C. Lamb, R. A. Lundy, T. B. Novey, and D. D. Yovanovitch, Phys. Rev. Letters 17, 1068 (1966); O. Sinanoğlu, B. Skutnik, and R. Tousey, Phys. Rev. Letters 17, 785 (1966); W. A. Chupka, J. P. Schiffer, and C. M. Stevens, Phys. Rev. Letters 17, 60 (1966); H. Kasha, L. B. Leipuner, and R. K. Adair, Phys. Rev. 150, 1140 (1966).

[4]O. W. Greenberg and D. Zwanziger, Phys. Rev. 150, 1177 (1966).

[5]Similar ideas were already expressed by M. Gell-Mann in his original paper about quarks, Phys. Letters 8, 214 (1964). I am indebted to Dr. R. E. Kreps for bringing this to my attention.

[6]The author is aware of the fact that some experiments have looked for all possible nonintegral charges.

[7]L. I. Schiff, Phys. Rev. Letters 17, 612 (1966). We use a special version of this model.

[8]On the basis of the model used the mass of F should not be lower than M. But we do not take the model too seriously and should allow for the possibility that $M_F < M$.

[9]S. Okubo, Phys. Rev. Letters 18, 256 (1967).

[10]For the baryons some suppression is perhaps at work to reduce the electromagnetic mass differences, e.g., see Ref. 1, p. 249.

[11]This formula is not correct for the neutron, because we have approximated the phase space assuming $E_m \gg m_e$ and we have neglected the Coulomb interaction between the electron and the final hadron.

REPRINT 10

Session 10

SYMMETRIES AND THE STRONG INTERACTIONS

R. H. Dalitz, Rapporteur

1. Higher Symmetries?

In 1964, Gursey and Radicati proposed SU(6) symmetry for the strong interactions as a plausible generalization of the established SU(3) symmetry. This proposal was based on analogy with the relationship between the SU(4) spin-isospin symmetry of Wigner, long known in the realm of low-energy nuclear physics, and the SU(2) isospin symmetry previously known there. This SU(6) symmetry quickly found many striking successes in accounting for experimental data on the properties of elementary particle systems.

The precise interpretation to be given to SU(6) symmetry was far from clear, however. This symmetry was based essentially on the static concepts of spin, and the unsatisfactoriness of this treatment of spin appeared to call for some relativistic generalization of the SU(6) symmetry group. Much effort has been given to this endeavor, and for a time there seemed to be hints of great things ahead. By the time of this Conference, the hope for such an all-embracing relativistic generalization had been essentially abandoned. This is illustrated by the rather small number of papers on such endeavors presented to this Conference.

Feldman and Matthews[1] have recently summarized the difficulties faced by any such endeavor:
(i) The Michel-O'Raifertaigh Theorem (Refs. 2, 3). This theorem states that any symmetry group which generalizes SU(3) symmetry and contains the inhomogeneous Lorentz group $\mathcal{P}$--i.e., any symmetry group which contains $\mathcal{P}\times SU(3)$ as a subgroup--necessarily requires that the energy-momentum vector have more than four components.
(ii) The Unitarity Theorem (Refs. 1, 4, 5). It is possible to avoid the above difficulty by combining the four relativistic spinor indices with the SU(3) indices (the natural attempt to use relativistic spin) and by confining attention to those transformations for this combined index which are independent of the momenta. In this situation, index invariance is required for the T matrix [as with the U(12) symmetry, for example, where the index A takes the values 1, 2, $\cdots$, 12]. However, it is then found that this invariance property leads necessarily to a conflict with the unitarity condition, unless the particle multiplets all have infinite dimensionality.
(iii) The Causality Theorem (Ref. 1). If these infinite-dimensional multiplets are degenerate (i.e., the group symmetry holds exactly), then the requirements of causality forbid Fermi statistics (i.e., anticommutation relations for the fields) for all particles, irrespective of their spin.

In this situation, the question is whether any sense can be given to the SU(6) symmetry. There is still one relativistic version, the collinear group[6,7] $SU(6)_W$, which requires only invariance with respect to Lorentz transformations along one particular axis. The rules for calculation with the collinear group seem clear, and there are considerable successes in their use, especially for two-body decay processes and for vertices generally. On the other hand, it is far from clear what this invariance group means in physical terms, i.e., what physical assumptions are being made about the invariance properties of the underlying Lagrangian.

Perhaps this means that it is now necessary to abandon the SU(6) symmetry, despite its qualitative and quantitative successes concerning the spectrum observed for elementary particle states and their decay properties. This is the conclusion which many workers seem to have reached during the past year. However, there is still one further hope of interpreting the successes of SU(6) symmetry as reflecting the existence of some quasi-static, nonrelativistic structure within these elementary particle states, such as is envisaged in the nonrelativistic quark model for them.

2. The Nonrelativistic Quark Model

Here, we shall confine attention to the simplest quark hypothesis, first put forward by Gell-Mann and by Zweig, that there is a basic triplet of quarks, consisting of an isospin doublet and an isospin singlet. For convenience, we use the notation (p, n) for the doublet quarks, and λ for the isosinglet quark. The quantum numbers for the quarks are as follows:

	Q	B	Y
p:	Q = 2 e/3	B = 1/3	Y = 1/3
n:	-e/3	1/3	1/3
λ:	-e/3	1/3	-2/3

The antiquarks are denoted by $\bar{q} = (\bar{p}, \bar{n}, \bar{\lambda})$ and have quantum numbers opposite those for the corresponding quark. The elementary particle states observed are then interpreted as composite systems of quarks and antiquarks. The simplest structure possible for the meson states is $\bar{q}$-q; the simplest structure possible for baryonic states is q-q-q.

The following situation is then possible (but by no means necessarily the case!): If the quarks are very heavy (mass M_q) and interact through a potential (range R) which is smooth (flat-bottomed, without any singular attraction, but possibly with a hard-core repulsion) and very deep (depth V), there are circumstances such that the quark motions in these strong potentials are essentially nonrelativistic, as was pointed out by Morpurgo[8] and by Bogoliubov et al.[9] In such a potential, the characteristic quark momentum is determined by the force range R, and is given by $\hbar/R$ according to the Uncertainty Principle. The condition for the motions to be nonrelativistic is then, simply,

$$\hbar/R \ll M_q c. \qquad (1)$$

If $M_q \gtrsim 10$ GeV, then this condition is satisfied for reasonable values for the force range R, of order 10^{-14} cm.

These bound states are characterized by exceedingly high binding energies, almost sufficient to cancel out the rest masses of the constituent quarks. The important question here is the nature of the relationship between the total energy E of the bound system and the potential depth V. At present, we do not know the proper functional form for this relationship, nor even what form the equation governing the quark motions should take. We can only be sure that the function $V(E^2)$ must have some singular behavior at $E^2 = 0$, and that this function will not be that characteristic of the Schrödinger equation.

This provides us with an unfamiliar situation, but one which has much qualitative correspondence to the pattern of the experimental data, as we shall see. This situation would imply that the "elementary particle" should be regarded as rather analogous to molecules whose constituent atoms are quarks. Such a molecular model appears especially unfamiliar in terms of the conventional ideas of field theory today, but there is nothing inherently self-contradictory about this model. If it works well, then it will be the task of field theory to show how such a model can arise from the basic equations of some field theory. I believe that we should investigate the possibility of such an unfamiliar situation with curiosity--at the least, it will be instructive, providing a concrete illustration of physical effects that will still be directly relevant to more complicated models for the elementary particles.

3. The Search for Quarks

The rough theoretical estimates available for the quark-production cross sections in high-energy collisions were reviewed in the parallel sessions by T. Fulton. Estimates based on the Landau statistical theory have been given by Domokos and Fulton[10] and by Chernavsky et al.[11] for the quark-pair production process

$$N + N \rightarrow N + N + q + \bar{q}. \quad (2)$$

These cross sections fall exponentially with increasing quark mass, and also depend strongly on the temperature T assumed for the "hot pot" resulting from the collision. The values given by Fulton are summarized in Table 10-I; those of Chernavsky et al. are much smaller (about 10^{-13} μb for $M_q = 3$ GeV) and fall off more rapidly with increasing M_q (by five orders of magnitude for each 1 GeV increase in M_q). Chilton et al.[12] have given an estimate based on the peripheral model, which gives much larger cross sections and a much slower fall-off with increasing M_q.

Table 10-I. Rough estimates for the quark-pair production cross section. The entries given here are the revised estimates discussed by T. Fulton in Session 10a of the Conference. (Values in μb.)

	M_q (GeV)	
	3	5
Peripheral model (Chilton et al.[12])	3.5	1.5
Landau statistical model ($T = m_\pi$)	10^{-9}	—
Landau statistical model ($T = 2m_\pi$)	10^{-3}	10^{-10}

The cross sections quoted by Fulton are to be taken as mean values, corresponding to averages over the cosmic ray spectrum for the incident particles. For a useful orientation, we give the counting rate which would then be expected in the setup used by Adair et al. in their cosmic ray search for quarks:

σ_q(μb) =	10^3	10^{-1}	10^{-5}	10^{-7}
Counting rate	1/sec	1/hr	1/yr	1/century

The experimental search for quarks was reviewed by E. Bowen. The accelerator experiments give the most sensitive limits on the mass. The Columbia experiment was sensitive to charge 2 e/3 and obtained an upper limit for the quark-production rate for 30-GeV protons incident on Fe and Be targets. Here the limit on M_q is obtained by normalizing the expected cross section to the observed $\bar{p}$ production in the same situation and assuming a plausible M_q dependence [like $(m_N/m_q)^4$] for the quark-production cross section; this leads to the lower limit, $M_q \geq 4.5$ GeV. Counter experiments sensitive to charge e/3 have also been carried out by Leipuner et al., and have been interpreted as giving the limit $M_q \geq 3$ GeV. A hydrogen bubble chamber experiment has also been carried out, based on an exposure to a 20-GeV/c beam, and gave $n_q/n_\pi \leq 10^{-10}$; this corresponds to a production cross section less than 10^{-5} μb if the quark mass is less than 4 GeV.

The cosmic ray experiments have the advantage of looking at the products of collisions at much higher energies. These experiments consist essentially of ionization measurements for the cosmic ray particles; they determine directly the flux of relativistic particles with charge $|e/3|$ or $|2e/3|$, which we denote by I_q (particle/cm^{2}sec sr). The upper limits obtained for I_q in recent experiments are as follows:

	e/3	2 e/3
Arizona 1966 (Bowen et al.)	$< 6\times10^{-9}$	$<2.5\times10^{-9}$
Brookhaven 1966 (Adair et al.)	$2.6^{+2.1}_{-1.3}\times10^{-9}$	
Argonne 1966 (Lamb et al.)	$< 0.5\times10^{-9}$	$<1.7\times10^{-9}$
CERN 1966	$< 1.5\times10^{-9}$	$<1.4\times10^{-9}$

These experimental results may be summarized by the statement

$$I_q < 1\times10^{-9} \text{ quark cm}^{-2}\text{sec}^{-1}\text{sr}^{-1}.$$

Adair has suggested that, for assumed mass M_q, this result may be expressed as a rough limit on the quark-pair production cross section,

$$M_q = 10 \text{ GeV}, \qquad \bar{\sigma}_q \leq 0.1 \ \mu\text{b},$$

$$M_q = 5 \text{ GeV}, \qquad \bar{\sigma}_q \leq 0.01 \ \mu\text{b},$$

where the production cross section $\bar{\sigma}_q$ is assumed constant for all energies above threshold. These limits lie far above the cross sections $\bar{\sigma}_q$ estimated from the statistical model, for mass values $M_q \geq 5$ GeV; they are comparable to or higher than those from the peripheral model for mass values exceeding about 10 GeV, but these latter calculations are likely to overestimate the production cross sections significantly.

Adair pointed out that if the cosmic ray flux of quarks had had the value I_q for the earth's lifetime of 10^9 years and if all those quarks had been stopped within a depth 300 kg/cm^2 in the earth's surface, then the density N_q of quarks in this surface layer of the earth would be 200 quarks/g, if these quarks were uniformly distributed in this layer. Some macroscopic experiments have already been carried out, using chemical and mass spectroscopic methods, giving rather strong limits,

$$\text{Sea water,} \qquad N_q < 0.25/\text{g},$$

$$\text{Air,} \qquad N_q < 3\times10^{-6}/\text{g}.$$

However, it is not really clear whether the quarks

that stop in the earth's surface are uniformly distributed, or whether they accumulate in some preferred situations. For these reasons, more extensive macroscopic searches for quarks are very desirable.

It was considered at the session that the sensitivity of the cosmic ray searches could still be improved by about two orders of magnitude. On the other hand, the macroscopic methods of search are already beyond that point in sensitivity (although it is not sure that the searches to date have necessarily been exploring the right domains). Macroscopic methods of still greater sensitivity have been proposed and will be tried out in the near future. If the quark-production cross sections are as low as suggested by the estimates based on the statistical model for mass values above 10 GeV, these macroscopic studies offer the greatest hope at present in the search for the quark.

4. The Mesonic States

Here we discuss the interpretation of the data on mesonic states, supposing that these are due to strong binding between quark and antiquark through their mutual potential $\overline{V}(r)$. Various aspects of this model have been discussed by many authors, including Ishida,[13] Iizuka,[14] Sinanoglu,[15] Bogoliubov et al.,[9] Hendry,[16] and Dalitz.[17, 18] This $\overline{q}q$ model allows only singlet and octet states, and it is satisfactory that no mesonic resonances have been established to date which cannot be attributed to the {1} and {8} representations.

We suppose that this $\overline{q}q$ binding arises from some superstrong force $\overline{V}$. The evidence for the mesonic states suggests that this force is almost independent of the spin (σ) and unitary spin (F) of the quarks. It is of interest to remark that this situation would arise naturally if these forces were transmitted by a vector field coupled with the baryon current, as proposed by Fujii.[19] A rough estimate for the strength f of this coupling may be obtained by solving the Bethe-Salpeter equation for two scalar particles of mass M_q, interacting through exchange of a scalar particle of mass m [potential $f^2M_q^2/(\Delta^2-m^2)$] and bound to zero total mass. This calculation[20] leads to values for $f^2/4\pi$ in the range 26 to 27 for various values of m/M_q in the range 0.01 to 0.3. When the inner part of the potential is modified by higher-order effects to a nonsingular form, the appropriate value for $f^2/4\pi$ is still higher. We note that this coupling strength is about an order of magnitude larger than the strength of the universal ρ coupling, for which Sakurai[21] gives the value $f_\rho^2/4\pi \approx 2.5$.

Other forces which may be needed are:

(i) Strong forces with σ and F dependence compatible with SU(6) symmetry. These can be written in the form

$$\overline{V}' = \{(1-\underline{\sigma}\cdot\underline{\overline{\sigma}})(1-F\cdot\overline{F})/36\}\ \overline{v}'(r), \qquad (3)$$

where the first factor represents the SU(6) projection operator, with values 0 for the 35 representation and 1 for the 1 representation.

(ii) Central forces with σ or F dependence, which do not conserve SU(6) symmetry, although still consistent with SU(3) symmetry. These have the forms $\overline{V}_\sigma = \underline{\sigma}\cdot\underline{\overline{\sigma}}\,\overline{v}_\sigma$ and $\overline{V}_F = F\cdot\overline{F}\,\overline{v}_F$.

(iii) Noncentral forces, consistent with SU(3) symmetry. These necessarily do not conserve the SU(6) symmetry. They may have spin-orbit or tensor character, with the forms

$$\overline{V}_{SO} = (\underline{\sigma}+\underline{\overline{\sigma}})\cdot\underline{L}\ \overline{v}_{SO}(r), \qquad (4)$$

$$\overline{V}_T = (\underline{\sigma}\cdot\underline{r}\,\underline{\overline{\sigma}}\cdot\underline{r} - \tfrac{1}{3}\,\underline{\sigma}\cdot\underline{\overline{\sigma}}\ r^2)\overline{v}_T(r). \qquad (5)$$

(iv) Moderately strong SU(3)-breaking interactions, which may also be spin-dependent or noncentral. Here we confine attention to the simplest hypothesis, that the SU(3) breaking is dominated by effects which can be represented by a one-body operator contributing linearly to $(\text{mass})^2$ for the $\overline{q}q$ state, greater for the λ (or $\overline{\lambda}$) quark by amount Δ than for the (n, p) [or $(\overline{n}, \overline{p})$] quarks. These interactions are still compatible with the SU(2) isospin symmetry.

It is not at all clear what equation governs the internal motion in this system. For the sake of discussion, we can start with the Bethe-Salpeter equation and make approximations to this appropriate to a static (nonretarded) potential (as observed in the c. m. frame); we confine attention to two spinless particles, since the potentials $\overline{V}$ chosen have a form such as to lead to nonrelativistic internal motions. We can then integrate out the internal energy variable, which leads us to the Blankenbecler-Sugar equation,

$$(E^2 - \underline{p}^2 - 4M^2)\phi(\underline{p}) = \frac{2M^2}{\sqrt{(4M^2+p^2}} \int V(\underline{p}, \underline{p}')\phi(\underline{p}')d_3\underline{p}'. \qquad (6)$$

This equation is quite akin to the Schrodinger equation, except that it is quadratic in E. We note that this equation does not have singular behavior at $E^2 = 0$, as we expect for the physically appropriate equation. [It is of interest to remark (as was pointed out to me by Dr. N. Dombey and Dr. G. Barton) that the equation

$$(E^2 - \underline{p}^2 - 4M^2)\phi(\underline{p}) = 2E\int V(\underline{p}, \underline{p}')\phi(\underline{p}')d_3\underline{p}'$$

does have singular behavior with respect to E = 0, in that the limit E = 0 can be reached only as the potential becomes infinitely strong. The natural form of the mass formula would not be simple with this equation, but would generally lie intermediate between linear and quadratic. This equation does not seem physically appropriate in that the $\overline{q}q$ potential in the π state would have to be $(m_K/m_\pi)^{1/2} \approx 1.9$ times as strong as that effective in the K state.] The use of Eq. 6 leads naturally to the use of E^2 in the SU(3) mass formula, and in other such mass relationships to be discussed below.

With the interactions listed above, the $\overline{q}q$ states for given spin and parity form nonets. Each set of nine states consists of an {8} and a {1} representation mixed together by the SU(3)-breaking forces. Each nonet can then be characterized by three parameters, m_1 = mass of the unitary pure {1} state, m_8 = mass of the unitary pure {8} state, and Δ. The masses of these nine states then satisfy the Schwinger relation obtained by eliminating these three parameters,

$$M_0'^2 - M_1^2)(M_0''^2 - M_1^2) - \tfrac{4}{3}(M_K^2 - M_1^2)(M_0'^2 + M_0''^2 - 2M_K^2)$$
$$= \tfrac{8}{9}(M_K^2 - M_1^2)^2(1 - \vartheta^2), \qquad (7)$$

where M_0', M_0'' denote the physical masses of the two I = 0, Y = 0 states, M_1 the mass of the I = 1, Y = 0 state, and M_K the mass of the I = 1/2, Y = ±1 states. The symbol ϑ denotes the spin-space overlap integral between the unitary pure singlet and octet states; $\vartheta = 1$ for the ideal nonet (for which $m_1 = m_8$).

The vector mesons appear to represent an almost ideal nonet. Their mass values satisfy the Schwinger relation with $\vartheta \approx 1$. The mass values m_1 = 810 MeV and m_8 = 769 MeV are not far from equality, so that we conclude that the potential $\overline{V}_F$ is rather small. The value of Δ is given by $(K^{*2} - \rho^2) = 2.0\times 10^5\ (\text{MeV})^2$. The isosinglet states

ϕ, ω are given by

$$\omega = \cos\theta_V \omega_1 + \sin\theta_V \phi_8,$$

$$\phi = -\sin\theta_V \omega_1 + \cos\theta_V \phi_8,$$

where the mixing angle θ_V has the value $\theta_V \approx 40°$.

The pseudoscalar mesons do not form an ideal nonet, presumably because the η' meson lies relatively far in mass from the other members of the nonet. The Schwinger relation requires $\vartheta \approx 0.68$, and the mass parameters are $m_1 = 828$ MeV, $m_8 = 140$ MeV. Since the η' mass lies among the vector meson masses, we conclude that the spin-dependent forces cannot be large. The estimate for Δ is $K^2 - \pi^2 = 2.3 \times 10^5$ (MeV)^2, in good agreement with the value from the vector mesons. The mixing angle obtained from the mass values is $\theta_P \approx -11°$.

The lowest states of the $\overline{q}q$ system are the S states. The lowest nonets observed are the vector and pseudoscalar mesons, and these do have the spin and parity appropriate for identification as the $^3S_1$ and $^1S_0$ states of the $\overline{q}q$ system. We may note here that electromagnetic transitions are possible between the vector and pseudoscalar states, $V \rightarrow P + \gamma$ and $P \rightarrow V + \gamma$, by M1 transition resulting from quark spin flip. Two such transitions are known, empirically, $\omega \rightarrow \pi^0 + \gamma$ and $\eta' \rightarrow \rho + \gamma$. The M1 amplitude for the ω decay has been calculated by many authors[9b,22-24] to have the value μ_p, the total proton magnetic moment, which leads to the prediction $\Gamma(\omega \rightarrow \pi^0\gamma) = 1.18$ MeV. This agrees well with the experimental value, $\Gamma(\omega \rightarrow \pi^0\gamma) = 1.1 \pm 0.15$ MeV, obtained from the full width $\Gamma(\omega) = 12.0 \pm 1.5$ MeV and the branching ratio $(\pi^0\gamma)/(\text{all } \omega \text{ modes}) = 9 \pm 0.4\%$. The radiative decay of the η' meson is well known, with a high branching ratio ($23 \pm 4\%$) relative to the $\eta' \rightarrow \eta\pi\pi$ mode, but no comparison can be made with theory, since the full width $\Gamma(\eta')$ is not known.

It is natural to expect a sequence of rotational levels stemming from these $^3S_1$ and $^1S_0$ nonets, corresponding to the rotation of the $\overline{q}$-q dumbbell in the singlet and triplet spin configurations. The next highest nonets will have L = 1, and therefore positive parity, as is observed for the states clustering around the mass region 1000 to 1400 MeV. The triplet states are $^3P_0$, $^3P_1$, and $^3P_2$, with charge conjugation parity $\mathcal{C} = +1$ for the neutral states with Y = 0; the singlet state is $^1P_1$, with $\mathcal{C} = -1$. With the potential $\overline{V}$ alone, these states would all have the same mass; they are separated into four nonets by the noncentral forces, as indicated for L = 1 in Table 10-II. The I = 1 states of these nonets appear known and are listed on this table. Spin (2++) has been established for the A2 meson. Spin (1+-) is believed to hold for the B meson from the S-wave character of its $\pi\omega$ decay. Spin (1++) has been established for the A1 meson from the characteristics of its $\pi\rho$ decay mode. The spin and parity are not known for the δ meson, since its decay modes have not yet been observed.[25] In the present context, interpretation of the δ meson as representing the $^3P_0$ configuration is the only possibility; this carries the implication that the dominant two-body decay mode is $\delta \rightarrow \eta\pi$. These four I = 1 states then form a sequence with approximately equal spacing in (mass)^2. As shown in Table 10-II, this situation can be interpreted directly as due to a spin-orbit interaction which is repulsive in the state of highest J, and we conclude that any tensor coupling is quite weak relative to the spin-orbit coupling. This interpretation also requires that the octet spin-spin force is rather weak, although such a force appears necessary in the L = 0 states to account for the ρ-π mass difference. This situation is quite possible if the spin-spin force is of short range relative to the dominant potential $\overline{V}$.

Not all the L = 1 nonet states are yet established. The known states are shown on Table 10-III. The spin and parity have not been determined uniquely even for all the established states; however, there is no real ambiguity about fitting the established states into the slots available in these four nonets, once it is assumed that the observed states have positive parity. The $K_C^*(1215)$ and $K^*(1080)$ states are not well established, although evidence for them has been reported.[26] $K^*(1080)$ undergoes decay to $K\pi$, so that the spin-parity can only be (0+) or (2+) (or higher even spin values not appropriate to these nonets); the (2+) K^* entry is already occupied by $K^*(1415)$, so only the assignment (0+) is available. $K_C^*(1215)$ has been observed in the reactions $\overline{p}p \rightarrow K\overline{K}\pi\pi$ and undergoes S-wave decay through the mode ($K\rho$), which requires the assignment (1+) for $K_C^*(1215)$. We note that $\Delta = (M_K^2 - M_1^2)$ has approximately the same value for these four L = 1 nonets, and that this is comparable with the values given above for the L = 0 nonets.

All of the states of the (2++) nonet are established, and Glashow and Socolow[27] have shown that the partial widths observed for the various two-body and three-body decay modes are quite consistent with this interpretation. The mixing angle obtained from the mass values is $\theta_T = 30°$. For each of the other nonets there is one state for which we have no candidate at present, and there are two mesonic states which do not fit naturally into these nonets:

(0++) S meson. There have been many reports in the last few years suggesting the existence of an S-wave $\pi\pi$ resonance (the σ or S meson) at various points in the mass range 350 to 750 MeV,[28-30] but the evidence has generally been rather indirect. A mass value as low as this for the S meson would be compatible with the Schwinger relation, but would require a rather small value for ϑ in the (0++) nonet.

(1++) D' meson. This would have G = +1. For mass values below 1000 MeV, the D' meson lies be-

Table 10-II. The L = 1 configurations and the pattern of their splitting by noncentral forces are compared with the I = 1 mesonic states observed in the mass range 900 to 1300 MeV.

	JPC			
	0++	1++	1+-	2++
Configuration	$^3P_0$	$^3P_1$	$^1P_1$	$^3P_2$
I = 1 meson state	δ(962)	A1(1080)	B(1200)	A2(1300)
Spin-orbit potential	-2	-1	0	+1
Tensor potential	-10	+5	0	-1

Table 10-III. The (I, Y) substates of the four L = 1 nonets. Entries with a single underline represent resonances for which there is some evidence in the literature but which are not yet regarded as established states. Entries with a double underline are purely speculative, and their mass values have been estimated by use of the Schwinger relation with $\mathcal{J} = 1$, appropriate to an ideal nonet; m_1 denotes the unitary singlet mass, after the SU(3)-breaking effects are turned off.

JPC	Nonet states (I, Y)				m_1	Δ
	(1, 0)	(1/2, ±1)	(0, 0)	(0, 0)	(MeV)	$(\text{MeV})^2$
2++	A2(1300)	$K^*(1415)$	f(1254)	f' (1514)	1238	3.1×10^5
1++	A1(1080)	$K_c^*(1215)$	D(1286)	D' (600-1000)?	?	3.1×10^5
0++	$\delta(962)$	$K^*(1080)$	S(1330?)	S' (1060)	1200?	2.4×10^5
1+-	B(1200)	$K^*(1313)$	H(1006)	H' (1385?)	964?	2.8×10^5

low all thresholds for the two-body modes (V + P) and (V + V). The three-body mode $D' \to \eta\pi\pi$ is allowed down to mass value about 830 MeV, as well as electromagnetic processes such as $\rho + \gamma$. It is an interesting conjecture whether or not the $X^0(959)$ may have quantum numbers (1++). In this case, the ninth pseudoscalar meson might be the E(1418) meson, for which the assignment (0-+) appears the most likely;[31] the E-meson mass would fit the Schwinger relation for pseudoscalar mesons better than does the X^0 mass. At present, the assignment (0-) for $X^0(959)$ is most clearly indicated by the angular correlations observed in the decay mode $X^0 \to \rho^0\gamma$; the data fit quite well $\sin^2\theta$, as required for the (0-) assignment, and disagree with $(1 + \cos^2\theta)$, appropriate to the (1+) assignment.[32] It would be desirable to have more evidence on the decay modes of the X^0 meson, especially on the mode $X^0 \to \gamma\gamma$, which would be strictly forbidden with the (1+) assignment.

(1 + -) H' meson. This would have G = -1, and would allow the decay modes $\pi\rho$ and $K\overline{K}^*$ (and $\overline{K}K^*$). The Schwinger mass relation indicates mass value about 1385 MeV for this meson, and it is still just conceivable that E(1418) meson may be this state. The present evidence on angular correlations in E-meson decay are not inconsistent with the assignment (1+), but the assignment $\mathcal{C} = -1$ appears rather unlikely in view of the observed final states $K_1^0K_1^0\pi^0$ and the absence of the final state $K_1^0K_2^0\pi^0$.

More effort will be needed to search for these three missing nonet states. We should emphasize here that the eight states observed for (0++), (1++), and (1+-) are not consistent with an octet structure, so that it is reasonable to expect at least one other resonant state with the same quantum numbers, which completes the octet or whose mixing effects generate the distortion from the octet mass relation in each case. More extensive and more detailed data on the widths and branching ratios of the established states are also needed, in order to test the nonet character of these sets of states.

The E(1418) meson provides a puzzle. To date, it has been observed only in the complicated reaction[31, 33]

$$\overline{p} + p \to E + \pi + \pi \to \overline{K} + K + \pi + \pi + \pi \qquad (8)$$

for antiproton interactions at rest. As mentioned above, the data on the decays $E \to K^0K^0\pi^0$ indicate $\mathcal{C} = +1$ rather strongly; the most probable spin-parity for the E meson is (0-), although (1+) is also acceptable. With (0-+), the E meson represents a tenth pseudoscalar meson; in the $\overline{q}q$ model, this could be assigned only to an excited ${}^1S_0$ state, involving internal radial oscillations. With (1++), the E meson could be assigned only to the (1++) nonet; Shen et al.[34] have explored the possibility that A1(1080), $K^*(1313)$, D(1286), and E(1418) may form a nonet and have found no inconsistencies with the data available; this is not palatable, in terms of the $\overline{q}q$ model, since it upsets the regularity found for Δ, and leaves $K^*(1215)$ (or some other K^* resonance) and B(1200) to be fitted into some other nonet.

Higher I = 1 levels have been investigated, particularly by Focacci et al.,[35, 36] using the missing-mass spectrometer method, for the measurement of the recoil proton spectra from the reaction

$$\pi^- + p \to p + M^- . \qquad (9)$$

The spectra observed show a series of sharp peaks corresponding to the excitation of successive I = 1, Y = 0 mesonic resonances up to mass value about 2400 MeV. It is natural for us to interpret these resonances as representing a sequence of rotational excitations of the $\overline{q}q$ system, with L = 2 for the R mesons with mass values around 1700 MeV, L = 3 for the S mesons at 1930 MeV, L = 4 for the T meson at 2195 MeV, and L = 5 for the U mesons at 2382 MeV.

The $\overline{q}q$ model implies that each rotational excitation should consist of four nonets, the states ${}^3L_{L+1}$, ${}^3L_L$, and ${}^3L_{L-1}$ with $C = (-1)^{L+1}$, and the state ${}^1L_L$ with $C = (-1)^L$. With spin-orbit coupling, the four I = 1 levels for orbital angular momentum L are shifted as follows:

	${}^3L_{L-1}$	${}^3L_L$	${}^1L_L$	${}^3L_{L+1}$
Coefficient of spin-orbit interaction	-2L-2	-2	0	2L

We note that the two states with J = L lie close relative to the states J = L ± 1, so that the pattern of states for given L will appear as a triplet until very high resolution is achieved or until the decay processes of these resonances are observed (since corresponding Y = 0 states ${}^3L_L$ and ${}^1L_L$ have opposite G and can therefore be distinguished according to whether they decay to an even or odd number of pions).

In the data of Focacci et al.,[35] the R-meson peak appears separated into three peaks, corresponding to states $R_\alpha(1632)$, $R_\beta(1699)$, and $R_\gamma(1748)$. With the $\overline{q}q$ model, the R_α state would be identified with the ${}^3D_1$ configuration (JPC = 1--) and R_γ with the ${}^3D_3$ configuration (JPC = 3--), and R_β would be presumed to consist of two unresolved states, corresponding to the ${}^3D_2$ and ${}^1D_2$ configurations (JPC

= 2-- and 2-+, respectively). It is of interest to note here that the I = 1 states and the two I = 0 states of the $^3D_1$ nonet are vector meson states which could have importance for the electromagnetic structure of the baryons.

Multipion resonance states have been reported in the mass region 1600 to 1700 MeV from bubble chamber studies of inelastic πp collisions, but in detail the experimental situation appears rather confusing. Our expectation from the $\bar{q}q$ model is that the I = 1 $^3D_1$ state R_α and the I = 1 $^3D_3$ state R_γ can undergo 2π decay, but that 2π decay is forbidden for all other D states; 3π decay is possible only from the I = 0 states of the ^3D nonets and from the I = 1 state of the $^1D_2$ nonet. The experimental evidence for an $I \geq 1\ \pi^\pm\pi^0$ resonance at about 1625 MeV is clear. This state has mass consistent with R_α (the width $\Gamma \approx 60$ MeV appears appreciably larger but this may result from a poorer resolution in the bubble chamber experiments), and this decay mode is consistent with the assignment (1--) suggested by the $\bar{q}q$ model, although the spin and isospin have not yet been determined directly. However, there is equally clear evidence for an $I \geq 1$ 3π resonance at about 1635 MeV, which cannot be attributed to the $^3D_1$ nonet. This could arise only from the I = 1 $^1D_2$ state, which would imply that this state has been displaced downwards from the $^3D_2$ state, to lie close to the $^3D_1$ state. There is also evidence in many experiments for a broad resonance ($\Gamma \approx 200$ MeV) for the $\pi^+\pi^-$ system in the mass region 1650 to 1700 MeV, a significantly higher mass value than 1625 MeV, the mass value for the $\pi^\pm\pi^0$ resonance referred to above; yet there are no I = 0 2π resonances permitted in the D configurations. The interpretation of these resonance states is far from clear at present.

Focacci et al.[35] have pointed out that if the ρ, A2, R, S, T, U mesons are labeled n = 1, 2, 3, 4, 5, 6, then the plot of $(\text{mass})^2$ versus n is approximately linear, as shown on Fig. 10-1. This suggests that these states may form a family of states. With the $\bar{q}q$ model, the simplest possibility is to suppose that this family consists of a rotational sequence, in which case n would specify the total spin for the corresponding meson. The plot of Fig. 10-1 then corresponds to a Regge trajectory for the J = L + 1 states with I = 1, Y = 0, in fact, to the leading Regge trajectory for (I, Y) = (1, 0) states. Its linear extrapolation downward in E^2 crosses the line $E^2 = 0$ at n = 0.45; this intercept agrees well with the value $n = 0.48 \pm 0.05$ [usually called $\alpha_\rho(0)$] obtained for the ρ trajectory from scattering and total-cross-section data corresponding to the region $E^2 \leq 0$ (i.e., for physical momentum transfers). We note that the trajectories of even and odd signatures are coincident here, for the ρ and A2 mesons lie on the same trajectory. This appears natural in the $\bar{q}q$ model; no significant exchange forces are expected to occur, since these would require the exchange of systems with baryon number 2/3, and the lowest such system is qq, with mass $2M_q$.

The excitation energy arising from the centrifugal term in Eq. 6 is given roughly by the expression

$$\delta_L(E^2) = L(L+1)\ \langle 1/r^2 \rangle_L \qquad (10)$$

The linear sequence observed for the J = L + 1 states corresponds to a linear dependence of E^2 on L. This differs from the situation usual in molecular physics, where $\langle 1/r^2 \rangle_L$ is roughly independent of L and $\delta_L(E^2)$ increases like L(L + 1). Here, $\langle 1/r^2 \rangle_L$ is required to fall with increasing L, more or less like 1/(2L + 1). This requires the potential $\bar{V}(r)$ effective in the low-lying excitations to be rather flat and open, like the function $(\bar{V}_0 + \lambda r^2)$, as for the

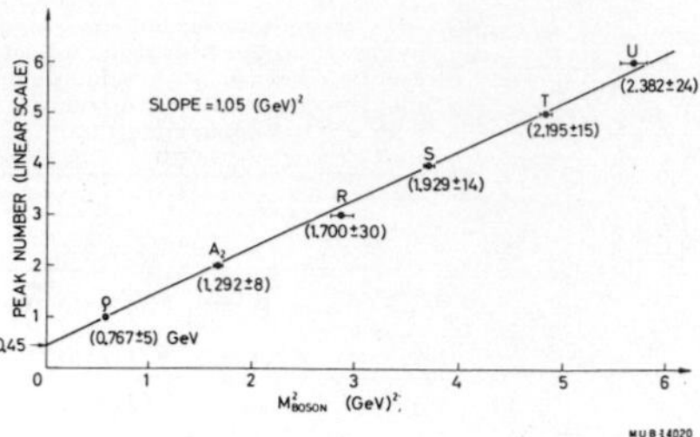

Fig. 10-1. A plot of the dominant mesonic excitations observed in the reaction $\pi^- + p \to p +$ (missing mass) studied with the missing-mass spectrometer by the Maglić group at CERN (Ref. 35). The peaks are numbered n in order of increasing mass, starting with the ρ meson, and n is plotted against $(\text{mass})^2$ for each mesonic excitation.

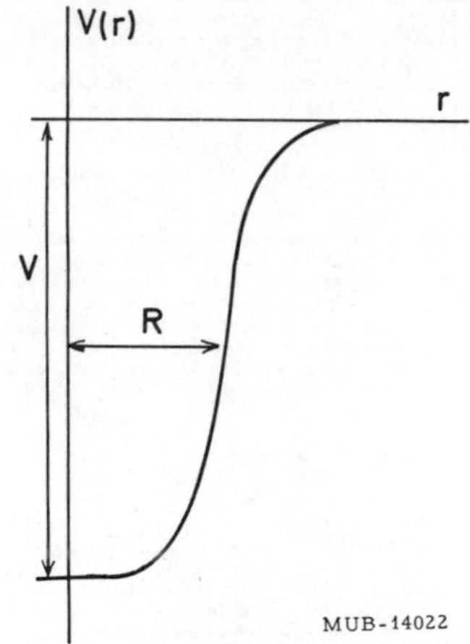

Fig. 10-2. Schematic representation of the $\bar{q}q$ potential within a meson.

potential form sketched in Fig. 10-2. In fact, if $\bar{V}(r)$ has this harmonic oscillator form over the region where the $\bar{q}q$ wave function is significant, then E^2 is precisely a linear function of L.

With the $\bar{q}q$ picture, the mesonic states already observed correspond to low-lying levels in a very deep potential $\bar{V}$ (depth close to $2M_q$). The rotational excitation of the ground levels leads to bound states in this potential up to very large L values (up to L_{max} with order of magnitude $4M_q^2/\alpha'_\rho(0)$, where $\alpha'_\rho(0) = 1.05\ (\text{GeV})^2$ is the slope of the Regge trajectory at $E^2 = 0$, thus $L_{max} \gtrsim 10^2$). Hence, this model suggests that the Regge trajectory should continue to move to the right with increasing J, up to spin values of order 10^2, before beginning their path back to the left.

For the states of high L, the mass range between the states $J = L \pm 1$ will have the order of magnitude

$$\delta E^2(L)_{SO} \approx 2M_q(2L+1)\langle \bar{v}_{SO}(r)\rangle_L. \qquad (11)$$

Since the data of Focacci et al.[35] show no splitting within the S, T, and U peaks, which are already exceedingly narrow (cf. Table 10-IV), we must conclude that the contribution $\delta E^2(L)_{SO}$ from the spin-orbit interaction must decrease rapidly with increasing L. For L = 2, the splitting is $\delta E^2(2)_{SO} = R_\gamma^2 - R_\alpha^2 \approx 0.39\ (\mathrm{GeV})^2$, compared with $\delta E^2(1)_{SO} = (A2)^2 - \rho^2 \approx 0.76\ (\mathrm{GeV})^2$ for L = 1; for L = 3, the empirical width for the S meson leads to the upper limit $\delta E^2(2)_{SO} \leq 0.14\ (\mathrm{GeV})^2$. This behavior requires that $\langle \bar{v}_{SO}(r)\rangle_L$ fall rapidly with increasing L; this is the case, for example, if the spin-orbit interaction $\bar{v}_{SO}$ has range appreciably less than that of the superstrong potential $\bar{V}(r)$.

With the $\bar{q}q$ model, there are four Regge trajectories associated with the ρ and π mesons, three corresponding to the triplet states $^3L_{L+1}$, ^3L_L, and $^3L_{L-1}$, and one corresponding to the singlet state ^1L_L. Insofar as the spin dependence of the $\bar{q}q$ force can be neglected, these four trajectories become parallel on the J-M^2 plot for large J, since the four states then become degenerate in energy (Fig. 10-3a).

This degeneracy is displayed more directly when these four trajectories are plotted as functions of L, rather than J, as shown in Fig. 10-3b.

The most surprising feature of the massive mesonic resonances established by Focacci et al.[35] is the sharpness of these resonance peaks. For example, the width reported for the T meson is less than 13 MeV, despite its high mass value, 2195 MeV. The most direct explanation for these narrow widths is to attribute them to their high angular momentum. The centrifugal barriers faced by the outgoing decay particles increase strongly with L. If R denotes the radius of the region of strong interactions from which the outgoing meson emerges, the barrier-penetration amplitude is adequately measured by the amplitude of an ingoing wave for angular momentum ℓ (normalized to unit amplitude at infinity) on the boundary R, thus

$$j_\ell(kR) \approx \frac{(kR)^\ell}{1,3,5,\cdots(2\ell+1)}\left[1 - \frac{(kR)^2}{4\ell+6} + \cdots\right]. \qquad (12)$$

The leading term is a good approximation, as long as $(kR)^2 \ll (4\ell+6)$. We note the large factor (ℓ!!) $= 1.3\cdots(2\ell+1)$ in the denominator; for example, with kR = 1 and ℓ = 4, this barrier-penetration amplitude is only about 10^{-3}. In the mass region ~2 GeV, two-body decay modes such as P+P, P+V, etc. typically involve momentum $k \lesssim 1$ GeV/c. If we assume an interaction radius $R \approx 0.2$ F for the pion emission process (the rms radius of the pion is about 0.3 F, according to the harmonic oscillator potential model considered above), then kR is sufficiently small for

Table 10-IV. The masses and widths of the higher I = 1, Y = 0 resonance states resolved in the "missing-mass spectrometer" experiments of the Maglić group at CERN (Ref. 35).

	Mesonic state					
	R			S	T	U
	R_α	R_β	R_γ			
Mass (MeV)	1632±10	1699±10	1748±10	1929±15	2195±15	2382±24
Width (Γ MeV)	< 21	< 30	< 38	≤ 35	≤ 13	≤ 30

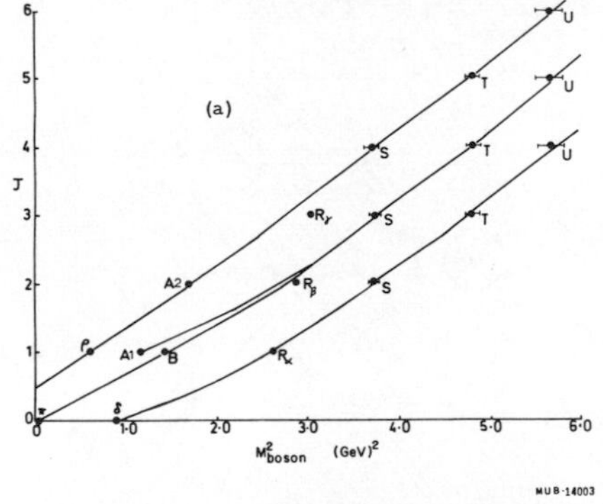

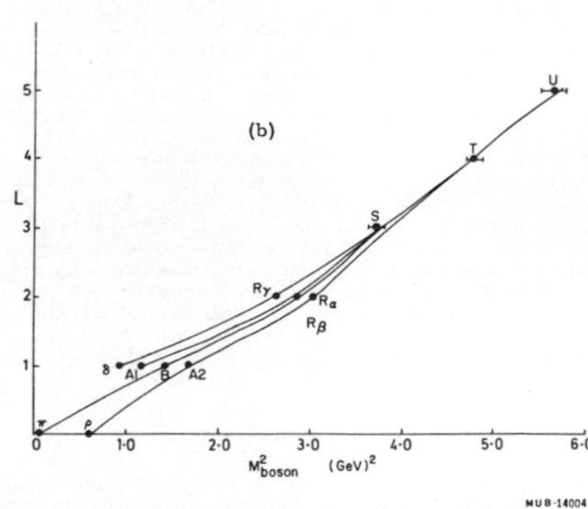

Fig. 10-3. Regge plots are made for the known I = 1, Y = 0 mesonic resonance states, according to the quark-model interpretation for these states. In (a), a conventional Regge plot is made of J versus $(\mathrm{mass})^2$. In (b), the plot is made of L versus $(\mathrm{mass})^2$, in which case the four trajectories become degenerate beyond sufficiently large mass values.

the use of the approximation 12. Taking the expression 12 and the phase space factor k/M, where M is the parent mass, we adopt the estimate

$$\Gamma(M \to 2P) = \gamma(k/M)[(kR)^{\ell}/(\ell!!)]^2. \qquad (13)$$

Comparison with the cases of the ρ meson and f meson suggest the order of magnitude $\gamma \approx 10^5$ MeV. If we now consider a meson with spin J = 4 with mass M ≈ 2 GeV, this expression leads to a partial width of order 0.1 MeV for two-body decay. More complicated two-body modes, such as VV, A2 P, etc., allow lower angular momenta for the outgoing particles, but also involve much lower outgoing momentum k and therefore a strong reduction in the factor $(kR)^{2\ell}$. For the more complicated modes of decay, such as the cascade sequences (L) → π + (L - 1), we may expect the matrix elements to fall rapidly with increasing L, because of the poor overlap between the initial and final radial wave functions, and because of the constraints involved in the coupling of the final angular momenta. Even though the number of available decay channels increases rapidly with increasing mass M for the parent particle, it is possible that the individual decay amplitudes may decrease even more rapidly, in the case in which the angular momentum of these particle states also increases with increasing mass for the parent particle, in such a way that the total decay width remains small (or even decreases) as M increases through this sequence of particle states. This situation is well known in atomic physics; for example, for a highly excited state (say n = 4) of the hydrogen atom, the decay width is much smaller than for the n = 2 P levels, even though the number of γ decays possible from an n = 4 state is considerably greater than from an n = 2 state, simply because the transition amplitudes fall rapidly in magnitude with increasing n. It is difficult to be completely quantitative about these remarks on the decay widths for the high-lying meson states. [It is of interest to recall that the possibility of strong centrifugal barriers associated with a high spin value was widely discussed about 15 years ago as a possible explanation for the long lifetimes (~ 10^{-10} sec!) observed for the low-lying mesonic and baryonic strange particles, which were known, from their copious production in high-energy collisions, to be strongly interacting particles.] However, the hypothesis that the sequence of mesonic states observed forms a Regge family carries the implication that the high-lying states must have high spin values, which leads directly to a natural and plausible qualitative interpretation for the narrowness of their decay widths, subject to the one further assumption that the radius R of the region of strong interaction from which the decay products emerge be sufficiently small. This interpretation still allows the possibility that there may exist high-mass mesons with low spin values, corresponding to lower Regge trajectories associated with radial excitations of the $\bar{q}$-q system, whose decay widths would be much larger in virtue of their low spin. Such broad mesonic states would be very difficult to detect with the "missing-mass spectrometer" method, owing to the large background subtractions which are necessary; their detection would certainly need more subtle observations, involving study of the statistics of a particular set of decay products as a function of their c. m. energy.

5. The Baryonic States

Next we discuss the interpretations of the data on baryonic states, supposing that these are due to the strong binding of three quarks through the qq potential V(r). Various aspects of this model have been discussed by many authors--by Bogoliubov et al.,[9] Dalitz,[17,18] Hori et al.,[37] Ishida,[38] Mitra,[39] Mitra and Ross,[40] Morpurgo,[41] Nambu,[42] Thirring,[43] and Werle,[44] among others. This qqq model allows only {1}, {8}, and {10} representations for baryonic states, and all the clearly established resonances are consistent with these representations. [However, it is important to mention a possible cloud on the horizon, namely the evidence from K^+p and K^+d total-cross-section measurements for a marked bump (about 8 mb) in the I = 0 KN total cross section at mass 1880 MeV.[45] If this bump were established to be due to a resonance state, this would require the existence of a $\{\overline{10}\}$ multiplet of resonance states. The simplest quark configuration which includes this representation is $qqqq\bar{q}$. Since the mass of this configuration lies within the mass range for the states we attribute to the configuration qqq here, there would be every reason to expect substantial mixing between these two configurations, which would vitiate the simple discussion given here, based on the qqq configuration alone.]

The L = 0+ Levels

The low-lying baryonic states are known to correspond to the 56 representation of SU(6), consisting of the ($1/2^+$) baryon octet and the ($3/2^+$) decuplet. The spin-unitary spin wave function corresponding to this representation is symmetric in the quark labels. Hence, with the natural assumption of Fermi statistics for the quarks, the space wave function is required to be totally antisymmetric in these labels. Since this representation lies lowest in mass, we expect L = 0 for the orbital angular momentum of this state. These two requirements can be met; however, they require nonzero internal orbital angular momenta. With the internal angular momenta (ℓ, ℓ') defined as in Fig. 10-4, these requirements imply $\ell' = \ell$ = odd. The lowest configuration (1, 1) is not totally antisymmetric; this requires the admixture of some (3, 3) configuration. The simplest wave function is of the form

$$\psi_{space} = (r_1^2 - r_2^2)(r_2^2 - r_3^2)(r_3^2 - r_1^2)\,\phi_{symm}(\underline{r}_1, \underline{r}_2, \underline{r}_3), \qquad (14)$$

where $\underline{r}_1$, $\underline{r}_2$, $\underline{r}_3$ denote the position vectors of the three quarks relative to their center of mass; in terms of the configurations (ℓ, ℓ'), this wave function takes the form

$$\psi_{space} = \underline{r}\cdot\underline{R}\left[\left(\tfrac{1}{4}r^2 - \tfrac{1}{3}R^2\right)^2 - \tfrac{1}{9}(\underline{r}\cdot\underline{R})^2\right]\phi_{symm}(r^2, R^2) \qquad (15a)$$

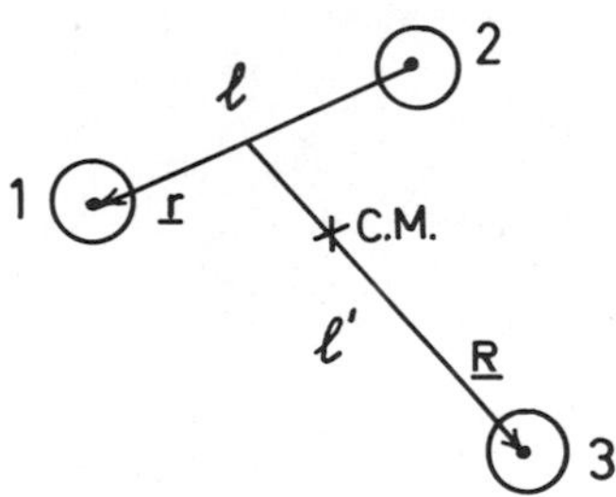

MUB-14021

Fig. 10-4. Diagram showing the coordinate system, and the definition of the internal angular momenta, in the space wave function for the three-quark system.

$$= rR \frac{r^4}{16} - \frac{7r^2R^2}{30} + \frac{R^4}{9} Y_1^0(\cos\theta)$$

$$- \frac{2r^3R^3}{45} Y_3^0(\cos\theta)\, \phi_{symm}(r^2, R^2), \quad (15b)$$

where $\underline{r} = \underline{r}_1 - \underline{r}_2$ and $R = \underline{r}_3 - \frac{1}{2}(\underline{r}_1 + \underline{r}_2)$, and θ is the angle between $\underline{r}$ and $\underline{R}$, so that $Y_\ell^0(\cos\theta)$ denotes the $L = 0$ function appropriate to $\ell' = \ell$.

The totally antisymmetric wave function 14 has at least three nodal planes, and therefore has relatively high kinetic energy, a surprising conclusion for a ground-state wave function.* However, this is possible if the qq potential has a strong exchange character, such that the qq interaction is strongly attractive in P states and repulsive in S states. The general form of a pure space-exchange potential is

$$V_{exch} = (1 + \underline{\sigma}_1 \cdot \underline{\sigma}_2)(1 + F_1 \cdot F_2)v(r). \quad (16)$$

Radicati[46] has pointed out that a potential of this form can be generated by the exchange of a pseudoscalar nonet and a vector nonet, which provides an SU(3) generalization of the Moller-Rosenfeld mixture.[47] This combination of meson exchanges is just such as to cancel out the qq tensor force. This model would mean that the qq potential V cannot be simply related with the $\bar{q}q$ potential $\bar{V}$, since the potential $\bar{V}$ corresponding to expression 16 would then be proportional to the SU(6) singlet projection operator $(1 - \sigma \cdot \bar{\sigma})(1 - F \cdot \bar{F})$ and would give no contribution to the $\bar{q}q$ attraction present in the 35 representation.

The predictions concerning the electromagnetic properties of the baryon octet and decuplet, which follow from their assignment to the 56 representation, have been quite successful. These predictions are:

(i) ratio of total magnetic moments for the nucleons is $\mu_p/\mu_n = -3/2$, compared with the empirical ratio $2.79/(-1.91)$;

(ii) E2 amplitude vanishes for the transition $\gamma N \rightarrow N^*(1238)$: the empirical ratio E2/M1 at resonance is at most several percent;

(iii) the value for the M1 amplitude is $(2\sqrt{2}\,\mu_p/3)$ for the transition $\gamma N \rightarrow N^*$; the empirical value is about 30% larger than this prediction.

SU(3)-Breaking Interactions

If the SU(3) breaking in the baryonic multiplets is attributed to a one-body operator, causing the energy of a λ quark to be Δ' greater than that for the (n, p) quarks, then the value $\Delta' \approx 147$ MeV is required to fit the decuplet states, and $\Delta' \approx 190$ MeV $[= (\Xi - N)/2]$ to fit the baryon octet states. This model then predicts Λ and Σ states to lie together at mass $(\Xi + N)/2 \approx 1130$ MeV. Although the mean mass for Λ and Σ is quite close to this prediction, the mass splitting $\Sigma - \Lambda \approx 80$ MeV represents a significant discrepancy from this model. It appears that it is necessary to include also some two-body interactions which violate SU(3) symmetry, a plausible possibility first envisaged by Zweig.[48] This possibility has been thoroughly explored by Federman et al.,[49] who showed that the SU(6) mass formula follows for the states of the 56 representation if the symmetry-breaking potentials W_{ab}^{SI} (where S = total spin, I =

---

*Since the Conference, Mitra and Majumdar (Phys. Rev. 150, 1194, 1966) have published a calculation of the baryon structure form factor $F(q^2)$ for an antisymmetric wave function of the form 14 with

$$\phi_{symm} = \exp[-\beta^2(r_1^2 + r_2^2 + r_3^2)], \quad (i)$$

$$= \exp[-\beta^2(\tfrac{2}{3}R^2 + \tfrac{1}{2}r^2)]. \quad (ii)$$

They found the result

$$F(q^2) = (1 - \frac{18}{11}z + \frac{14}{11}z^2 - \frac{82}{165}z^3 + \frac{41}{660}z^4 - \frac{1}{110}z^5)\exp(-z), \quad (iii)$$

where $z = q^2/12\beta^2$, and q here refers to momentum transfer to the photon. The function iii has a zero at about $z = 1.44$. Assuming rigid charge and magnetic moment distributions, the nucleon charge form factors would then be

$$F_{Ep} = [\tfrac{4}{3}F_{E1}(q^2) - \tfrac{1}{3}F_{E2}(q^2)]\, F(q^2), \quad (iva)$$

$$F_{En} = [\tfrac{2}{3}F_{E1}(q^2) - \tfrac{2}{3}F_{E2}(q^2)]\, F(q^2), \quad (ivb)$$

where $F_{Ei}(q^2)$ denotes the charge form factor for quark q_i, and the nucleon magnetic form factors (neglecting any possible contributions from exchange currents) would be

$$F_{Mp} = [\tfrac{8}{9}F_{M1}(q^2) + \tfrac{1}{9}F_{M2}(q^2)]\, F(q^2), \quad (va)$$

$$F_{\mu n} = [\tfrac{1}{3}F_{M1}(q^2) + \tfrac{2}{3}F_{M2}(q^2)]\, F(q^2). \quad (vb)$$

Exact SU(3) symmetry requires $F_{E1} \equiv F_{E2}$ and $F_{M1} \equiv F_{M2}$, of course. We note that a zero in $F(q^2)$ leads to a zero at the same q^2 for all of the nucleon form factors.

If this result--that the body form factor of the baryon has a node--is typical for antisymmetric space wave functions, then the fact that the measured form factors show no evidence for a node, up to momentum transfers $q^2 = 100\ F^{-2}$, provides a very strong argument against the relevance of antisymmetric space wave functions to the baryons, unless β is so large that this node lies beyond the region of q^2 explored to date. The rms radius associated with the three-quark distribution is $R_q = (29/22\beta^2)^{1/2}$; if the node is to occur outside the explored region, this requires $\beta \geqslant 2.4\ F^{-1}$, so that we must have $R \leqslant 0.5$ F. A value for the rms radius for the quark distribution smaller than this limit is by no means excluded. We note that the result $(dF_{En}/dq^2) = 0.021\ F^2$ implies $R_1^2 - R_2^2 = 0.126\ F^2$, where R_1 and R_2 are the rms charge radii for the quarks q_1 and q_2. The rms radius for the proton is then $[(4/3)R_1^2 - (1/3)R_2^2 + R_q^2] = (0.79)^2 F^2$; this requires $R_1^2 + R_q^2 = 0.50\ F^2$, and the above limit for R_q requires the $R_1 \geqslant 0.5$ F. Insofar as the charge distribution within the quarks may be mediated by the ρ, ω, and ϕ mesons, the allowed region for R_1 corresponds to rather reasonable values for the charge radius of the p quark q_1.

If we take $R_q = 0.2$ F as a reasonable estimate for the rms radius for the quark distribution in the baryons (a sum rule given by A. de Shalit, in lectures at Varenna, July 1965, suggests the inequality $R_q \leqslant 0.4/\sqrt{M_q}$ F, for quark mass M_q GeV), then the node in the form factor $F(q^2)$ would occur at squared momentum transfer $q^2 \approx 500\ F^{-2}$. It will be of the greatest interest to see whether any such node is found when electron-proton scattering experiments are carried out at the highest electron energies available at SLAC.

If no node is found in the nucleon form factors, and if it appears (as seems likely) that such a node is quite a general property of the form factor for an antisymmetric space wave function, then this will be a serious difficulty which could be avoided only with the assumption of parastatistics for the quarks, since this allows the three-quark space wave function to be symmetric and the three-body form factor of the three-quark system to be free of nodes.

breaking potentials W_{ab}^{SI} (where S = total spin, I = total isospin, for two interacting quarks of types a, b) satisfy the relation

$$2W_{N\lambda}^{1\frac{1}{2}} = W_{NN}^{11} + W_{\lambda\lambda}^{10} , \qquad (17)$$

irrespective of the values taken by the singlet potentials W_{ab}^{0I}. Equation 17 states the condition that the potential W^{1I} is the O_3^3 component of an octet, so that it is not so surprising that the decuplet masses then satisfy the Gell-Mann–Okubo formula. We note that the singlet potentials must have isospin dependence, since the Σ-Λ mass difference is proportional to the difference $(W_{N\lambda}^{0\frac{1}{2}} - W_{NN}^{00})$.

At this point, it is appropriate to underline our lack of understanding of the origin of the mass splitting by drawing attention to "Lipkin's Crazy Mass Formula," which reads

$$K - \pi \overset{Q}{=} K^* - \rho \overset{L}{=} Y^* - N^* \overset{L,Q}{=\!=\!=} \Xi - \Sigma , \qquad (18)$$

where Q denotes that the equality is to be taken for $(\text{mass})^2$, and L denotes that the equality is for (mass). Earlier, we pointed out that the left-hand equality corresponded to equality for $(\epsilon_\lambda^2 - \epsilon_N^2)$ in the S = 0 and S = 1 $q\bar{q}$ spin states, where $\epsilon_q^2 = \epsilon_{\bar{q}}^2$ is a one-body operator giving the contribution of each quark q or antiquark $\bar{q}$ to E^2 for the $q\bar{q}$ state. The right-hand equality corresponds to equality for $(\epsilon_\lambda' - \epsilon_N')$ or $(\epsilon_\lambda'^2 - \epsilon_N'^2)$ in the S = 1/2 and S = 3/2 states of the qqq system, where ϵ_q' or $\epsilon_q'^2$ is a one-body operator giving the contribution of each quark q to E or E^2, respectively, for the qqq system. Since the decuplet and the baryon octet masses are comparable, it is not crucial for the validity of the baryonic mass equality whether (mass) or $(\text{mass})^2$ is used. The puzzle lies in the central equality, which would be grossly in error if $(\text{mass})^2$ were used. The only thing which appears clear after perusal of Eq. 18 is that the differences $(\epsilon_\lambda - \epsilon_N)$ and $(\epsilon_\lambda' - \epsilon_N')$ are not to be interpreted simply as giving the quark mass difference $(M_\lambda - M_N)$. It is quite possible that the central equality is simply accidental.

The L = 1- Levels

The baryonic resonances believed to have negative parity are tabulated in Table 10-V. We notice that the N^* masses range from 1518 to 1700 MeV, with a substantial gap in mass values until $N_{\frac{1}{2}}^*(2190)$. This gap may simply reflect our lack of knowledge about πN scattering in the region of pion kinetic energy 1000 to 2000 MeV. However, the spin-parity known for $N_{\frac{1}{2}}^*(2190)$ allow its interpretation as the first Regge recurrence of $N_{\frac{1}{2}}^*(1518)$, and we assume that $N_{\frac{1}{2}}^*(2190)$ belongs to some higher supermultiplet.

A simple and reasonable hypothesis is that these negative-parity baryonic states belong to a qqq state with rotational excitation L = 1 and negative parity. As has been discussed,[18] the appropriate state of spin and unitary spin for the qqq system is then the 70 representation of SU(6). This representation has mixed (M) symmetry with respect to permutations of the quark labels. This appears quite natural for an L = 1- wave function, since the position vectors $(\underline{\lambda}, \underline{\rho})$, with

$$\underline{\lambda} = (\underline{r}_1 + \underline{r}_2 - 2\underline{r}_3)/\sqrt{6} , \qquad \underline{\rho} = (\underline{r}_1 - \underline{r}_2)/\sqrt{2} , \qquad (19)$$

form the basis for an M representation of this permutation group. A space wave function $\psi_m(\underline{r}_1, \underline{r}_2, \underline{r}_3)$

Table 10-V. The baryonic resonance states with negative parity are tabulated. They are grouped in the SU(3) multiplets suggested by their spin determination or by their qualitative agreement with the mass systematics for baryonic multiplets, or according to our knowledge of their decay branching ratios. $\Xi^*(1820)$ has been assigned to a decuplet on the basis of its $(\Sigma\bar{K})/(\Lambda\bar{K})$ ratio. The relationship of $Y_0^*(2110)$ and $N_{1/2}^*(2190)$ is quite uncertain at present; on the basis of mass systematics, it appears rather likely that $Y_0^*(2110)$ will be found to be a unitary singlet state.

Spin-parity	Representation	Baryonic resonance states
$(1/2^-)$	{1}	$Y_0^*(1405)$
	{8}	$N_{1/2}^*(1570)$, $Y_0^*(1670)$, $Y_1^*(1750)$,.
	{8}	$N_{1/2}^*(1700)$, ···
	{10}	$N_{3/2}^*(1670)$, ···
$(3/2^-)$	{1}	$Y_0^*(1520)$
	{8}	$N_{1/2}^*(1518)$, $Y_0^*(1700)$?, $Y_1^*(1660)$,.
	{10}	···, $\Xi^*(1820)$
$(5/2^-)$	{8}	$N_{1/2}^*(1688)$, $Y_1^*(1765)$, $Y_0^*(1840)$?,.
$(7/2^-)$	{8?}	$N_{1/2}^*(2190)$, $Y_0^*(2110)$, ···

with L = 1- and M symmetry can then be written as a product of the representation (λ, ρ) and a scalar function $\phi(\underline{r}_1, \underline{r}_2, \underline{r}_3)$, which may be either symmetrical or antisymmetrical, or belong to an M representation of the permutation group.

These unitary multiplets are separated by the effect of SU(6)-breaking interactions. Central interactions of the type $V_\sigma = \underline{\sigma}_1 \cdot \underline{\sigma}_2 v_\sigma$ and $V_F = F_1 \cdot F_2 v_F$ lead to the mass formula

$$M(\underline{S}, F^2) = M_0 + a\underline{S}^2 + bF^2, \tag{20}$$

and to the pattern of masses shown on Fig. 10-5. Since F^2 takes the values 0, 18, and 36 for the representations {1}, {8}, and {10}, this expression implies equal spacing for the S = 1/2 representations in this order. The term aS^2 separates the ^4P and ^2P configurations. Each of these multiplets is then split further by the noncentral interactions, leading to the pattern of states shown in Fig. 10-5. As seen from Table 10-V, the spin, parity, and unitary spin for each of the known baryonic resonance states are compatible with their assignment to one of these unitary multiplets. Apart from the two singlet states, $Y_0^*(1405)$ and $Y_0^*(1520)$, none of these unitary multiplets is known completely; for one unitary multiplet, a $(3/2^-)$ octet, there are no known candidates at present. [The assignment of $\Xi^*(1820)$ is unclear. It has been pointed out by Marinov[50] and by Goldberg et al.[51] that the branching ratios for $\Xi^*(1820)$ decay, especially the $\Lambda\bar{K}/\Sigma\bar{K}$ ratio, are inconsistent with its assignment to the same octet as $N_{1/2}^*(1518)$ and $Y_1^*(1660)$. $\Xi^*(1820)$ could well belong to the other $(3/2^-)$ octet shown on Fig. 10-5; in Table 10-V, we have followed the assignment given by Mitra and Ross[40] (see below). The assignment of $Y_0^*(1700)$ is even more uncertain; indeed, its spin and parity have not been established.]

The Spin-Orbit Splittings

Our discussion of the noncentral interactions is confined to the spin-orbit interaction for the present, since this would have a very natural origin in terms of vector meson exchange. The spin-orbit interaction gives a diagonal contribution to the energy of each state of the form $A(S, \{a\})\underline{S} \cdot \underline{L}$. [The spin-orbit interaction also couples the $^4\{8\}$ and $^2\{8\}$ states with the same total angular momentum. The effect of this off-diagonal term on the $(1/2^-)$ and $(3/2^-)$ octet states has been neglected in the remarks made here.] An F-independent spin-orbit interaction

$$U_{SO}(ij) = (\underline{\sigma}_i + \underline{\sigma}_j) \cdot \underline{L}_{ij}\, U_{SO}(r_{ij}) \tag{21}$$

would give the same sign to the coefficient A for each multiplet, and this does not appear compatible with the data. For the singlet states, the coefficient A is positive; on the other hand, the $N_{1/2}^*$ of lowest mass has spin-parity $(3/2^-)$, which suggests A negative for the $^2\{8\}$ states. Since the superstrong potential V includes octet vector exchange, it seems natural to consider the possibility of an F-dependent spin-orbit interaction,

$$U_{SO}(ij) = (1 + a F_i \cdot F_j)(\underline{\sigma}_i + \underline{\sigma}_j) \cdot \underline{L}_{ij}\, U_{SO}(r_{ij}). \tag{22}$$

This leads to a diagonal contribution

$$(A + BF^2)\, \underline{S} \cdot \underline{L} \tag{23}$$

to the energy of each multiplet. A > 0 holds for the singlet states; the coefficient is (A + 18 B) for octet states, and (A + 36 B) for decuplet states. (A + 18 B) < 0 for the $^2\{8\}$ states then implies (A + 36 B) < 0 strongly for the decuplet states. This result requires that the $(3/2^-)$ $N_{3/2}^*$ lie well below the $(1/2^-)$

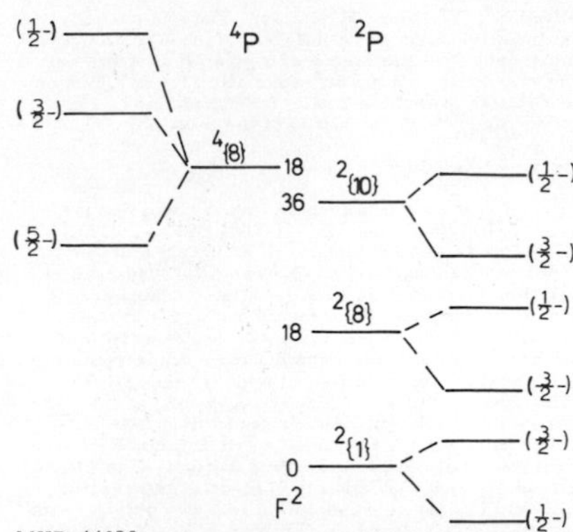

Fig. 10-5. Schematic representation of the unitary multiplets contained in the configuration (L = 1-, 70), after the degeneracy has been broken by spin-spin forces, by unitary spin–unitary spin forces, and by spin-orbit forces.

$N_{3/2}^*(1670)$. Although this mass region is well explored in pion-nucleon scattering, there is not yet any evidence for an I = 3/2 $d_{3/2}$ resonance in this region. [The phase-shift analysis by Bransden et al.[52] attributes the well-known shoulder in the π^+p total cross section to a d_{33} resonance, whereas the analyses by Bareyre et al.[53] and Auvil et al.[54] attribute this to an S_{13} resonance. If $\Xi^*(1820)$ belongs to a $(3/2^-)$ decuplet, the corresponding $N_{3/2}^*$ state is likely to lie in the range 1500 to 1600 MeV; for assumed mass 1585 MeV, Mitra and Ross[40] estimate that it may have width about 12 MeV. It is not clear whether such a narrow resonance would necessarily have been detected in this mass region.] Owing to the uncertainties in the identification of the unitary multiplets at present, it is unclear whether or not the empirical pattern of spin-orbit splittings is in agreement with the interaction 22 alone.

The pattern of levels may also be strongly distorted from the simple unitary patterns by the mixing effects introduced by the SU(3)-breaking interactions (δH, say). If δH has no noncentral components, then δH does not mix the S = 1/2 and S = 3/2 states; however, the spin-orbit interactions observed (which can mix the S = 1/2 and S = 3/2 states) are of the same order of magnitude (≈ 100 MeV) as the splittings due to δH, so that these two mixing effects probably need to be treated together. For both $(1/2^-)$ and $(3/2^-)$ cases, δH mixes the {1} and $^2\{8\}$ Y_0^* states, the latter being mixed with the $^4\{8\}$ Y_0^* state by U_{SO}; δH mixes the {10} and $^2\{8\}$ Y_1^* states, the latter being mixed with the $^4\{8\}$ Y_1^* state by U_{SO}; and δH mixes the {10} and $^2\{8\}$ $\Xi_{1/2}^*$ states, the latter being mixed with the $^4\{8\}$ $\Xi_{1/2}^*$ state by U_{SO}. δH generally has a different effect in the $^4\{8\}$ and $^2\{8\}$ $N_{1/2}^*$ states, which then causes a modification in their mixing by U_{SO}. Since the unmixed states have energy separations typically about 300 MeV (due to V_σ and V_F), the amount of mixing in the physical states could well be quite large. These mixing effects may introduce a serious complication in the task of untangling the multiplet relationships between the observed N^*, Y^*, and Ξ^* states. They cause substantial deviations from the Gell-Mann–Okubo mass relationship for the states of a given multiplet, and they are likely to have an especially strong effect on the relative branching ratios for the various decay modes for each of the states of the multiplet.

The L = 2+ Levels

The next sets of baryonic levels observed are the $(5/2^+)$ resonances, $N^*_{1/2}(1688)$ and $Y^*_0(1815)$, which appear to be members of an octet, and the $(7/2^+)$ resonances, $N^*_{3/2}(1920)$ and $Y^*_1(2030)$, which appear to be members of a decuplet. It appears natural to attribute these levels to the rotational excitation L = 2+. Since the L = 2+ space wave function can have the same permutation symmetry as the L = 0+ space wave function, it appears natural for the spin–unitary spin wave function to belong to the 56 representation again. This state is then to be regarded simply as a rotational excitation (or Regge recurrence) of the ground configuration. The interactions V_q and V_F and the spin-orbit interactions split this (56, 5) representation into two octets, with spin-parity $(5/2^+)$ and $(3/2^+)$, and into four decuplets, with spin-parity $(7/2^+)$, $(5/2^+)$, $(3/2^+)$, and $(1/2^+)$. Only states of the $(5/2^+)$ octet and the $(7/2^+)$ decuplet are known; the remaining positive-parity states just listed presumably lie in the higher mass regions, where the pion-nucleon scattering data and its analysis are still in a relatively primitive state. With our present uncertainties concerning the nature of the qq spin-orbit interaction, which have been seen above in our attempts to interpret the (L = 1-, 70) supermultiplet states, we are unable to predict the mass relationship between these missing states and the observed $(5/2^+)$ octet and $(7/2^+)$ decuplet.

Thus, the I = 1/2 $(5/2^+)$ N^* state and I = $3/2^+$ $(7/2^+)$ N^* state have a natural interpretation as the first excited states in the leading Regge rotational sequence for the 56 representation. This rotational sequence continues to higher mass values, corresponding to L = 4+, 6+, 8+ in turn. In view of the tight binding of the qqq states, we may expect this sequence to continue to the right on the J-vs-M^2 plot, up to J values of the order 10^3 [given roughly by $(3M_q)^2/\alpha'_N(0)$, with $\alpha'_N(0) \approx 1.1$ (GeV)$^{-2}$ obtained from the slope of the line joining the L = 2+ states with the L = 0+ states on the J-vs-M^2 plot], before the Regge trajectory turns back to the left.

The next positive parity configuration has L = 4+. This generates octet states with spin-parity $(9/2^+)$ and $(7/2^+)$, and decuplet states with spin-parity $(1/2^+)$, $(9/2^+)$, $(7/2^+)$, and $(5/2^+)$. These six unitary multiplets represent a further rotational excitation of the six unitary multiplets for L = 2+, so that there are six Regge rotational sequences associated with the 56 representation.

I = 3/2 N^* states are known up to high mass values,[55] as shown on Table 10-VI. As is well known, these states lie on a smooth curve, almost on a straight line, on the J-vs-M^2 plot, and this suggests that they are members of a common rotational sequence, corresponding to L = 0+, 2+, 4+, 6+, and 8+, in turn. It is of interest to note that the width of these states does not increase much with increasing L, over this range; the observed widths could well correspond only to upper limits, owing to the possibility of overlap of these levels with I = 3/2 negative-parity levels of the L = odd rotational sequence [of which only the L = 1- $(1/2^-)$ state $N^*_{1/2}(1680)$ is known at present]. The narrowness of these high-mass levels is again to be understood in terms of their high angular momentum J and the corresponding suppression of their decay by the large centrifugal barriers.

In the same way, a rotational sequence of negative-parity levels is expected to occur, based on the (L = 1-, 70) configuration, with L = 3-, 5-, 7-, and so on. The first excited configuration is (L = 3-, 70); this generates a large number of unitary multiplets: two singlet states, with $(5/2^-)$ and $(7/2^-)$, six octets, $(5/2^-)$ and $(1/2^-)$ for S = 1/2 and $(3/2^-)$, $(5/2^-)$, $(7/2^-)$, and $(9/2^-)$ for S = 3/2, and two decuplets, $(5/2^-)$ and $(7/2^-)$, ten multiplets in all. Of these multiplets, only two $(7/2^-)$ states are known, $N^*_{1/2}(2190)$ and $Y^*_0(2110)$; it seems most probable that the octet based on $N^*_{1/2}(2190)$ is the rotational excitation of the $N^*_{1/2}(1518)$ octet, and the $Y^*_0(2110)$ is a singlet state, the first rotational excitation of $Y^*_0(1520)$. Rather little is known of the branching ratios of $Y^*_0(2110)$, to check this singlet assignment.

Photoexcitation

Moorhouse[56] has considered the photoexcitation of these negative-parity N^* resonances,

$$\gamma + N \rightarrow N^* , \qquad (24)$$

according to the quark model. The most interesting result is that this transition is forbidden for the $(5/2^-)$ N^{*+}. This transition involves $^2S \rightarrow {}^4P$; the spin change excludes the normal E3 transition, and direct calculation of the M2 amplitude leads to zero. This is in accord with experiment; it is known that the γp resonance excitation observed near total energy 1690 MeV is dominantly due to $(5/2^+)$ excitation, the relative strengths of the two excitations being $(5/2^-)/(5/2^+) \approx 0.05$ in intensity.[57] It has been pointed out by Lipkin[58] that the vanishing of this M2 excitation is accidental. The magnetic moment operator transforms under SU(6) like Σ_i (charge $\times\, \underline{\sigma})_i$, which is a member of a 35 representation; the Clebsch-Gordan coefficient for 56 × 35 → 70, appropriate to the charge states in the transition $\gamma p \rightarrow N^{*+}$, happens to vanish. Lipkin pointed out further that the corresponding Clebsch-Gordan coefficient for the neutral excitation does not vanish, so that the excitation

Table 10-VI. Mass and width for the I = 3/2 N^* resonances which are believed to have positive parity. Note that $(\text{mass})^2$ increases uniformly [J/M^2 slope, 1.15 (GeV)$^{-2}$] through this sequence; the spin-parity values queried are purely speculative and based on the assumption that these five states form a Regge rotational sequence.

	JP				
	$3/2^+$	$7/2^+$	$(11/2^+)$?	$(15/2^+)$?	$(19/2^+)$?
Mass (GeV)	1.236	1.920	2.423±0.010	2.850±0.12	3.23
$(\text{Mass})^2$	1.53	3.69	5.86	8.12	10.43
Width Γ (MeV)	120	200	155±10	200±20	220

$$\gamma + n \to N^*_{1/2}(5/2^-)^0 \qquad (25)$$

is predicted to occur quite strongly through M2 excitation. It would be very interesting to see this prediction tested.

We should add here that photoexcitation of the ($\underset{\sim}{56}$, L = 2+) states is allowed; in particular, the observed photoexcitation process $\gamma p \to N^*_{1/2}(1688, 5/2^+)^+$ is permitted, through E2 and M3 transitions.

Resonance Decay Processes

The branching ratios for the various decay modes of the resonance states have been calculated by Mitra and Ross[40] and by Lipkin et al.[59] on the basis of the quark model, assuming the basic decay interaction to be the one-quark transition

$$q \to q + \text{meson}. \qquad (26)$$

This mechanism should not be taken too literally. This model is really a device for calculating the relevant Clebsch-Gordan coefficients appropriate to related transitions (i.e., transitions involving the same initial and the same final quark configurations, and the same orbital angular momentum for the outgoing meson).

Lipkin et al. point out[59] that the assumption of the quark model together with the interaction $q \to q + \pi$ leads exactly to the decay amplitudes (apart from a normalizing factor) corresponding to the assumption of $SU(6)_W$ without the quark model. The same is true for all decays involving emission of a K meson and for all decays involving an η meson. At this stage, these predictions of the quark model do not involve the assumption of SU(3) symmetry, but also they do not relate the π, K, and η amplitudes. To obtain their relationship it is necessary to assume SU(3) explicitly for interaction 26. Lipkin et al. use interaction 26 for calculation of the amplitudes for the decays $B^* \to B + M$, where B^* denotes the states $(5/2^+)$ and $(7/2^+)$ appropriate to the L = 2+ qqq configurations ($\underset{\sim}{56}$, 5) (see above). They point out that there generally are unknown form factors whose values may vary widely from decay mode to decay mode owing to the variations in the c.m. momentum of the decay, in consequence of the large mass differences within the SU(6) multiplets, and they recommend that the comparison with experiment should confine attention to ratios of partial decay widths for decay modes giving comparable c.m. momenta. Unfortunately rather few of their predictions can be tested at present, owing to the incompleteness of the data for these resonance states.

Mitra and Ross[40] make calculations for all the states of the L = 1 $\underset{\sim}{70}$ representation, using the coupling form

$$(\bar{q}\underset{\sim}{\sigma} \cdot (\underset{\sim}{q} - \frac{\omega}{M_q}\underset{\sim}{P})\, F_i q)\, P_i, \qquad (27)$$

the static meson-quark interaction together with the term appropriate to Galilean invariance. The decay modes to be considered are S- and D-wave decays of the type $B^*(\underset{\sim}{70}, 3) \to B(\underset{\sim}{56}, 1) + P$ and P-wave decays of the type $B^*(\overline{\underset{\sim}{70}}, 3) \to B^*(\overline{\underset{\sim}{70}}, 3) + P$, where P denotes the pseudoscalar meson octet. We shall not discuss their results in detail, but they do serve as the basis for a number of general remarks, as follow.

A. In this model, the rate for S- and D-wave decays has an additional factor ω^2, besides the phase-space and centrifugal-barrier factors $p[p^2X^2/(p^2+X^2)]^\ell$, which are normally included and which are strongly affected by the mass differences within the initial- and final-particle multiplets. This additional factor favors a heavy meson for a decay occurring near its threshold. For example, this factor may help to account for the strong $B\eta$ partial width for the octet of $(1/2^-)$ resonances which happen to lie close to the $B\eta$ thresholds.

B. Some of the resonance states are found to be quite narrow, or to be strongly inelastic relative to the channel most convenient for experiment. These features may be the reason why there has been no observation of some of the resonance states belonging to the ($\underset{\sim}{70}$, 3) configuration, even though there has been considerable exploration of the relevant mass range. For example, Mitra and Ross speculatively suggest that the $N^*_{3/2}$ state belonging to $^2\{10\}_{3/2}$ may lie at mass about 1585 MeV; in this event, its only decay modes would be $N\pi$, with width only 12 MeV, and $N^*\pi$, with width < 1 MeV. Another prediction is that the Y^*_0 state belonging to the configuration $^4\{8\}_{5/2}$ should have an exceedingly small partial width (calculated value zero) for the $\bar{K}N$ channel (the estimate given for this resonance by Leith in Session 9a was $x_{el} = 0.11 \pm 0.05$).

C. The $f/(d+f)$ ratios for the various $\{8\} \to \{8\}$ transitions $B^* \to B + P$ are predicted by the model, apart from the uncertainty about the amount of $^4\{8\}$-$^2\{8\}$ mixing. Several experimental papers have been presented, which give new methods for obtaining further limits on these ratios. Heusch et al.[60] consider the $(p\eta)/(p\pi^0)$ ratio for the photoexcitation $\gamma p \to N^*_{1/2}(1688, 5/2^+)^+$, for which they determine the upper limit 0.08 from the available data. The phase-space ratio {based on the expression $q[q^2X^2/(q^2+X^2)]^\ell$} lies between 0.22 and 0.54 as X runs from $M_N/2$ to m_π. The squared ratio of the matrix elements is 3 if this resonance belongs to a {27} representation, or $(1-4f)^2/3$ if it belongs to an {8} representation. Clearly, the observed ratio excludes the {27} representation, and requires the limits $0 \leq f \leq 0.5$ for the $B^*(5/2^+) \to B + P$ decay from an {8} representation.

Kernan and Smart[61] point out that it is possible to obtain additional information about the f values by making use of the relative phase for reaction amplitudes through different resonant states, deduced from the character of their interference terms. They consider particularly the reaction

$$K^- + n \to \Lambda + \pi^-. \qquad (28)$$

Angular distribution data have been obtained by Smart et al.[62] over the energy range including $Y^*_1(1660)$, $Y^*_1(1765)$, $Y^*_1(1915)$, and $Y^*_1(2030)$, and have been analyzed by them in terms of resonant amplitudes for these partial waves [$(3/2^-)$, $(5/2^-)$, $(5/2^+)$, and $(7/2^+)$, in turn], together with constant background amplitudes in S and P waves. These resonant amplitudes are of the form

$$T_1(\bar{K}N \to \Lambda\pi) = \phi(g_{N\bar{K}Y^*}\, g_{\Lambda\pi Y^*})/(E_R - E - i\Gamma/2), \qquad (29)$$

where ϕ includes an undetermined phase common to all the resonance amplitudes. The value expected for the quantity $(g_{N\bar{K}Y^*}\, g_{\Lambda\pi Y^*})$ depends on the representation $\{\alpha\}$, as follows:

$\{\alpha\}$	{8}	{10}	$\{\overline{10}\}$	{27}
$(g_{N\bar{K}Y^*}\, g_{\Lambda\pi Y^*})$	$-g_8^2(1-f)(1-2f)$	$+g_{10}^2$	$-g_{\overline{10}}^2$	$+g_{27}^2$

The new information given by the analysis of these angular-distribution data in terms of the amplitudes 29 is the relative sign of this quantity (··) for each of the four resonances in this region:

Y^* resonance at	1660	1765	1915	2030
Sign of $(g_{N\bar{K}Y^*}\, g_{\Lambda\pi Y^*}$	+	-	-	+

Here, the phase of ϕ has been chosen to make the expression $(\cdot\cdot)$ positive for $Y_1^*(2030)$, since this $(7/2^+)$ resonance is believed to belong to a decuplet containing the $(7/2^+)$ resonance $N_{3/2}^*(1920)$ and since this expression is expected to be positive for a decuplet Y_1^*, according to the preceding table. Comparison of these tables then leads to the following conclusions:

(i) $Y_1^*(1765)$ can belong only to a $\{\overline{10}\}$ representation, or to an $\{8\}$ representation with $f > 1$ or $f < 0.5$. A study of the branching ratios for $Y_1^*(1765)$ by Yodh et al.[63] favors the $\{8\}$ assignment with $f = -1.5^{+0.7}_{-1.1}$ or $-0.5^{+0.2}_{-0.3}$; either of these solutions is in accord with the limits just obtained.

(ii) $Y_1^*(1915)$ is believed to belong to a $(5/2^+)$ octet, together with $N_{1/2}^*(1688)$ and $Y_0^*(1815)$. This octet must have $f > 1$ or $f < 0.5$.

(iii) $Y_1^*(1660)$ is believed to belong to a $(3/2^-)$ octet, together with $N_{1/2}^*(1518)$. For this octet, the observed sign for $(\cdot\cdot)$ requires $0.5 < f < 1.0$.

D. The assignment for the well-known resonance $\Xi_{1/2}^*(1820)$ has been a difficulty.[64] Direct measurement of its spin and parity led to the possibilities $(3/2^-)$ and $(5/2^+)$; the location of its mass relative to the other known $(5/2^+)$ resonances favors the assignment $(3/2^-)$. If $\Xi_{1/2}^*(1820)$ belongs to the same octet as $N_{1/2}^*(1518)$ and $Y_1^*(1660)$, then, as emphasized by Marinov[50] and by Goldberg et al.,[51] the partial widths observed for the BP decay modes of those latter resonances imply an f value such that the $\Sigma\overline{K}/\Lambda\overline{K}$ ratio should be large (typically of order 10) for $\Xi_{1/2}^*(1820)$ decay. Experimentally, the mode $\Xi_{1/2}(1820) \to \Sigma\overline{K}$ has not yet been established; the upper limit for the branching ratio is $\Sigma\overline{K}/\Lambda\overline{K} \leq 0.1$, within one standard deviation.[65] If $\Xi_{1/2}^*(1820)$ is assigned to the $(5/2^+)$ octet containing $N_{1/2}^*(1688)$ and $Y_0^*(1815)$, overlooking the difficulties with the mass formula in this event, a similar discrepancy is found for this branching ratio.

Mitra and Ross[40] have pointed out the possibility that $\Xi_{1/2}^*(1820)$ could belong to the unidentified $(3/2^-)$ decuplet predicted by the $(\underset{\sim}{70}, 3)$ representation for negative parity resonances. This decuplet state has the form $(\overline{K}\Sigma + \pi\Xi + \overline{K}\Lambda - \eta\Xi)/2$; with the larger phase space for the $\Lambda\overline{K}$ channel relative to the $\Sigma\overline{K}$ channel, the branching ratio prediction is $(\Sigma\overline{K})/(\Lambda\overline{K}) = 0.3$. Mitra and Ross point out that this ratio is quite sensitive to a moderate admixture of octet state. Since we expect the $(3/2^-)$ octet Ξ^* to lie not far from 1800 MeV, on the basis of the systematics of baryonic masses, the octet and decuplet $(3/2^-)$ Ξ^* states must lie quite close in mass, so that quite strong mixing would be expected to occur through the SU(3)-breaking interactions. With the state $(\sqrt{0.9}\ {}^2\{10\} + \sqrt{0.1}\ {}^2\{8\})$, they find satisfactory values for the partial widths, their predictions then being $\Gamma(\Lambda\overline{K}) = 10$ MeV, $\Gamma(\Sigma\overline{K}) = 0.1$ MeV, $\Gamma(\Xi\pi) = 1$ MeV, and $\Gamma(\Xi\pi) = 8$ MeV; however, there is no theoretical basis for this particular admixture. Mitra and Ross emphasize that a satisfactory fit cannot be obtained by a small $\{10\}$ admixture with a dominant $\{8\}$ state.

E. With definite predictions for the decay amplitudes for all the states ${}^{2S+1}\{\alpha\}_J$ of the $(\underset{\sim}{70}, 3)$ representation, as provided by the Mitra-Ross calculation, there are more clues to the problem of assigning the observed resonances to these configurations. For the $(1/2^-)$ states, the $B\eta$ resonance states $N_{1/2}^*(1570)$, $Y_0^*(1670)$, and $Y_1^*(1750)$ must be assigned to the ${}^4\{8\}$ configurations, on the basis of their observed widths. The very broad state $N_{1/2}^*(1700)$ must then be assigned to the ${}^2\{8\}$ configuration, leading to the conclusion that ${}^2\{8\}_{1/2}$ lies above the ${}^4\{8\}_{1/2}$ configuration. For the $(3/2^-)$ states, $N_{1/2}^*(1518)$ and $Y_1^*(1660)$ are fitted adequately by the decay properties of the ${}^2\{8\}_{3/2}$ configuration. The ${}^4\{8\}_{3/2}$ configurations are all predicted to have rather small partial widths for decay to BP, their dominant decay modes being $B^*(3/2^+) + P$; however, no candidates are yet known for this configuration. The assignment of $\Xi_{1/2}^*(1820)$ to ${}^2\{10\}_{3/2}$ implies the existence of a corresponding Y_1^* at about 1650 to 1750 MeV, a corresponding $N_{3/2}^*$ at about 1500 to 1650 MeV, and an Ω^- state at about 1900 to 2000 MeV (which would appear as a narrow $\Xi\overline{K}$ resonance state). No candidates are known for these decuplet states; their BP partial widths are predicted to be relatively small (being due to D-wave emission), their dominant decay modes being predicted to be $PB^*(3/2^+)$, which can occur through S-wave emission. The pattern of N^* levels, as assigned to fit the Mitra-Ross decay-width calculations, is shown on Fig. 10-6. This pattern of spin-orbit splittings is not understood at present. As discussed above, its generation may be quite a complicated resultant of the joint effect of spin-orbit interactions and SU(3)-breaking interactions.

Unwanted States

As pointed out above, the requirement of antisymmetry for the space wave function for the L = 0 baryon ground state implies that there are internal angular momenta $\underset{\sim}{\ell}, \underset{\sim}{\ell}'$ in this state, summing to give $\underset{\sim}{\ell} + \underset{\sim}{\ell}' = \underset{\sim}{L} = 0$. Thirring has pointed out[43] another antisymmetric wave function that can be constructed

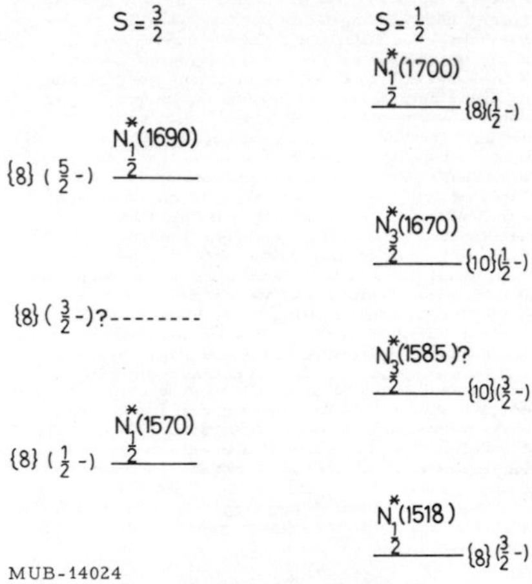

$S = \frac{3}{2}$ $S = \frac{1}{2}$

$N_1^*(1700)$ $\frac{1}{2}$ $\{8\}(\frac{1}{2}-)$

$\{8\}(\frac{5}{2}-)$ $N_1^*(1690)$ $\frac{1}{2}$

$N_3^*(1670)$ $\frac{1}{2}$ $\{10\}(\frac{1}{2}-)$

$\{8\}(\frac{3}{2}-)$?

$N_3^*(1585)$? $\frac{3}{2}$ $\{10\}(\frac{3}{2}-)$

$\{8\}(\frac{1}{2}-)$ $N_1^*(1570)$ $\frac{1}{2}$

$N_1^*(1518)$ $\frac{1}{2}$ $\{8\}(\frac{3}{2}-)$

MUB-14024

Fig. 10-6. The pattern of N^* levels for the negative-parity supermultiplet (L = 1-, $\underset{\sim}{70}$), following the assignments of Mitra and Ross (Ref. 40) based on the partial widths calculated by them for the various decay modes of these resonance states. The level $N_{3/2}^*(1585)$ is speculative, its location being estimated following the assignment of $\Xi_{1/2}^*(1820)$ to a $(3/2^-)$ decuplet. The S = 3/2 octet level $(3/2^-)$ has not yet been identified. We note that the sign of the spin-orbit coupling corresponds to repulsion in the state where $\underset{\sim}{L}$ and $\underset{\sim}{S}$ are parallel for the ${}^4\{8\}$ and ${}^2\{1\}$ configurations, and to attraction for the ${}^2\{8\}$ and ${}^2\{10\}$ configurations, according to this figure.

from the same internal angular momenta $\ell = \ell' = 1$, to give total orbital angular momentum L = 1+. This space wave function has the form

$$\psi_{space}(\underline{r}_1, \underline{r}_2, \underline{r}_3) = (\underline{r}_{12} \times \underline{r}_{23} + \underline{r}_{23} \times \underline{r}_{31} + \underline{r}_{31} \times \underline{r}_{12}) \times \phi_{symm}(\underline{r}_1, \underline{r}_2, \underline{r}_3). \quad (30)$$

Thirring pointed out that this wave function has less severe nodes than the L = 0+ space wave function, so that these states might well be expected to lie lower in mass than those for the L = 0+ baryon configuration discussed. At least, these positive parity states would be expected to occur at quite low excitation energy, relative to the baryons. This L = 1+ configuration would lead to a (56, 3) representation, consisting of {8} states for spin-parity $(1/2^+)$ and $(3/2^+)$ and {10} states for spin-parity $(1/2^+)$, $(3/2^+)$, and $(5/2^+)$.

There exists no experimental evidence for all these positive parity states. [There does exist evidence for a resonance $N^*_{1/2}(1400)$, especially from the reaction $pp \to pN^*$ at high energies. This resonance is usually identified with the P_{11} state of the πN system, since the P_{11} phase does show a rapid variation in this region, which may be consistent with the existence of a strongly inelastic resonance in this I = 1/2 $(1/2^+)$ state.] However, it has been pointed out by Morpurgo[66] that the decay of states $B^*_{56}(L = 1+)$ is governed by some very restrictive selection rules. Their decay by meson emission to the octet and decuplet states of the supermultiplet $B_{56}(L = 0+)$ is forbidden, as long as this meson emission takes place through one-quark interactions; the decay amplitude would then be proportional to the matrix element $\langle (L = 0+) | \Sigma_i \exp(ik \cdot r_i) | (L = 1+) \rangle$, which necessarily vanishes. Their decay by γ emission to these states is also strongly suppressed, since the large electromagnetic interaction of the quarks, the interaction with their anomalous moments, similarly leads to a vanishing space factor in the amplitude. These $B^*_{56}(L = 1+)$ states can still decay through the emission of two uncorrelated mesons, and the channels $[B_{56}(L = 0+) + \pi + \pi]$ are likely to be their most probable decay modes. With these selection rules, the direct formation of these $B^*_{56}(L = 1+)$ states could well be quite difficult; they would probably be formed most readily as decay products from the decay of heavier B^* resonances.

Parastatistics for Quarks

Greenberg[67] has considered the possibility that quarks do not follow Fermi statistics, but rather para-Fermi statistics of order p = 3. Essentially, this is equivalent to the introduction of three quark triplets q^i_α, with i = 1, 2, 3, with the proviso that the three fields q^1_α, q^2_α, q^3_α enter into all interactions in a completely symmetrical way, so that it is impossible to distinguish physically between these three quark triplets. These quark fields q^i_α are such that commutation relations appropriate to Bose statistics hold for two fields q^i_α, q^j_α with $i \neq j$, and that anticommutation relations appropriate to Fermi statistics hold when i = j. Hence, for a three-quark system, it is possible to build up a wave function for the space, spin, and unitary-spin variables which is symmetrical in the labels of the three quarks. With parastatistics of order 3, therefore, the three-quark wave function belonging to the 56 representation of SU(6) corresponds to a symmetrical space wave function, as one normally expects for the ground-state configuration.

Greenberg has investigated the excited three-quark configurations on the basis of a shell-model representation for the quarks. Naturally, he finds that the first excited configuration, belonging to the S^2P^1 shell, corresponds to the representation (70, 3). The two-quantum excitations lead to a number of supermultiplets, to the L = 2+ representations (56, 5) and (70, 5), the L = 1+ representations (70, 3) and (20, 3), and the L = 0+ representations (56, 1) and (70, 1). The relative masses of these supermultiplets depend on the detailed assumptions about the qq interactions.

Mitra has presented[68] some dynamical calculations on the qqq supermultiplets, on the basis of parastatistics. For this hypothesis, he argues that a form factor corresponding to the antisymmetrical space wave function necessarily has nodes (see note following Eq. 15), contrary to the evidence from the baryon form factors; the symmetrical space wave function then permitted for the ground state 56 would be free from this serious objection. Mitra finds that the relatively low-lying position found for the first excited state (the L = 1-, 70 configuration, naturally) requires a very strong P-wave attraction. Mitra then finds the problem of unwanted states of positive parity, discussed by Thirring[43] for the case of normal statistics for the quarks. With this very strong P-wave attraction, it becomes energetically favorable to excite two P-wave quarks, by far the most favorable configuration being that for which L = 1+ and the space wave function is totally antisymmetric. With parastatistics, this configuration corresponds to the totally antisymmetric SU(6) representation 20, whose SU(3) content is given by

$$\underline{20} \to (\{8\},\ S = \tfrac{1}{2}) + (\{1\},\ S = \tfrac{3}{2}). \quad (31)$$

The spin-orbit coupling then splits these states (20, 3) into the following SU(3) multiplets: two octets, with spin-parity $(1/2^+)$ and $(3/2^+)$, and three singlet states, with spin-parity $(5/2^+)$, $(3/2^+)$, and $(1/2^+)$. The remarks made by Morpurgo[66] about the strongly restrictive selection rules governing the decay modes for the L = 1+ configurations again apply to these states. These states have not been observed [unless the state $N^*_{1/2}(1400)$ observed in inelastic pp collisions is a member of this $(1/2^+)$ octet], but they would be difficult to excite directly, through photoexcitation or meson-baryon collisions. Until there is some evidence for them, they appear to provide a difficulty for the quark model of baryonic states, whether Fermi statistics or parastatistics are adopted.

6. Higher Representations for Excited Mesonic and Baryonic States

An alternative proposal which has frequently been made to account for the higher mesonic and baryonic resonances is that of assigning them to larger SU(6) representations. In terms of group theory (rather than dynamics) this is equivalent to considering more complicated configurations of quarks and antiquarks, however, keeping always to S-wave states. The positive-parity mesons can be assigned to configurations $qq\bar{q}\bar{q}$. Since the P and V mesons belong to the 35 representation, the representations which allow the decay modes P + P and P + V are contained in the reduction

$$\underline{35} \times \underline{35} = \underline{1} + 2.\underline{35} + \underline{189} + \underline{280} + \underline{280}^* + \underline{405}. \quad (32)$$

The representations which have been considered for the positive-parity mesons are the 189 and the 405 representations. The SU(3) multiplets contained in these representations are listed in Table 10-VII.

The negative-parity baryons are assigned to configurations $qqqq\bar{q}$. The representations which

Table 10-VII. SU(3)-spin reduction table for SU(6) representations.

Representation	189	405	700	1134
{35}			$5/2^-, 3/2^-$	$3/2^-, 1/2^-$
{27}	0^+	$2^+, 1^+, 0^+$	$3/2^-, 1/2^-$	$5/2^-, 3/2^-, 3/2^-, 1/2^-, 1/2^-$
$\{\overline{10}\}$	1^+	1^+	$1/2^-$	$3/2^-, 1/2^-$
{10}	1^+	1^+	$5/2^-, 3/2^-, 1/2^-$	$5/2^-, 3/2^-, 3/2^-, 1/2^-, 1/2^-$
{ 8}	$2^+, 1^+, 1^+, 0^+$	$2^+, 1^+, 1^+, 0^+$	$3/2^-, 1/2^-$	$5/2^-, 3/2^-, 3/2^-, 3/2^-, 1/2^-, 1/2^-, 1/2^-$
{ 1}	$2^+, 0^+$	$2^+, 0^+$		$3/2^-, 1/2^-$

allow decay to (meson + baryon) states are contained in the reduction

$$\underline{35} \times \underline{56} = \underline{56} + \underline{70} + \underline{700} + \underline{1134}. \qquad (33)$$

The SU(3) multiplets contained in these representations are listed in Table 10-VII. Spin $(5/2^-)$ states are contained only in the 700 and 1134 representations. Only the 1134 representation includes the $(5/2^-)$ octet and the $(3/2^-)$ and $(1/2^-)$ singlet states observed. Coyne et al.[69] have discussed the fitting of the partial-width data for $Y_1^*(1765)$ and $Y_0^*(1520)$ by their assignment to the 1134 representation. They find that all these decays are governed by the same amplitude, so that the relative partial widths are determined only by Clebsch-Gordan coefficients and phase-space factors; the agreement with the data is tolerable. The main difficulty with this assigment is the rather large number of SU(3) multiplets which are then predicted, but for which there are no experimental indications at present. However, many of these predicted resonances cannot decay to (P+B) states, or may be difficult to excite.

Horn et al. have pointed out[70] that there can be rather restrictive $SU(6)_W$ selection rules governing the decay of states belonging to these large SU(6) representations, analogous to the $SU(6)_W$ selection rule, which forbids the decay $\phi \to \pi\rho$. They discuss particularly Z spin, a particular set of generators for a subgroup of $SU(6)_W$, given by $Z_z = W_z$ and $Z_{x,y} = (1/3 + 2Y)W_{x,y}$. For any system containing only nonstrange quarks and only strange antiquarks, Z-spin conservation is equivalent to ordinary spin conservation. Then, for example, the decay of a system (usually referred to as a Z particle) with Y = 2 to K+N is forbidden for $J \geq 3/2$; this selection rule can be extended to other states of the same SU(3) multiplet by use of the Wigner-Eckart theorem. Other selection rules can be obtained by performing I-spin and U-spin transformations on the definition of Z spin.

Selection rules of particular interest are as follows:

(a) (2+) mesonic states belonging to a {27} multiplet in an SU(6) 405 representation are forbidden to decay to PP or $\overline{P}$V final states.

(b) $(5/2^-)$ baryonic states belonging to a {27} or {35} multiplet within a 700 or 1134 SU(6) representation are forbidden to decay to $\overline{PB}$, VB, or PD final states [where D denotes the $(3/2^+)$ decuplet].

(c) $(3/2^-)$ baryonic states belonging to a $\{\overline{10}\}$, {27}, or {35} multiplet within a 700 or 1134 SU(6) representation are forbidden to decay to PB final states.

(d) $(1/2^-)$ baryonic states belonging to a $\{\overline{10}\}$, {27}, or {35} multiplet within a 700 or 1134 SU(6) representation are forbidden to decay to PD final states.

These selection rules mean that many states belonging to the unfamiliar SU(3) multiplets contained within these large SU(6) multiplets cannot be formed by one-meson exchange mechanisms (resonance production cross sections to which these mechanisms cannot contribute are usually suppressed by one or two orders of magnitudes), nor by meson-baryon collisions (so that they will be difficult to detect from total-cross-section measurements). Since KN resonances necessarily belong to $\{\overline{10}\}$ or {27} multiplets, it is possible that these selection rules may account in part for the relative lack of structure found in the KN cross sections. All these resonances can occur as decay products from still more massive resonance states, so that a search for them would best be made in reactions leading to relatively complicated multiparticle final states.

The 405 representation has also been adopted by Elitzur et al.[71] to account for the spin 2+ nonet. These authors do not insist on SU(3) symmetry, but adopt a principle of conservation of the total number n_λ of λ and $\bar{\lambda}$ quarks for classification of the 405 substates and for discussion of their decay processes. The nine states f, f', A2, and K^* given by this classification are definite superpositions of the states of the {1}, {8}, and {27} representations of SU(3). The decay amplitudes are calculated by carrying out a quark-spin recoupling, followed by quark rearrangement to give the final PP and VP states; SU(3) is then conserved in the PP decays, but this procedure necessarily breaks SU(3) for the VP decays. The decay rates calculated for these modes correspond to partial widths which naturally differ from those of the SU(3) analysis by Glashow and Socolow,[72] but which agree equally well with the available data when the η-η' mixing angle is chosen sufficiently small (actually, $|\alpha| \leq 10°$, which value is quite compatible with the mixing angle suggested by the deviation of the pseudoscalar meson masses from the Gell-Mann–Okubo mass formula). This work serves to illustrate again that agreement with experiment can often be obtained without the assumption of SU(3) symmetry. This underlines the continuing need for accurate and detailed tests of SU(3) symmetry over the widest possible range of phenomena.

The quark rearrangement hypothesis was discussed also by Rubinstein and Stern[73] for $p\bar{p}$ annihilation. However, as discussed by Harte et al.[74] and by Kirz,[75] it appears that this hypothesis leads to considerable disagreement with the experimental data for that situation.

7. Meson Mixing Angles

It is well known that the I = 0 meson states (denoted here by ψ_0' and ψ_0'') in a nonet are not generally unitary pure. Their SU(3) character is defined by a mixing angle θ, such that

$$\psi_0' = \psi_8 \cos\theta - \psi_1 \sin\theta, \quad (34a)$$

$$\psi_0'' = \psi_8 \sin\theta + \psi_1 \cos\theta, \quad (34b)$$

where ψ_8, ψ_1 denote the pure octet and singlet states, respectively. In the quark model, these states ψ_8 and ψ_1 have the unitary structure

$$\psi_8 = (\bar{p}p + \bar{n}n - 2\bar{\lambda}\lambda)/\sqrt{6}, \quad (35a)$$

$$\psi_1 = (\bar{p}p + \bar{n}n + \bar{\lambda}\lambda)/\sqrt{3}. \quad (35b)$$

At present, the mixing angle is deduced from the observed masses for all the particles in the nonet. This calculation assumes the exact validity of the first-order mass formula, that due to Gell-Mann and Okubo. These nine masses are known for three nonets, the (0-), (1-), and (2+) nonets. The mixing angles calculated in this way (using the quadratic form of the mass formula, for the reasons given in Sec. 4) are:

(i) pseudoscalar meson nonet, $\theta_P = -11°$,
(ii) vector meson nonet, $\theta_V = +40°$,
(iii) spin-2+ meson nonet, $\theta_T = +30°$.

The sign of the mixing angle is not given from the analysis of the masses; the signs given here are those corresponding to the quark model.

For the vector mesons, an estimate of the mixing angle θ_V can be obtained in several independent ways, involving further assumptions. The assumption of $SU(6)_W$ symmetry leads to the conclusion that $\psi_8 \to \rho\pi$ is forbidden, whereas $\psi_1 \to \rho\pi$ is allowed. The physical ϕ meson corresponds to the state ψ_0''; the physical ω meson corresponds to the state ψ_0'. Then the decay rates $\Gamma(\omega \to 3\pi)$ and $\Gamma(\phi \to \rho\pi)$ are governed by the same matrix element, namely $M(\psi_1 \to \rho\pi)$, and their ratio can be expressed in terms of the physical mixing angle. The calculation by Glashow and Socolow[72] gives

$$\Gamma(\phi \to \rho\pi) \approx 17 \tan^2(\theta_V - \theta)\,\Gamma(\omega \to 3\pi), \quad (36)$$

where θ denotes the ideal mixing angle, $\theta = 35.3°$ corresponding to $\tan\theta = 1/\sqrt{2}$. This allows two solutions, the larger solution being $39 \pm 1°$. The second procedure cannot be carried through at present, as the necessary data are incomplete. This depends on the assumption (valid with the simple quark model) that the electromagnetic current transforms like the U = 0 member of an octet. In this case, the coupling $\psi_1 \to \gamma$ is forbidden, and the decay processes $\omega \to e^+e^-$ and $\phi \to e^+e^-$, which are mediated by the electromagnetic field, both depend on the same matrix element, the ratio of their decay rates being[76, 77]

$$\Gamma(\omega \to e^+e^-)/\Gamma(\phi \to e^+e^-) = (m_\omega/m_\phi)\tan^2\theta_V. \quad (37)$$

At present, there are available only a rough value for $\Gamma(\omega \to e^+e^-)$ (branching ratio $\approx 2 \times 10^{-4}$ on the basis of three events) and an upper limit (branching ratio $< 3 \times 10^{-3}$) for $\Gamma(\phi \to e^+e^-)$. Improved data on these partial widths would provide a valuable check on our present interpretation of the ω and ϕ mesons.

Alexander et al.[78] have pointed out the possibility of determining these mixing angles from meson-production data. Here the assumption made is that, for any reaction of the type

$$\text{meson} + A \to \text{meson} + A', \quad (38)$$

the amplitude is equal to the sum of the two contributions for the quark and the antiquark in the meson; that is, the quark and antiquark are assumed to act independently and their scattering amplitudes are assumed additive. With these assumptions, there is a restriction on the relationship between the initial and final meson states; not both quarks can change type. If ψ_λ, ψ_{NO} denote the states

$$\psi_\lambda = \bar{\lambda}\lambda, \quad (39a)$$

$$\psi_{NO} = (\bar{p}p + \bar{n}n)/\sqrt{2}, \quad (39b)$$

then it follows that an incident pion, being composed of a p, n quark and a $\bar{p}$, $\bar{n}$ antiquark, cannot change to the state ψ_λ in these reactions, so that we have many relationships of the kind

$$\langle \pi^- p | \psi_\lambda n \rangle = \langle \pi^+ n | \psi_\lambda p \rangle = \langle \pi^+ p | \psi_\lambda N^{*++} \rangle = \langle \pi^- p | \psi_\lambda N^{*0} \rangle = 0. \quad (40)$$

Since we have, from Eqs. 34, 35, and 39

$$\psi_\lambda = \{(\cos\theta - \sqrt{2}\sin\theta)\,\psi_0'' - (\sqrt{2}\cos\theta + \sin\theta)\,\psi_0'\}/\sqrt{3}, \quad (41)$$

the relations 40 lead to a relation between the ψ_0' and ψ_0'' production cross sections which depends on the mixing angle for the nonet considered. For example, the mixing angle θ_V can be obtained from the cross-section ratio

$$\frac{\sigma(\pi^+ p \to \phi N^{*++})}{\sigma(\pi^+ p \to \omega N^{*++})} = \left(\frac{\cos\theta_V - \sqrt{2}\sin\theta_V}{\sin\theta_V + \sqrt{2}\cos\theta_V}\right)^2 \quad (42)$$

Owing to the mass differences between the two mesons ψ_0' and ψ_0'', there are kinematical corrections, discussed by Alexander et al.,[78] which need to be made to the data before their cross sections can be compared in this way.

Estimates of the mixing angles θ_P, θ_V, and θ_T have been made on this basis by Benson et al.[79] and by Lai and Schumann.[80] For reactions of the type $\pi^+ p \to \eta N^{*++}$ and $\eta' N^{*++}$ at various energies they obtain estimates $-28 \pm 7°$ and $-19 \pm 7°$ for θ_P; for reactions of the type $\pi^+ n \to p\eta'$ and $p\eta$, they obtain $-28 \pm 7°$ and $-31 \pm 5°$. For the η, η' comparisons, the kinematical corrections are necessarily rather large, owing to the large η, η' mass difference; in each case, there is also a second solution for θ_P, in the range $-80°$ to $-90°$, which is far from the expected value. For the reactions $\pi^+ n \to p\phi$ and $p\omega$, Benson et al. obtain the estimate $27 \pm 4°$ or $43 \pm 4°$ for θ_V; Lai and Schumann obtain the estimate $\theta_V = 35 \pm 7°$ from data on the reactions $\pi^+ p \to \phi N^{*++}$ and ωN^{*++} at various energies. From data on the reactions $\pi^- p \to nf$ and nf' at various energies, Lai and Schumann obtain the estimate $\theta_T = 26 \pm 2.5°$ or $47 \pm 3°$. In each case the cross-section data lead to one solution for the mixing angle which is comparable with the angle expected from the analysis of the nonet masses; in particular, the data on η and η' production definitely require a mixing angle θ_P with sign opposite to that of the vector and 2+ mixing angles.

Another set of relationships of this kind can be obtained for reactions induced by K mesons. For example, the ρ^0 meson corresponds to the $\bar{q}q$ state $(\bar{p}p - \bar{n}n)/\sqrt{2}$. An incident K^- meson (quark configuration $\bar{p}\lambda$) can change into $\bar{p}p$, but not into $\bar{n}n$, so that, for example,

$$\langle K^- A | \psi_{NO} B \rangle = \langle K^- A | \rho^0 B \rangle . \quad (43)$$

Owing to the closeness of θ_V and θ, the state ψ_{NO} can be replaced by the ω meson, to a rather good approximation. An example of relation 43 is provided by the K^-p reactions, where the prediction is

$$\frac{d\sigma}{d\Omega}(K^- p \to \Lambda\omega) = \frac{d\sigma}{d\Omega}(K^- p \to \Lambda\rho^0). \quad (44)$$

Up to about 3 BeV, the data are in contradiction with this prediction; the data of London et al.[81] at 2.24 BeV give a $\Lambda\omega$ cross section very much larger than that for $\Lambda\rho^0$, and the $\Lambda\omega$ cross section is roughly isotropic, whereas the $\Lambda\rho^0$ cross section is peripheral in character. However, recent data for K^-p interactions at 4.1 and 5.5 GeV/c give quite good agreement with the prediction.[82] The $\Lambda\omega$, $\Lambda\rho^0$, and $\Lambda\phi$ production angular distributions at 4.1 GeV/c are shown on Fig. 10-7. The ω and ρ^0 distributions agree in showing a strong forward peak, together with a secondary backward peak, whereas the ϕ distribution differs from them by showing only the peripheral forward peak. The total cross sections for the $\Lambda\omega$ and $\Lambda\rho^0$ reactions are not yet well known. The preliminary estimates at 4.1 GeV/c are $\sigma(\Lambda\rho^0) = 41 \pm 17$ μb and $\sigma(\Lambda\omega) = 41 \pm 15$ μb, compatible with equality for these reactions.

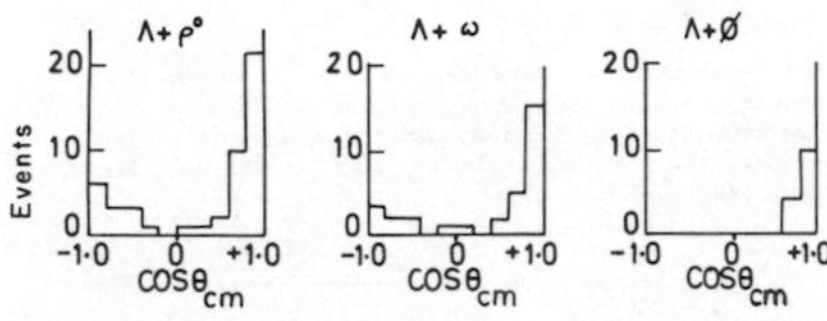

Fig. 10-7. The angular distributions for $\Lambda\rho^0$, $\Lambda\omega$, and $\Lambda\phi$ final states from K^-p collisions at 4.1 GeV/c, as reported by Davis et al. (Ref. 81), where $\theta_{c.m.}$ denotes the meson production angle in the barycentric system.

One further example discussed by Alexander et al.[78] involves the comparison of two rather different reactions. In a reaction leading from $K^- = (\bar{p}\lambda)$ to $\psi_\lambda = (\bar{\lambda}\lambda)$, only the interaction of the antiquark is effective; the same is true for the corresponding reaction leading from $\pi^- = (\bar{p}n)$ to $K^0 = (\bar{\lambda}n)$. Since the same antiquark transition occurs, the two reaction amplitudes are equal; for example,

$$\langle K^-p|\psi_\lambda\Lambda\rangle = \langle\pi^-p\,|\,K^0\Lambda\rangle \qquad (45)$$

Alexander et al. compare data on the production cross sections for vector states; then ψ_λ is approximately ϕ and the $(\bar{\lambda}n)$ state represents K^{*0}. The data at Q value 460 MeV are $\sigma(K^-p \to \Lambda\phi) = 40 \pm 8$ μb (for 3.0 GeV/c incident momentum) and $\sigma(\pi^-p \to \Lambda K^{*0}) = 53 \pm 8$ μb (for 2.7 GeV/c incident momentum), in satisfactory agreement.

8. Conclusion

Let us conclude by summarizing briefly the elements of success, and the difficulties, of the nonrelativistic quark model for the elementary particle states, in its attempt to provide a basis for an understanding of SU(6) symmetry. For the mesonic states, the $\bar{q}q$ model has the following features:

(i) It allows only nonet states.

(ii) The nonets occur in supermultiplets of four nonets with the same parity. The quantum numbers of these states are those $[P = (-1)^{L+1},\ C = (-1)^{L+S}]$ corresponding to the states formed by the addition of an internal spin S, which can take the values 0 and 1, to an internal orbital angular momentum L, to give the total angular momentum $J = L$ or $L \pm 1$ (for $L = 0$, the situation is special; there are only two nonets, for $S = 0$ and $S = 1$).

(iii) The four nonets are separated in mass by a spin-orbit force giving a mass contribution proportional to $L \cdot S$.

(iv) The higher-mass mesons are Regge rotational excitations of the $L = 0$ configurations. Along the Regge trajectory, the meson states occur at intervals $\Delta J = 1$. Owing to the large quark mass, these meson states are tightly bound. A natural and qualitative conclusion from this is that there is a long sequence of rotational states (i.e., the Regge trajectory continues moving to the right), up to J values of order 10^2. The J-vs-M^2 plot is observed linear; this is not an unreasonable situation for the low-lying states, since the $\bar{q}q$ potential might well be approximated by a harmonic oscillator potential near the bottom of the well, but we have no reason to expect this linear dependence to persist much further than $J \approx 10$.

(v) The high-mass meson states (mass~2 GeV) are observed to have quite small widths (typically 20 to 30 MeV, at most--much of this width may be due to the resolution curve). A natural, qualitative explanation of the narrowness of these states is provided by their high angular momentum, the small decay probabilities being due primarily to the rapid fall of the penetration factors with increasing J. However, the large width (130 MeV) observed for the ρ meson does appear to pose something of a problem.[83] Although it is not clear what is the natural scale for lifetimes for strongly interacting particle decay, this width is sufficiently large relative to 1 GeV to suggest a substantial reduced width for 2π state (i.e., $qq\bar{q}\bar{q}$ component) in the ρ-meson wave function, contrary to the assumption of a $\bar{q}q$ structure.

For the baryonic states, there has been less progress in our understanding of the phenomena in terms of the nonrelativistic quark model. There are a number of serious difficulties and obscurities, as follow:

(i) The assumption of Fermi statistics for quarks, and the observation that the low-lying states of positive parity form a 56 representation, lead to the requirement that the $L = 0$ space wave function for the qqq ground state be totally antisymmetric. The dynamics leading to this situation are not easy to understand; even with space-exchange forces which are repulsive in the S state, there is some doubt whether the $L = 0+$ configuration would necessarily lie lowest in mass. Further, there is a serious possibility that antisymmetry for the baryon space wave function may require a zero in the baryon structure form factor for quite low momentum transfer q^2. This would require a zero for the same q^2 in both electric and magnetic form factors, for a value of q^2 most probably in the range of momentum-transfers already well explored. These difficulties could be avoided if the quarks obeyed parastatistics, but this is an unattractive possibility, since it represents a very drastic and far-reaching hypothesis which may raise more difficulties than it solves.

(ii) The hypothesis that the low-lying baryonic resonant states of negative parity belong to an $L = 1^-$ configuration belonging to the 70 representation of SU(6) offers the possibility of accounting for all the observed unitary multiplets of this type in a single supermultiplet. The observed masses show appreciable mass splitting of the type due to noncentral qq interactions. However, the pattern of mass splittings does not appear to correspond to a simple spin-orbit force, and this pattern is not understood at present.

(iii) The data on higher baryonic resonances appear consistent with the notion that these arise as Regge rotational excitations of the two low-lying configurations ($L = 0+$, 56) and ($L = 1-$, 70). Here, the $L =$ even configurations are distinguished from the $L =$ odd configurations by differing internal symmetries, so that the baryonic states in a rotational sequence occur at intervals $\Delta L = 2$. The N^* states which have $I = 3/2$ and are believed to have positive parity [therefore representative of the configurations (L = 2n+, 56) for n integral] have masses which lie on a smooth Regge trajectory which is approximately linear. Owing to the tight binding of these baryonic states, the Regge rotational sequence is expected to continue, with the Regge trajectory continuing to move to the right, up to J values of order 10^3 [for $M_q \approx 10$ GeV; more generally, up to $J \approx (3M_q)^2$].

(iv) The widths of the baryonic resonances which correspond to the leading 56 Regge trajectory do not increase rapidly with increasing mass. For example, $N^*_{3/2}(2850)$ has width 200 MeV, to be compared with 120 MeV for $N^*_{3/2}(1236)$. This behavior can be understood qualitatively in terms of the high angular momentum attributed to these states, corresponding primarily to the rapid fall of the penetration factor for the centrifugal barriers with increasing J.

(v) There is evidence for one further low-lying baryonic resonance state, lying outside the configurations mentioned above, namely $N^*_{1/2}(1400)$, believed to have spin-parity ($1/2^+$). Its internal configuration is not at all understood. Its identification with the (L = 1+, 56) configuration implies the existence of four other unitary multiplets, none of which is known. Its identification with the (L = 0+, 20) configuration is more economical, implying the existence of only a $3/2^+$ unitary singlet in addition to the octet counterparts of the observed $N^*_{1/2}$ state; however, this requires the space wave function to have symmetry opposite that for the baryon octet states (i.e., symmetric with Fermi statistics for quarks, antisymmetric with parastatistics), which would be a surprising situation for such a low-lying state.

(vi) There is no understanding why the attraction in multiquark states should saturate for N = 3. If qqq form a tightly bound state, why should there not be still greater binding with more complicated systems qqqq, and so on? With Fermi statistics, this saturation property is not understood, although various suggestions have been made in the literature, such as the necessity for relativistic effects for additional quarks,[84] repulsive three-body forces[85] and other possibilities.[86] With parastatistics, this could follow from the order p = 3 required to give a unique structure to the baryon states. The octet character of the baryons requires a three-quark structure, and this structure must be possible in only one way (if not, an isolated proton would have statistical weight greater than unity). This octet state is constructed from $Q^i_\alpha(1)Q^j_\beta(2)Q^k_\gamma(3)$ with $i \neq j \neq k$; with i, j, k = 1, 2, ··· p, uniqueness for this state requires p = 3. For a state formed from more than three quarks, the overall wave function must then have some antisymmetry in the quark labels (since some of the quark superficies must then be equal), and this will be energetically unfavorable.

In conclusion, I feel a pressing need to apologize to the many persons who submitted papers to the Conference about the symmetries of the strongly interacting particles, and on the experimental evidence relating to them, that I have not been able to include discussion of their work here. A one-hour talk on such a broad field necessarily involves a severe selection of topics, necessarily with a personal flavor, from the many diverse facets of elementary particle phenomena which are now relevant to our questions about these symmetry properties. Impending deadlines for publication have prevented extension of the Rapporteur talk to a review of the papers on all these facets.

Finally, I would like to give thanks to the leaders of the Discussion Sessions, Dr. R. Adair, Dr. R. L. Cool, Dr. S. C. Frautschi, Dr. S. L. Glashow, and Dr. H. J. Lipkin for their efficient organization of these informative meetings, and to the scientific secretaries, especially Dr. G. Shapiro and Dr. F. von Hippel, for their support.

Footnotes and References

1. G. Feldman and P. T. Matthews, Unitarity, Causality, and Fermi Statistics, to be published, 1966.
2. L. Michel, Phys. Rev. 137, B405 (1965).
3. L. O'Raifertaigh, Phys. Rev. 139, B1052 (1965).
4. J. M. Cornwall, P. G. O. Freund, and K. T. Mahanthappa, Phys. Rev. Letters 14, 515 (1965).
5. R. Blankenbecler, M. L. Goldberger, K. Johnson, and S. B. Treiman, Phys. Rev. Letters 14, 518 (1965).
6. R. F. Dashen and M. Gell-Mann, Phys. Letters 17, 142 (1965).
7. H. Harari and H. J. Lipkin, Phys. Rev. 140, B1617 (1965).
8. G. Morpurgo, Physics 2, 95 (1965).
9. (a) N. Bogoliubov, B. Struminsky, and A. Tavkhelidze, JINR Preprint D-1968 (Dubna, 1965); (b) Dynamical Models of Elementary Particles, Paper 10d.12.
10. G. Domokos and T. Fulton, Phys. Letters 20, 546 (1966).
11. D. Chernavsky, E. Feinberg, and I. Sissakian, Heavy Pair Production, with Application to the Problem of Quark Search, Paper 12c.4.
12. F. Chilton et al., Argonne National Laboratory, quoted by T. Fulton in Session 10a.
13. S. Ishida, Progr. Theoret. Phys. (Kyoto) 32, 922 (1964); 34, 64 (1965).
14. J. Iizuka, Progr. Theoret. Phys. (Kyoto) 35, 117 and 309 (1966).
15. O. Sinanoglu, Phys. Rev. Letters 16, 207 (1966).
16. A. Hendry, Nuovo Cimento 43A, 1191 (1966).
17. R. H. Dalitz, Quark Models for the Elementary Particles, chapter in High Energy Physics (Gordon and Breach, New York, 1966), p. 253.
18. R. H. Dalitz, in Proceedings of the Oxford International Conference on Elementary Particles (Rutherford High-Energy Laboratory, Chilton, January 1966), p. 157.
19. Y. Fujii, Progr. Theoret. Phys. (Kyoto) 21, 232 (1959).
20. This calculation was carried out by D. Holdsworth (Oxford).
21. J. Sakurai, Phys. Rev. Letters 17, 1021 (1966).
22. W. Thirring, Phys. Letters 16, 335 (1965).
23. C. Becchi and G. Morpurgo, Phys. Rev. 140, B687 (1965).
24. (a) L. Soloviev, Phys. Letters 16, 345 (1965); (b) Y. Anisovitch, A. Anselm, Y. Azimov, G. Damlov, and I. Dyatlov, Phys. Letters 16, 194 (1965).
25. W. Kienzle, B. Maglić, B. Levrat, F. Lefebvres, D. Freytag, and H. Blieden, Phys. Letters 19, 438 (1965); J. Oostens, P. Chavanon, M. Crozon, and J. Tocqueville, Production of Isospin 1 Resonances in the Reaction p + p = D + (Missing Mass), Paper 7a.51.
26. The case for $K^*_C(1215)$ has been made clearly by R. Armenteros, in Proceedings of the XIIth International Conference on High Energy Physics, Dubna, 1966, p. 617. The evidence for K*(1080) was presented by Y. Goldschmidt-Clermont at Session 9a.
27. S. Glashow and R. Socolow, Phys. Rev. Letters 15, 325 (1965).
28. The evidence on the scalar σ meson has been nicely summarized in a recent paper, Scalar Mesons, by L. M. Brown (Northwestern University).
29. C. Lovelace, R. Heinze, and A. Donnachie, Phys. Letters 22, 332 (1966).
30. M. Feldman, W. Frati, J. Halpern, A. Kanofsky, M. Nussbaum, S. Richert, P. Yamin, A. Choudry, S. Devons, and J. Grunhaus, Phys. Rev. Letters 14, 869 (1965); V. Hagopian, W. Selove, J. Alitti, J. Baton, and M. Neveu-René, Phys. Rev. Letters 14, 1077 (1965).

31. P. Baillou, D. Edwards, B. Marechal, L. Mortanet, M. Tomas, C. d'Andlau, A. Astier, J. Cohen-Gannou, M. Della-Negra, S. Wojcicki, M. Baubillier, J. Duboc, F. James, and F. Levy, Further Study of the E Meson in Antiproton-Proton Annihilations at Rest, Report CERN-TC-Phys. 66-24, Oct. 1966.
32. G. Kalbfleisch, O. Dahl, and A. Rittenberg, Phys. Rev. Letters 13, 349 (1964).
33. N. Barash, L. Kirsch, D. Miller, and T. Tan, Annihilations of Antiprotons at Rest in Hydrogen. VI: Kaonic Final States, Nevis Rept. 154, Sept. 1966.
34. B. C. Shen, I. Butterworth, C. Fu, G. Goldhaber, S. Goldhaber, and G. H. Trilling, Evidence for a K^*(1320) Resonance, UCRL-16930, July 18, 1966; see also p. 63 of Ref. 36.
35. M. Focacci, G. Chikovani, W. Kienzle, B. Levrat, B. Maglić, and M. Martin, Mass Spectrum of Charged Bosons from 550 to 2450 MeV Observed by Missing Mass Spectrometer, Paper 7a.38; see also G. Chikovani et al., Phys. Letters 22, 233 (1966).
36. Pictorial Atlas of Boson Resonances, supplement to the Rapporteur talk by G. Goldhaber in Session 9 of this Conference.
37. S. Hori, J. Iizuka, K. Matumoto, E. Yamada, and M. Yamazaki, A Systematics and Phenomenology of Hadrons (Kanazawa University preprint, July 1966).
38. S. Ishida, Progr. Theoret. Phys. (Kyoto) 34, 64 (1965).
39. A. Mitra, Phys. Rev. 142, 1119 (1966).
40. A. Mitra and M. Ross, Meson-Baryon Couplings in a Quark Model (Rutherford High Energy Laboratory, Chilton, August 1966).
41. G. Morpurgo, The Nonrelativistic Quark Model, lecture at Balatonvilagos Symposium of the Hungarian Physical Society, June 1966.
42. Y. Nambu, in Symmetry Principles at High Energy (Coral Gables Conference, 1965), p. 274.
43. W. Thirring, Triplet Model of Elementary Particles, Lectures at International University Week in Nuclear Physics, March, 1966.
44. J. Werle, Symmetric Three-Quark Interactions (Warsaw, June 1966).
45. R. Cool, G. Giacomelli, T. Kycia, B. Leontic, K. Li, A. Lundby, and J. Teiger, Phys. Rev. Letters 17, 102 (1966).
46. L. Radicati, The SU(6) Model of Elementary Particles, Lectures given at the Cargese Summer School, 1966 (in press).
47. See L. Rosenfeld, Nuclear Forces (North Holland, Amsterdam, 1948).
48. G. Zweig, in Symmetries in Elementary Particle Physics (Academic Press, N. Y., 1965), p. 192.
49. P. Federman, H. R. Rubinstein, and I. Talmi, Phys. Letters 22, 208 (1966).
50. M. S. Marinov, Soviet J. Nucl. Phys. 2, 228 (1966).
51. M. Goldberg, J. Leitner, R. Musto, and L. O'Raifertaigh, Strong Decay Rates and SU_3--A Comparison and Critique (1966).
52. B. Bransden, P. J. O'Donnell, and R. G. Moorhouse, Phys. Letters 19, 420 (1965).
53. P. Bareyre, C. Bricman, A. V. Stirling, and G. Villet, Phys. Letters 18, 342 (1965).
54. P. Auvil, A. Donnachie, A. T. Lea, and C. Lovelace, Phys. Letters 19, 148 (1965).
55. A. Citron, W. Galbraith, T. Kycia, B. Leontic, R. Phillips, A. Rousset, and P. Sharp, Phys. Rev. 144, 1101 (1966).
56. G. Moorhouse, Phys. Rev. Letters 16, 771 (1966).
57. R. L. Walker and S. Eklund, California Institute of Technology, 1966.
58. H. Lipkin, oral report in Session 1a.
59. H. Lipkin, H. Rubinstein, and H. Stern, Strong Decays with Meson Emission in the Quark Model, Paper 10d.33.
60. C. Heusch, C. Prescott, and R. Dashen, Phys. Rev. Letters 17, 1019 (1966).
61. A. Kernan and W. M. Smart, Phys. Rev. Letters 17, 832 (1966).
62. W. Smart, A. Kernan, G. Kalmus, and R. Ely, Phys. Rev. Letters 17, 556 (1966).
63. G. Charlton, P. Condon, R. Glasser, and G. Yodh, quoted by Kernan and Smart (Ref. 61).
64. G. Smith, J. Lindsey, J. Button-Shafer, and J. Murray, Phys. Rev. Letters 14, 25 (1965).
65. J. Meyer (Saclay) private communication, 1966.
66. G. Morpurgo, Phys. Letters 22, 214 (1966).
67. O. Greenberg, Phys. Rev. Letters 13, 598 (1964).
68. A. N. Mitra, A Dynamical Model for Baryon Resonances, Phys. Rev. (to be published, 1966).
69. J. Coyne, S. Meshkov, and G. Yodh, Phys. Rev. Letters 17, 666 (1966).
70. D. Horn, H. Lipkin, and S. Meshkov, Missing SU(3) Multiplets and $SU(6)_W$ Selection Rules, Paper 10d.27.
71. M. Elitzur, H. Rubinstein, H. Stern, and H. Lipkin, Phys. Rev. Letters 17, 420 (1966).
72. S. Glashow and R. Socolow, Phys. Rev. Letters 15, 329 (1964).
73. H. Rubinstein and H. Stern, Phys. Letters 21, 447 (1966).
74. J. Harte, R. Socolow, J. Vandermeulen, and K. Zalewski, Nucleon-Nucleon Annihilation at Rest is not a Simple Quark Rearrangement, CERN preprint TH 701, Aug. 1966.
75. J. Kirz, Phys. Letters 22, 524 (1966).
76. R. Dashen and D. Sharp, Phys. Rev. 133, B1585 (1964).
77. R. Dalitz, in Proceedings of the Siena International Conference on Elementary Particles (Italian Physical Society, Bologna, 1963), vol. II, p. 171.
78. G. Alexander, H. Lipkin, and F. Scheck, Phys. Rev. Letters 17, 412 (1966).
79. G. Benson, L. Lovell, C. Murphy, B. Roe, D. Sinclair, and J. Vander Velde, Production Cross Sections for η, ω, η', ϕ and f^0 Mesons in π^+d Collisions at 3.65 BeV/c, Paper 10d.8(7a.16).
80. K. Lai and T. Schumann, A New Experimental Determination of the Mixing Angles of Meson Nonets Using a Recent Quark Model Prediction, Paper 10d.32.
81. G. London, R. Rau, N. Samios, S. Yamamoto, M. Goldberg, S. Lichtman, M. Primer, and J. Leitner, Phys. Rev. 143, 1034 (1966).
82. R. Davis, C. Hwang, W. Kropac, J. Mott, R. Ammar, A. Cooper, M. Derrick, T. Fields, L. Hyman, J. Loken, F. Schweingruber, and J. Simpson, Two-Body Processes in K^-p Interactions at 4.1 and 5.5 GeV/c, Paper 8a.23.
83. E. Squires and P. Watson, The Dynamics of Quark Models, May 1966.
84. G. Morpurgo, Phys. Letters 20, 684 (1966).
85. T. Kobayashi and M. Namiki, Progr. Theoret. Phys. (Kyoto) (1966).
86. O. Greenberg and D. Zwanziger, Phys. Rev. 150, 1177 (1966).

REPRINT 11

Reprinted from THE PHYSICAL REVIEW, Vol. 140, No. 3B, B687–B690, 8 November 1965
Printed in U. S. A.

Test of the Nonrelativistic Quark Model for "Elementary" Particles: Radiative Decays of Vector Mesons

C. BECCHI AND G. MORPURGO
Istituto di Fisica dell'Università, Genova, Italy
and
Istituto Nazionale di Fisica Nucleare, Sezione di Genova, Genova, Italy

(Received 19 May 1965)

An experimental test of the nonrelativistic quark model proposed by one of the authors (G.M.) to decribe the internal dynamics of elementary particles is suggested and discussed. The idea is the following: In the nonrelativistic quark model mentioned above, one can obtain not only the ratio $-\frac{3}{2}$ of the magnetic moment of the proton to that of the neutron, but also the absolute value of the magnetic moment of the proton in terms of the quark magnetic moment. By using the value of the quark magnetic moments determined in this way, we calculate the rates of the $M1$ radiative transitions $V \to P+\gamma$, where V is a vector meson and P a pseudoscalar meson. The following results for the widths are obtained (in MeV): $\omega \to \pi^0\gamma$ (1.17); $\omega \to \eta\gamma$ (6.4×10^{-3}); $\rho \to \pi\gamma$ (1.2×10^{-1}); $\rho_0 \to \eta\gamma$ (4.4×10^{-2}); $K^{*+} \to K^+\gamma$ (7×10^{-2}); $K^{*0} \to K^0\gamma$ (2.8×10^{-1}); $\varphi \to \eta\gamma$ (3.04×10^{-1}). The result for the ω agrees with the present experimental data, assuming that the $\pi^0\gamma$ decay dominates the neutral decay rate of the ω; no experimental data are available for the other decays and it is suggested that the $K^{*0} \to K^*\gamma$ and $\varphi \to \eta\gamma$ decay rates are sufficiently large to deserve a measurement. Two possible reasons for uncertainty are discussed in detail: (a) dependence of the vertex function upon the masses, and (b) choice of the ω and η unitary spin functions.

1. THE PROBLEM

IT has been remarked by one of us[1] that if quarks do exist as real massive particles, the internal dynamics of "elementary" particles might be nonrelativistic. In particular it could be possible, at least as a convenient approximation, to write an Hamiltonian for an "elementary" particle in terms of the quark coordinates only in the same way in which one writes an Hamiltonian for a nucleus in terms of the nucleon coordinates only.

For instance, the proton and the neutron might be conceived as being three-quark structures in much the same way as He^3 and H^3 are three-nucleon systems. If,

[1] G. Morpurgo, report presented at the Frascati meeting of the Istituto Nazionale di Fisica Nucleare (to be published).

in this nonrelativistic model of the proton and of the neutron the space part of the three-quark wave function is taken to be completely antisymmetric, one obtains[1] the well-known $-\frac{3}{2}$ ratio between the magnetic moments of the proton and of the neutron; but this fact, as emphasized particularly by Bég, Lee, and Pais,[2] is not a test of the model because it can also be derived quite generally if one assumes that SU_6 is valid in the nonrelativistic limit and that the proton and the neutron belong to the representation **56** of SU_6. However, it is possible to have a definite test of the model, as we shall now show. Indeed, if one takes the three-quark model seriously, one can not only derive the ratio $-\frac{3}{2}$ between the magnetic moments, but also the individual values of the magnetic moments of the proton and the neutron in terms of the magnetic moments of the quarks. One obtains[1]

$$\boldsymbol{\mu}_i=\mu_p(e_i/e)\boldsymbol{\sigma}_i\,, \tag{1}$$

where the index $i=1$, 2 specifies the kind of quark (respectively, the p quark and n quark), and $(e_1, e_2) = (\frac{2}{3}, -\frac{1}{3})$). In Eq. (1) μ_p is the magnetic moment of the real proton, $\mu_p=2.79eh/2M_pc$, where M_p is the proton mass.[3]

We can at this point state the test of the model which we propose: It consists in using the values (1) of the magnetic moments of the quarks obtained from fitting the n and p magnetic moments to predict the electromagnetic properties of other particles. One of the simplest possibilities appears to be that of calculating the rates of the $V\rightarrow P+\gamma$ processes, where V and P are, respectively, the mesons of the vector octet and of the pseudoscalar octet. These transitions, being pure $M1$ transitions, depend essentially on the quark magnetic moments. We list below the transitions which we shall consider:

$$\begin{array}{llll} (1) & \omega\rightarrow\pi^0+\gamma\,, & (2) & \omega\rightarrow\eta+\gamma\,, \\ (3) & \rho\rightarrow\pi+\gamma\,, & (4) & \rho^0\rightarrow\eta+\gamma\,, \\ (5) & K^{*+}\rightarrow K^++\gamma\,, & (6) & K^{*0}\rightarrow K^0+\gamma\,. \end{array} \tag{2}$$

There are also other matrix elements of interest, like those involving the φ and X_0 particles and that corresponding to the $\omega\rho_0\gamma$ vertex, but we shall, for the moment, concentrate our attention on the matrix elements (1) to (6) above.

[2] M. A. Bég, B. W. Lee, and A. Pais, Phys. Rev. Letters **13**, 514 (1964).

[3] Of course it must be strongly emphasized that underlying the values (1) of the magnetic moments of the quarks, is the assumption that such magnetic moments are proportional to the charges. As has already been often observed [M. A. Bég and A. Pais, Phys. Rev. **137**, B1514 (1965)], this is, however, the only assumption which gives rise to the ratio $-\frac{3}{2}$ in the **56**, representation. Note also that the magnetic moments of the quarks (1) are very anomalous; for a quark mass of 5 GeV, the g factor of the quark is 18.6. This indicates that the quarks are, themselves, very far from being "elementary"; but they could hardly be expected to be, since they interact strongly. The only important point is that in the same way that nucleons (which are certainly not elementary) behave as the elementary constituents of nuclei, the quarks should behave as elementary in the internal dynamics of the lower states of particles.

2. GENERAL DISCUSSION OF THE MATRIX ELEMENTS FOR THE $V\rightarrow P+\gamma$ TRANSITIONS

To obtain a real test of the model, two conditions must be satisfied: (a) that in the calculation of the matrix element no uncertainties occur, and (b) that the process considered has a nonzero degree of likelihood of being experimentally accessible. For instance, the static magnetic moments of the ρ and K^* would be ideal as far as the condition (a) is concerned but do not easily satisfy condition (b). For this reason we omit giving the results for them and concentrate our attention on the transition moments (1) to (6). The uncertainties which occur in the matrix elements for these transitions can be divided into two classes:

(1) Relativistic uncertainties: Although the internal dynamics is nonrelativistic, the transitions (1) and (2) are relativistic transitions in the sense that the π^0 is clearly relativistic. As already pointed out in Ref. 1. this has consequences of two different kinds: (a) Dynamical effects: The relativistic form of the interaction between quarks and electromagnetic field must be used instead of the nonrelativistic form (7) of which we shall make use in this paper. (b) Kinematical effects: The wave function of a bound state of two particles in motion at a relativistic velocity must be appropriately transformed. In more conventional language, what we shall do is to calculate the transition rates without taking into account the dependence of the vertex function on the masses of the particles involved in the decay. In other words, the vertex function will be calculated assuming all the masses equal. The results presented in Table I, as we shall explain in more detail later, are based on this approximation. We hope to be able, in the future, to give an estimate of the reliability of this approximation.

(2) Uncertainties arising from violations of SU_3: The main point of the model is that the bosons are describable in terms of the coordinates of a quark and an antiquark, in the same way as positronium is describable in terms of the coordinates of an electron and a positron. Now if SU_3 were exactly true, this would fix the unitary spin structure of all the bosons. This is

TABLE I. The rates of the decays $V\rightarrow P+\gamma$ as calculated in the model. Column 1: the process; 2: the effective coupling constant; column 3: the momentum of the γ; column 4: the calculated width in MeV; column 5: the branching ratio.

Process	$\lvert f_{iJ}\rvert^2$	k (MeV)	Γ_{iJ} (MeV)	Γ_{iJ}/Γ
$\omega\rightarrow\pi^0+\gamma$	2/3	380	1.17	1.2×10^{-1}
$\omega\rightarrow\eta+\gamma$	2/81	200	6.4×10^{-3}	6.8×10^{-4}
$\rho\rightarrow\pi+\gamma$	2/27	370	1.2×10^{-1}	1.1×10^{-3}
$\rho_0\rightarrow\eta+\gamma$	2/9	184	4.4×10^{-2}	4.15×10^{-4}
$K^{*+}\rightarrow K^++\gamma$	2/27	308	7×10^{-2}	1.4×10^{-5}
$K^{*0}\rightarrow K^0+\gamma$	8/27	308	2.8×10^{-1}	5.6×10^{-3}
$\varphi\rightarrow\eta+\gamma$	16/81[a]	362	3.04×10^{-1} [a]	10^{-1}

[a] This calculation of the φ decay rate is performed with the conventional choice of the φ and η unitary-spin functions, namely, $\varphi=D_3{}^3$, $\eta=(1/\sqrt{6})\times(D_1{}^1+D_2{}^2-2D_3{}^3)$; note that if the η were, like the ω, a pure $(1/\sqrt{2})\times(D_1{}^1+D_2{}^2)$ state, the rate would vanish.

not the case, however, if violations of SU_3 of the kind T_3^3 are present; violations of this kind do not affect the unitary spin structure of the particles with isotopic spin different from zero, but may affect that of the particles with isotopic spin zero, since T_3^3 corresponds to isotopic spin zero. For instance, if the ω were a member of the vector octet, its unitary spin wave function would be

$$\omega_8 = (1/\sqrt{6})(D_1^1 + D_2^2 - 2D_3^3)\,, \tag{3}$$

while in the conventional solution of the so-called ω-φ problem the ω is mixed with the unitary singlet

$$\omega_1 = (1/\sqrt{3})(D_1^1 + D_2^2 + D_3^3)$$

in such a way that

$$\omega = (1/\sqrt{2})(D_1^1 + D_2^2)\,. \tag{4}$$

This conventional solution of the ω-φ problem appears very plausible, especially in view of the fact that presumably[1] the main part of the violating term T_3^3 is exhausted by the mass difference among quarks; and it is also the solution suggested by SU_6. However, some uncertainty remains. In other words, on writing

$$\omega = (2 + \lambda_\omega^2)^{-1/2}(D_1^1 + D_2^2 - \lambda_\omega D_3^3) \tag{5}$$

we prefer to think that the choice $\lambda_\omega = 0$ should be considered as extremely probable but not, as yet, absolutely certain. A situation in a sense more obscure holds for the η. Here it is usually accepted, mainly because of the success of the Gell-Mann–Okubo mass formula for the P octet, that the η is a pure (or practically pure) octet meson, and therefore has a unitary spin structure $(1/\sqrt{3})(D_1^1 + D_2^2 - 2D_3^3)$. Particularly in view of the fact that a clear justification of the *quadratic* mass formula for bosons is lacking (in spite of the success of such a formula), we do not consider this structure either as definitely established, and we prefer to write

$$\eta = (2 + \lambda_\eta)^{-1/2}(D_1^1 + D_2^2 - \lambda_\eta D_3^3) \tag{6}$$

where the choice $\lambda_\eta = 2$ appears to be not improbable, but not certain.

Finally, another reason for uncertainty, different from the ones described above, appears for the decays (5) and (6): Though the proton and the neutron determined the magnetic moments of quarks 1 and 2, they do not, of course, give any information on the magnetic moment of the third quark, whose knowledge is necessary for the calculations of the $K^* \to K + \gamma$ matrix element. In the following we shall calculate the rate of the $K^* \to K + \gamma$ transitions under the assumption that the third quark too has a magnetic moment proportional to its charge with the same constant of proportionality as for the proton and of the neutron; that is, we assume that (1) is valid not only for $i = 1, 2$ but also for $i = 3$ with of course $e_3/e = -\frac{1}{3}$. This assumption appears plausible. Indeed the SU_3-violating interaction T_3^3 has an order of magnitude such that it only changes the mass of the third quark with respect to that of the other two by ~ 200 MeV, a very small difference compared with the quark mass itself (say 5 GeV). It is therefore not unreasonable to presume that a (negligible) correction of the same order of magnitude affects the magnetic moment.

We end this section with the following remark: The uncertainties due to the poor knowledge of λ_ω, λ_η, or the magnetic moment of the third quark can eventually be eliminated through appropriate experiments: For instance, the magnetic moment of the third quark might be determined through a measurement of the Λ magnetic moment and λ_ω might be determined by the methods discussed, for example, by Dalitz.[4] Therefore the only theoretical uncertainty is the mass dependence of the vertex function.[5]

3. A FEW DETAILS OF THE CALCULATIONS

In Table I we give the rates of the transitions (1) to (6) calculated in the way outlined in the previous section. To be sure, however, that the meaning of the numbers given in the table is clear, it appears appropriate to give some details of the calculations:

(a) The operator $\mathfrak{M}_i^\theta$ which induces an $M1$ transition with polarization $\boldsymbol{\varepsilon}_a$ of the photon for the ith quark will be written in its nonrelativistic form:

$$\mathfrak{M}_i^a = \left[\frac{eh}{2Mc}\mathbf{L}_i \cdot (\mathbf{k} \times \boldsymbol{\varepsilon}_a) + \mu_p \frac{e_i}{e} \boldsymbol{\sigma}_i \cdot (\mathbf{k} \times \boldsymbol{\varepsilon}_a)\right] \exp i\mathbf{k} \cdot \mathbf{r}_i\,. \tag{7}$$

The orbital magnetic-moment term is proportional to the quark magneton $eh/2Mc$ (M = quark mass). For a value of $M = 5$ GeV its order of magnitude is ~ 15 times smaller than that of the spin term; since in addition the contribution of the orbital term vanishes in the long-wavelength approximation ($k = 0$) for the transitions in which we are interested here ($L = 0$), we are entitled to neglect the orbital term in the ensuing calculations.

(b) The states of the particles which enter into the calculation can be written as follows (for ρ, ω, and K^* the component with $S_z = +1$ will be given):

$$\begin{aligned}
\pi^0 &= \tfrac{1}{2}[(\alpha_1\beta_{\bar{1}} - \alpha_{\bar{1}}\beta_1) - (\alpha_2\beta_{\bar{2}} - \alpha_{\bar{2}}\beta_2)]f(r)\,,\\
\eta^0 &= [2(2+\lambda_\eta^2)]^{-1/2}[(\alpha_1\beta_{\bar{1}} - \alpha_{\bar{1}}\beta_1) + (\alpha_2\beta_{\bar{2}} - \alpha_{\bar{2}}\beta_2)\\
&\qquad - \lambda_\eta(\alpha_3\beta_{\bar{3}} - \alpha_{\bar{3}}\beta_3)]f(r)\,,\\
K^+ &= (1/\sqrt{2})(\alpha_1\beta_{\bar{3}} - \alpha_{\bar{3}}\beta_1)f(r)\,,\\
K^0 &= (1/\sqrt{2})(\alpha_2\beta_{\bar{3}} - \alpha_{\bar{3}}\beta_2)f(r)\,,\\
\rho^0 &= (1/\sqrt{2})(\alpha_1\alpha_{\bar{1}} - \alpha_2\alpha_{\bar{2}})f(r)\,,\\
\omega^0 &= (2+\lambda_\omega^2)^{-1/2}[\alpha_1\alpha_{\bar{1}} + \alpha_2\alpha_{\bar{2}} - \lambda_\omega\alpha_3\alpha_{\bar{3}}]f(r)\,,\\
K^{*+} &= \alpha_1\alpha_{\bar{3}}f(r)\,,\\
K^{*0} &= \alpha_2\alpha_{\bar{3}}f(r)\,.
\end{aligned} \tag{8}$$

[4] R. H. Dalitz, *Proceedings of the Sienna International Conference on Elementary Particles, 1963*, edited by G. Bernardini and G. Puppi (Italian Physical Society, Bologna, 1963), Vol. II, p. 171.

[5] If the vertex function is assumed to depend on the masses only through the three-momentum of the photon (whether this is so questionable), and if the radius of the decaying $9\bar{9}$ system, that is, the radius of the vector boson, is taken of the order of $(5m_\pi)^{-1}$ or larger, the dependence of the vertex function on the masses is almost negligible.

In the above expressions we have indicated by α_i and β_i the spin functions (with spin up and spin down, respectively) for a quark ($i=1, 2, 3$) and by $\bar{\alpha}_i$, $\bar{\beta}_i$ the spin functions (with spin up and spin down, respectively) for an antiquark ($i=1, 2, 3$). The vector particles have been assumed in pure $^3S_1$ states (no mixing with $^3D_1$ states); the space part of the wave function $f(r)$ has been assumed to be the same for all P and V mesons. These last two assumptions may be regarded, if one prefers, as consequences of SU_6. Using (7) and (8), the squares $(|\langle V|P\rangle|^2)_{\text{av}}$ of the matrix elements for the transitions of interest, summed over the polarization of the final photon and averaged over the spin direction of the initial vector meson, are immediately calculated as follows:

$$|f_{\omega\pi0}|^2 \equiv \mu_p^{-2}k^{-2}(|\langle\omega|\pi^0\rangle|^2)_{\text{av}} = 4/3(2+\lambda_\omega^2),$$

$$|f_{\omega\eta}|^2 \equiv \mu_p^{-2}k^{-2}(|\langle\omega|\eta\rangle|^2)_{\text{av}} = \frac{8}{27}\frac{1}{(2+\lambda_\omega^2)}\frac{1}{(2+\lambda_\eta^2)}(1-\lambda_\eta\lambda_\omega)^2, \quad (9)$$

$$|f_{\rho\pi}|^2 \equiv \mu_p^{-2}k^{-2}(|\langle\rho^0|\pi^0\rangle|^2)_{\text{av}} = 2/27,$$

$$|f_{\rho\eta}|^2 \equiv \mu_p^{-2}k^{-2}(|\langle\rho^0|\eta\rangle|^2)_{\text{av}} = 4/3(2+\lambda_\eta^2),$$

$$|f_{k^{*+}k^+}|^2 \equiv \mu_p^{-2}k^{-2}(|\langle K^{*+}|K^+\rangle|^2)_{\text{av}} = 2/27,$$

$$|f_{k^{*0}k^0}|^2 = \mu_p^{-2}k^{-2}(|\langle K^{*0}|K^0\rangle|^2)_{\text{av}} = 8/27.$$

Here a long-wavelength approximation has been used ($\exp ikr=1$). Note that owing to charge independence, the $\rho^{0,\pm}\to\pi^{0,\pm}+\gamma$ transition probabilities are equal. Note also that the following relations among matrix elements due to *nonviolated* SU_3 also hold quite generally, independently of the model[6]:

$$\langle\rho^0|\pi\rangle = \langle K^{*+}|K^+\rangle = -\tfrac{1}{2}\langle K^{*+}|K^0\rangle = (1/\sqrt{3})\langle\rho^0|\eta\rangle = (1/\sqrt{3})\langle\omega_8|\pi^0\rangle.$$

These relations are obviously satisfied by our results (9) (the η appearing in these relations corresponds to the choice $\lambda_\eta=+2$).

The decay rates are obtained on multiplying the expressions (9) by $(2\pi\rho_f/2k)\times N$. Here $2\pi\rho_f$ is the usual phase-space factor, which we shall take in its *relativistic* form

$$2\pi\rho_f = 2\pi\frac{4\pi}{(2\pi)^3}k^2\frac{\omega_k}{M_V} = \frac{k^2}{\pi}\frac{\omega_k}{M_V} \quad (10)$$

where k is the energy of the photon, ω_k the energy of the pseudoscalar meson, and M_V the mass of the decaying vector meson; $1/2k$ is the standard factor arising from the normalization of the photon; and the factor N, given by

$$N = M_V/\omega_k \quad (11)$$

is a relativistic factor which requires a more careful discussion. This factor M_V/ω_k serves to take into account all the requirements of relativity except one, as we shall now explain. (We might omit this factor, but then, to be consistent, we should have to use the nonrelativistic phase space; the result is the same.)

To clarify this point imagine that we try to write the vertex for our process relativistically. This is uniquely determined as

$$f_{ij}\epsilon^{\alpha\beta\delta\gamma}\partial_\alpha A_\beta\partial_\gamma V_\delta^{(i)}P^{(J)} \quad (12)$$

where $A_\beta(X)$ is the electromagnetic field, $V_\delta(X)$ is the vector field and $P(X)$ is the pseudoscalar field; f_{iJ} is an effective coupling constant which depends on the kind i of vector meson and on the kind J of the pseudoscalar meson involved; f_{iJ} will depend on the masses M_{V_i} and M_{P_J}. But assume for a moment that this dependence is not strong and that we are allowed to use the value of $f_{iJ}(0)$ when the masses of the particles are taken to be equal. *We may consider our previous calculation of the matrix elements as a calculation of* $|f_{iJ}(0)|^2$. *What we have called the relativistic uncertainties is the fact that we really do not know how strongly* f_{iJ} *depends on the existing differences in masses.* But if we neglect this dependence our previous calculation is relativistically correct, provided that we insert the factor M_V/ω_k mentioned above, as results immediately on using (12).

4. RESULTS

The rates of the various decays given by the formula

$$\Gamma_{iJ} = |f_{iJ}|^2\frac{(2.79)^2}{2}\frac{1}{137}\left(\frac{k}{M_p}\right)^2 k \quad (13)$$

obtained by putting together the expressions (9) (which we have called $|f_{iJ}|^2$), (10), and (11), are given in Table I. For the ω and the η we have assumed, in the table, the standard solution $\lambda_\omega=0$. $\lambda_\eta=+2$, but the general dependence on λ_ω and λ_η is of course contained in the previous formulas (9).

We only add that the present experimental value of the ratio $(\omega\to\text{neutrals})/(\omega\to\pi^++\pi^-+\pi^0)$ is given as 11×10^{-2}.[7] Since the total width of the ω is given as 9 MeV and since the $\omega\to\pi^0+\pi^0+\pi^0$ decay is forbidden by isotopic spin, it is possible, though not certain, that practically all the neutral decays are $\omega\to\pi^0+\gamma$. In such a case the rate would be in striking agreement with the value given in Table I. It is clearly very important to have a determination of the nature of the neutral decay mode of the ω. It appears also important to try to obtain some information on the $K^{*0}\to K^0+\gamma$ and $\varphi\to\eta+\gamma$ decays, which might not be entirely beyond experimental possibility.

[6] S. Okubo, Phys. Letters 4, 14 (1963); S. L. Glashow, Phys. Rev. Letters 11, 48 (1963); K. Tanaka, Phys. Rev. 133, B1509 (1964).

[7] A. H. Rosenfeld, A. Barbaro-Gualtieri, W. H. Barkas, P. L. Bastien, J. Kirz, and M. Roos, Rev. Mod. Phys. 36, 977 (1964).

REPRINT 12

Sonderabdruck aus Supplementum II, 1966, der

ACTA PHYSICA AUSTRIACA

Unter Mitwirkung der Österreichischen Akademie der Wissenschaften herausgegeben von Fritz Regler, Wien, und Hans Thirring, Wien

Schriftleitung: Paul Urban, Graz

Springer-Verlag / Wien · New York

Electromagnetic Properties of Hadrons in the Static SU_6 Model*

By

W. Thirring

Institute for Theoretical Physics, University of Vienna

In the current thinking about strongly interacting particles one usually imagines that they are mixtures of certain bare particles e.g. the proton being partly a bare proton and partly a bare proton with a virtual p-wave pion around it. This picture was never very successful in explaining the electromagnetic properties of the baryons. The reason is that the well-explored outer part of the pion cloud does not contain much charge and magnetic moment and the core is rather complicated. It is the more remarkable that an alternative model where the baryons consist of three spin 1/2 particles called quarks is numerically very successful in predicting the electromagnetic properties. In this model one assumes that the quark interaction is spin- and unitary spin-independent and that there are no orbital contributions to the magnetic moments. The following table lists the quantum numbers of the three fundamental entities:

	Q	Y	N	T_3	μ
p	2/3	1/3	1/3	1/2	2/3
n	$-1/3$	1/3	1/3	$-1/2$	$-1/3$
λ	$-1/3$	$-2/3$	1/3	0	$-1/3$

μ is the magnetic moment measured in quark magnetons.

For the antiparticles they all change their sign. In the following we shall draw the state vectors of the physical particles regarding their spin and quark content. These vectors can be found by simple symmetry considerations. In the four columns we list the following expectation values

* Lecture given at the IV. Internationale Universitätswochen für Kernphysik, Schladming, 25 February—10 March 1965.

$$\mu = \left\langle \sum_i Q_i \sigma_i^{(z)} \right\rangle$$

$$\delta m_0 = \left\langle \sum 3 N Q_i \right\rangle$$

$$\delta m_e = \left\langle \sum_{i>k} Q_i Q_k \right\rangle$$

$$- \delta m_m = \left\langle \sum_{i>k} Q_i Q_k (\vec{\sigma}_i \cdot \vec{\sigma}_k) \right\rangle.$$

δm_0 corresponds to a mass difference of the quarks with $|Q| = 1/3$ and $2/3$. δm_e is the electrostatic interaction and should be multiplied with e^2/R where R is a mean distance of the quarks. δm_m is the magnetic interaction and for s-states one expects a factor $2/3\ (\mu_0{}^2/R^3)$.

In this model all particles are constructed from 3 2-component fields which we unite in one entity ψ_α, $\alpha = 1 - 6$. In a more physical notation we shall give the spin direction and the quark content, e.g.

$$\psi_\alpha = \underset{p}{\uparrow}, \underset{p}{\downarrow}, \underset{n}{\uparrow}, \underset{n}{\downarrow}, \underset{\lambda}{\uparrow}, \underset{\lambda}{\downarrow}.$$

The 9 vector and 8 pseudoscalar bosons are in a $3 \times 9 + 8 = 35$ representation of the quark-antiquark states $\psi_\alpha \psi_\beta{}^+$. They are orthogonal to the ninth pseudoscalar meson.

$$x = \frac{1}{\sqrt{6}} \psi_\alpha \psi_\alpha{}^+ = \frac{1}{\sqrt{6}} (\underset{\bar{p}\ p}{\uparrow\downarrow} - \underset{\bar{p}\ p}{\downarrow\uparrow} + \underset{\bar{n}\ n}{\uparrow\downarrow} - \underset{\bar{n}\ n}{\downarrow\uparrow} + \underset{\bar{\lambda}\ \lambda}{\uparrow\downarrow} - \underset{\bar{\lambda}\ \lambda}{\downarrow\uparrow})$$

which is an $S\,U_6$ singulet. Assuming that the space wave function corresponds to an s-state we note that the particles have the correct parity and the neutral vector and pseudoscalar particles have charge conjugation -1 and $+1$ resp.

	μ	δm_0	δm_e	δm_m
$\varrho^+ = \underset{\bar{n}\ p}{\uparrow\uparrow}$	1	$\frac{1}{3}$	$\frac{2}{9}$	$-\frac{2}{9}$
$\varrho^- = \underset{\bar{p}\ n}{\uparrow\uparrow}$	-1	$\frac{1}{3}$	$\frac{2}{9}$	$-\frac{2}{9}$
$\varrho^0 = \frac{1}{\sqrt{2}} (\underset{\bar{p}\ p}{\uparrow\uparrow} - \underset{\bar{n}\ n}{\uparrow\uparrow})$	0	$\frac{1}{3}$	$-\frac{5}{18}$	$\frac{5}{18}$
$K^{*+} = \underset{\bar{\lambda}\ p}{\uparrow\uparrow}$	1	$\frac{1}{3}$	$\frac{2}{9}$	$-\frac{2}{9}$

	μ	δm_0	δm_e	δm_m
$K^{*-} = \underset{\bar{p}\,\lambda}{\uparrow\uparrow}$	-1	$\frac{1}{3}$	$\frac{2}{9}$	$-\frac{2}{9}$
$K^{*0} = \underset{\bar{\lambda}\,n}{\uparrow\uparrow}$	0	$-\frac{2}{3}$	$-\frac{1}{9}$	$+\frac{1}{9}$
$\bar{K}^{*0} = \underset{\bar{n}\,\lambda}{\uparrow\uparrow}$	0	$-\frac{2}{3}$	$-\frac{1}{9}$	$+\frac{1}{9}$
$\phi_8 = \frac{1}{\sqrt{6}}(2\underset{\bar{\lambda}\,\lambda}{\uparrow\uparrow} - \underset{\bar{p}\,p}{\uparrow\uparrow} - \underset{\bar{n}\,n}{\uparrow\uparrow})$	0	$-\frac{1}{3}$	$-\frac{1}{6}$	$\frac{1}{6}$
$\omega_1 = \frac{1}{\sqrt{3}}(\underset{\bar{\lambda}\,\lambda}{\uparrow\uparrow} + \underset{\bar{p}\,p}{\uparrow\uparrow} + \underset{\bar{n}\,n}{\uparrow\uparrow})$	0	0	$-\frac{5}{27}$	$\frac{5}{27}$
$\phi = \underset{\bar{\lambda}\,\lambda}{\uparrow\uparrow}$	0	$-\frac{2}{3}$	$-\frac{1}{9}$	$+\frac{1}{9}$
$\omega = \frac{1}{\sqrt{2}}(\underset{\bar{p}\,p}{\uparrow\uparrow} + \underset{\bar{n}\,n}{\uparrow\uparrow})$	0	$\frac{1}{3}$	$-\frac{5}{18}$	$\frac{5}{18}$
$\pi^+ = \frac{1}{\sqrt{2}}(\underset{\bar{n}\,p}{\uparrow\downarrow} - \underset{\bar{n}\,p}{\downarrow\uparrow})$	0	$\frac{1}{3}$	$\frac{2}{9}$	$\frac{2}{3}$
$\pi^- = \frac{1}{\sqrt{2}}(\underset{\bar{n}\,p}{\uparrow\downarrow} - \underset{\bar{n}\,p}{\downarrow\uparrow})$	0	$\frac{1}{3}$	$\frac{2}{9}$	$\frac{2}{3}$
$\pi^0 = \frac{1}{2}(\underset{\bar{p}\,p}{\uparrow\downarrow} - \underset{\bar{p}\,p}{\downarrow\uparrow} - \underset{\bar{n}\,n}{\uparrow\downarrow} + \underset{\bar{n}\,n}{\downarrow\uparrow})$	0	$\frac{1}{3}$	$-\frac{5}{18}$	$-\frac{5}{6}$
$K^+ = \frac{1}{\sqrt{2}}(\underset{\bar{\lambda}\,p}{\uparrow\downarrow} - \underset{\bar{\lambda}\,p}{\downarrow\uparrow})$	0	$\frac{1}{3}$	$\frac{2}{9}$	$\frac{2}{3}$
$K^- = \frac{1}{\sqrt{2}}(\underset{\bar{p}\,\lambda}{\uparrow\downarrow} - \underset{\bar{p}\,\lambda}{\downarrow\uparrow})$	0	$\frac{1}{3}$	$\frac{2}{9}$	$\frac{2}{3}$
$K^0 = \frac{1}{\sqrt{2}}(\underset{\bar{\lambda}\,n}{\uparrow\downarrow} - \underset{\bar{\lambda}\,n}{\downarrow\uparrow})$	0	$-\frac{2}{3}$	$-\frac{1}{9}$	$-\frac{1}{3}$
$\bar{K}^0 = \frac{1}{\sqrt{2}}(\underset{\bar{n}\,\lambda}{\uparrow\downarrow} - \underset{\bar{n}\,\lambda}{\downarrow\uparrow})$	0	$-\frac{2}{3}$	$-\frac{1}{9}$	$-\frac{1}{3}$
$\eta = \frac{1}{\sqrt{12}}(2\underset{\bar{\lambda}\,\lambda}{\uparrow\downarrow} - 2\underset{\bar{\lambda}\,\lambda}{\downarrow\uparrow} - \underset{\bar{p}\,p}{\uparrow\downarrow} + \underset{\bar{p}\,p}{\downarrow\uparrow} - \underset{\bar{n}\,n}{\uparrow\downarrow} + \underset{\bar{n}\,n}{\downarrow\uparrow})$	0	$-\frac{3}{9}$	$-\frac{1}{6}$	$-\frac{1}{2}$

For spin 0 mesons $\langle\mu\rangle$ is, of course, zero but they have a sort of inner magnetic moment which manifests itself in transitions to the spin 1 states. Thus for the transition moment $\langle I=0, I_z=0\,|\mu_Z|\,I=1, I_z=0\rangle$ one finds

$$\langle\pi^+|\mu|\varrho^+\rangle = \langle\pi^0|\mu|\varrho^0\rangle = \langle\pi^-|\mu|\varrho^-\rangle = -1/3$$

$$\langle\pi^0|\mu|\omega\rangle = -1, \langle\pi^0|\mu|\phi\rangle = 0$$

$$\langle\eta|\mu|\omega\rangle = -\frac{1}{3\sqrt{3}}, \langle\eta|\mu|\phi\rangle = -\frac{2\sqrt{2}}{3\sqrt{3}}, \langle\eta|\mu|\varrho^0\rangle = -\frac{1}{\sqrt{3}}$$

$$\langle K^+|\mu|K^{*+}\rangle = \langle K^-|\mu|K^{*-}\rangle = \frac{1}{3}, \langle K^0|\mu|K^{*0}\rangle = \langle \bar{K}^0|\mu|\bar{K}^{*0}\rangle = \frac{2}{3}.$$

The baryons are composed of three quarks $\psi_\alpha\,\psi_\beta\,\psi_\gamma$ in an SU_6 symmetric state. Thus the radial wave-function must be rather complicated if they are in an s-state and obey Fermi statistics.

	μ	δm_0	δm_e	δm_m
$\Omega^- = \underset{\lambda}{\uparrow}\underset{\lambda}{\uparrow}\underset{\lambda}{\uparrow}$	-1	-1	$\frac{1}{3}$	$-\frac{1}{3}$
$\Xi^{*-} = \frac{1}{\sqrt{3}}(\underset{\lambda}{\uparrow}\underset{\lambda}{\uparrow}\underset{n}{\uparrow} + \underset{\lambda}{\uparrow}\underset{n}{\uparrow}\underset{\lambda}{\uparrow} + \underset{n}{\uparrow}\underset{\lambda}{\uparrow}\underset{\lambda}{\uparrow})$	-1	-1	$\frac{1}{3}$	$-\frac{1}{3}$
$\Xi^{*0} = \frac{1}{\sqrt{3}}(\underset{\lambda}{\uparrow}\underset{\lambda}{\uparrow}\underset{p}{\uparrow} + \underset{\lambda}{\uparrow}\underset{p}{\uparrow}\underset{\lambda}{\uparrow} + \underset{p}{\uparrow}\underset{\lambda}{\uparrow}\underset{\lambda}{\uparrow})$	0	0	$-\frac{1}{3}$	$+\frac{1}{3}$
$Y^{*-} = \frac{1}{\sqrt{3}}(\underset{\lambda}{\uparrow}\underset{n}{\uparrow}\underset{n}{\uparrow} + \underset{n}{\uparrow}\underset{\lambda}{\uparrow}\underset{n}{\uparrow} + \underset{n}{\uparrow}\underset{n}{\uparrow}\underset{\lambda}{\uparrow})$	-1	-1	$\frac{1}{3}$	$-\frac{1}{3}$
$Y^{*0} = \frac{1}{\sqrt{6}}(\underset{\lambda}{\uparrow}\underset{n}{\uparrow}\underset{p}{\uparrow} + \underset{\lambda}{\uparrow}\underset{p}{\uparrow}\underset{n}{\uparrow} + \underset{n}{\uparrow}\underset{\lambda}{\uparrow}\underset{p}{\uparrow} + \underset{p}{\uparrow}\underset{\lambda}{\uparrow}\underset{n}{\uparrow} + \underset{p}{\uparrow}\underset{n}{\uparrow}\underset{\lambda}{\uparrow} + \underset{n}{\uparrow}\underset{p}{\uparrow}\underset{\lambda}{\uparrow})$	0	0	$-\frac{1}{3}$	$+\frac{1}{3}$
$Y^{*+} = \frac{1}{\sqrt{3}}(\underset{\lambda}{\uparrow}\underset{p}{\uparrow}\underset{p}{\uparrow} + \underset{p}{\uparrow}\underset{\lambda}{\uparrow}\underset{p}{\uparrow} + \underset{p}{\uparrow}\underset{p}{\uparrow}\underset{\lambda}{\uparrow})$	1	1	0	0
$N^{*-} = \underset{n}{\uparrow}\underset{n}{\uparrow}\underset{n}{\uparrow}$	-1	-1	$\frac{1}{3}$	$-\frac{1}{3}$
$N^{*0} = \frac{1}{\sqrt{3}}(\underset{n}{\uparrow}\underset{n}{\uparrow}\underset{p}{\uparrow} + \underset{n}{\uparrow}\underset{p}{\uparrow}\underset{n}{\uparrow} + \underset{p}{\uparrow}\underset{n}{\uparrow}\underset{n}{\uparrow})$	0	0	$-\frac{1}{3}$	$+\frac{1}{3}$
$N^{*+} = \frac{1}{\sqrt{3}}(\underset{p}{\uparrow}\underset{p}{\uparrow}\underset{n}{\uparrow} + \underset{p}{\uparrow}\underset{n}{\uparrow}\underset{p}{\uparrow} + \underset{n}{\uparrow}\underset{p}{\uparrow}\underset{p}{\uparrow})$	1	1	0	0

	μ	δm_0	δm_e	δm_m
$N^{*++} = \underset{p}{\uparrow}\underset{p}{\uparrow}\underset{p}{\uparrow}$	2	2	$\frac{4}{3}$	$-\frac{4}{3}$
$P = \frac{1}{\sqrt{18}}(2\underset{p}{\uparrow}\underset{n}{\downarrow}\underset{p}{\uparrow} + 2\underset{p}{\uparrow}\underset{p}{\uparrow}\underset{n}{\downarrow} + 2\underset{n}{\downarrow}\underset{p}{\uparrow}\underset{p}{\uparrow} - \underset{p}{\uparrow}\underset{p}{\downarrow}\underset{n}{\uparrow} - \underset{p}{\uparrow}\underset{n}{\uparrow}\underset{p}{\downarrow} - \underset{p}{\downarrow}\underset{n}{\uparrow}\underset{p}{\uparrow} - \underset{n}{\uparrow}\underset{p}{\downarrow}\underset{p}{\uparrow} - \underset{n}{\uparrow}\underset{p}{\uparrow}\underset{p}{\downarrow} - \underset{p}{\downarrow}\underset{p}{\uparrow}\underset{n}{\uparrow})$	1	1	0	$-\frac{4}{3}$
$N = \frac{1}{\sqrt{18}}(-2\underset{n}{\uparrow}\underset{p}{\downarrow}\underset{n}{\uparrow} - 2\underset{n}{\uparrow}\underset{n}{\uparrow}\underset{p}{\downarrow} - 2\underset{p}{\downarrow}\underset{n}{\uparrow}\underset{n}{\uparrow} + \underset{p}{\uparrow}\underset{n}{\downarrow}\underset{n}{\uparrow} + \underset{n}{\uparrow}\underset{p}{\uparrow}\underset{n}{\downarrow} + \underset{n}{\downarrow}\underset{p}{\uparrow}\underset{n}{\uparrow} + \underset{n}{\uparrow}\underset{n}{\downarrow}\underset{p}{\uparrow} + \underset{p}{\uparrow}\underset{n}{\uparrow}\underset{n}{\downarrow} + \underset{n}{\downarrow}\underset{n}{\uparrow}\underset{p}{\uparrow})$	$-\frac{2}{3}$	0	$-\frac{1}{3}$	-1
$\Sigma^{+} = \frac{1}{\sqrt{18}}(2\underset{p}{\uparrow}\underset{\lambda}{\downarrow}\underset{p}{\uparrow} + 2\underset{p}{\uparrow}\underset{p}{\uparrow}\underset{\lambda}{\downarrow} + 2\underset{\lambda}{\downarrow}\underset{p}{\uparrow}\underset{p}{\uparrow} - \underset{p}{\uparrow}\underset{p}{\downarrow}\underset{\lambda}{\uparrow} - \underset{p}{\uparrow}\underset{\lambda}{\uparrow}\underset{p}{\downarrow} - \underset{p}{\downarrow}\underset{\lambda}{\uparrow}\underset{p}{\uparrow} - \underset{\lambda}{\uparrow}\underset{p}{\downarrow}\underset{p}{\uparrow} - \underset{\lambda}{\uparrow}\underset{p}{\uparrow}\underset{p}{\downarrow} - \underset{p}{\downarrow}\underset{p}{\uparrow}\underset{\lambda}{\uparrow})$	1	1	0	$-\frac{4}{3}$
$\Sigma^{-} = \frac{1}{\sqrt{18}}(-2\underset{n}{\uparrow}\underset{\lambda}{\downarrow}\underset{n}{\uparrow} - 2\underset{n}{\uparrow}\underset{n}{\uparrow}\underset{\lambda}{\downarrow} - 2\underset{\lambda}{\downarrow}\underset{n}{\uparrow}\underset{n}{\uparrow} + \underset{\lambda}{\uparrow}\underset{n}{\downarrow}\underset{n}{\uparrow} + \underset{n}{\uparrow}\underset{\lambda}{\uparrow}\underset{n}{\downarrow} + \underset{n}{\downarrow}\underset{\lambda}{\uparrow}\underset{n}{\uparrow} + \underset{n}{\uparrow}\underset{n}{\downarrow}\underset{\lambda}{\uparrow} + \underset{\lambda}{\uparrow}\underset{n}{\uparrow}\underset{n}{\downarrow} + \underset{n}{\downarrow}\underset{n}{\uparrow}\underset{\lambda}{\uparrow})$	$-\frac{1}{3}$	-1	$\frac{1}{3}$	$\frac{1}{3}$
$\Sigma^{0} = \frac{1}{\sqrt{36}}(+2\underset{n}{\uparrow}\underset{\lambda}{\downarrow}\underset{p}{\uparrow} - \underset{n}{\downarrow}\underset{\lambda}{\uparrow}\underset{p}{\uparrow} - \underset{\lambda}{\uparrow}\underset{n}{\downarrow}\underset{p}{\uparrow} + 2\underset{\lambda}{\downarrow}\underset{n}{\uparrow}\underset{p}{\uparrow} + 2\underset{p}{\uparrow}\underset{n}{\uparrow}\underset{\lambda}{\downarrow} -$	$\frac{1}{3}$	0	$-\frac{1}{3}$	0

	μ	δm_0	δm_e	δm_m
$-\underset{p\,n\,\lambda}{\uparrow\downarrow\uparrow}-\underset{p\,\lambda\,n}{\uparrow\uparrow\downarrow}+2\underset{p\,\lambda\,n}{\uparrow\downarrow\uparrow}+$ $+2\underset{\lambda\,p\,n}{\downarrow\uparrow\uparrow}-\underset{\lambda\,p\,n}{\uparrow\uparrow\downarrow}-\underset{n\,p\,\lambda}{\downarrow\uparrow\uparrow}+$ $+2\underset{n\,p\,\lambda}{\uparrow\uparrow\downarrow}-\underset{\lambda\,p\,n}{\uparrow\downarrow\uparrow}-\underset{p\,\lambda\,n}{\downarrow\uparrow\uparrow}-$ $-\underset{n\,\lambda\,p}{\uparrow\uparrow\downarrow}-\underset{n\,p\,\lambda}{\uparrow\downarrow\uparrow}-\underset{p\,n\,\lambda}{\downarrow\uparrow\uparrow}-$ $-\underset{\lambda\,n\,p}{\uparrow\uparrow\downarrow})$				
$\Lambda=\frac{1}{\sqrt{12}}(\underset{p\,n\,\lambda}{\uparrow\downarrow\uparrow}-\underset{p\,n\,\lambda}{\downarrow\uparrow\uparrow}-\underset{n\,p\,\lambda}{\uparrow\downarrow\uparrow}+$ $+\underset{n\,p\,\lambda}{\downarrow\uparrow\uparrow}+\underset{\lambda\,p\,n}{\uparrow\uparrow\downarrow}-\underset{\lambda\,p\,n}{\uparrow\downarrow\uparrow}-$ $-\underset{\lambda\,n\,p}{\uparrow\uparrow\downarrow}+\underset{\lambda\,n\,p}{\uparrow\downarrow\uparrow}+\underset{n\,\lambda\,p}{\downarrow\uparrow\uparrow}-$ $-\underset{n\,\lambda\,p}{\uparrow\uparrow\downarrow}-\underset{p\,\lambda\,n}{\downarrow\uparrow\uparrow}+\underset{p\,\lambda\,n}{\uparrow\uparrow\downarrow})$	$-\frac{1}{3}$	0	$-\frac{1}{3}$	$-\frac{2}{3}$
$\Xi^0=\frac{1}{\sqrt{18}}(-2\underset{\lambda\,p\,\lambda}{\uparrow\downarrow\uparrow}-2\underset{\lambda\,\lambda\,p}{\uparrow\uparrow\downarrow}-$ $-2\underset{p\,\lambda\,\lambda}{\downarrow\uparrow\uparrow}+\underset{p\,\lambda\,\lambda}{\uparrow\downarrow\uparrow}+\underset{\lambda\,p\,\lambda}{\uparrow\uparrow\downarrow}+$ $+\underset{\lambda\,p\,\lambda}{\downarrow\uparrow\uparrow}+\underset{\lambda\,\lambda\,p}{\uparrow\downarrow\uparrow}+\underset{p\,\lambda\,\lambda}{\uparrow\uparrow\downarrow}+$ $+\underset{\lambda\,\lambda\,p}{\downarrow\uparrow\uparrow})$	$-\frac{2}{3}$	0	$-\frac{1}{3}$	-1
$\Xi^-=\frac{1}{\sqrt{18}}(2\underset{\lambda\,n\,\lambda}{\uparrow\downarrow\uparrow}+2\underset{\lambda\,\lambda\,n}{\uparrow\uparrow\downarrow}+$ $+2\underset{n\,\lambda\,\lambda}{\downarrow\uparrow\uparrow}-\underset{\lambda\,\lambda\,n}{\uparrow\downarrow\uparrow}-\underset{\lambda\,n\,\lambda}{\uparrow\uparrow\downarrow}-$ $-\underset{\lambda\,n\,\lambda}{\downarrow\uparrow\uparrow}-\underset{n\,\lambda\,\lambda}{\uparrow\downarrow\uparrow}-\underset{n\,\lambda\,\lambda}{\uparrow\uparrow\downarrow}-$ $-\underset{\lambda\,\lambda\,n}{\downarrow\uparrow\uparrow})$	$-\frac{1}{3}$	-1	$\frac{1}{3}$	$\frac{1}{3}$

The transition moments are found to be (in absolute value)

$$\langle P|\mu|N^{*+}\rangle=\langle\Sigma^+|\mu|Y^{*+}\rangle=\langle N|\mu|N^{*0}\rangle=2\,\langle\Sigma^0|\mu|Y^{*0}\rangle=$$
$$=\frac{\sqrt{3}}{2}\,\langle\Lambda|\mu|Y^{*0}\rangle=\langle\Xi^0|\mu|\Xi^{*0}\rangle=\frac{2\sqrt{2}}{3}\,.$$

For the electromagnetic mass splittings the following relations follow from the table.

$$Y_1^{*0} - Y_1^{*0} = N^{*0} - N^{*+} = \frac{1}{3}(N^{*-} - N^{*++})$$

$$N^{*-} - N^{*0} = Y_1^{*-} - Y_1^{*0} = \Xi^{*-} - \Xi^{*0} = N - P + \Sigma^- + \Sigma^+ - 2\Sigma_0.$$

The following experimental data are available on that.

Magnetic moments in nuclear magnetons:

$$\mu_p = 2.78, \qquad \mu_N = -1.91, \qquad \mu_\Lambda = -0.7 \pm 0.3, \qquad \mu_{\Sigma^+} = 2.2 \pm ?$$

Thus if the quark magneton equals the proton moment we get excellent agreement with the known moments; the transition moments $N \to N^*$ are experimentally somewhat bigger than the predictions. Regarding the mass differences we can calculate from $N - P, \Sigma^+ - \Sigma^0, \Sigma^0 - \Sigma^-$ the three parameters and find

$$\delta m = -(1.9 \pm 0.2)\,\delta m_0 + (3.5 \pm 0.1)\,\delta m_e + (1.6 \pm 0.3)\,\delta m_m.$$

Giving experimental numbers in parenthesis this compars as follows with the data.

$$\Xi^- - \Xi^0 = 6.3 \pm 0.3 \quad (6.5 \pm 1)$$
$$\Xi^{*-} - \Xi^{*0} = 3.1 \pm 0.3 \quad (6 \pm 3)$$
$$N^{*0} - N^{*++} = 0.7 \pm 0.6 \quad (0.4 \pm 0.8)$$
$$N^{*-} - N^{*++} = 3.6 \pm 0.6 \quad (0.6 \pm 5)$$
$$Y_1^{*-} - Y_1^{*+} = 4.4 \pm 0.5 \quad (4.3 \pm 2).$$

Thus the theoretically expected sign of δm_e and δm_m reproduces the data within the errors. They correspond to a mean quark distance $R \sim 0.4 \cdot 10^{-13}$ cm in reasonable agreement with the expected order of the Compton wavelength of the vector mesons.

For the Bosons only the $\pi^+ - \pi^0, K^+ - K^0$ mass splitting are experimentally known. They do not determine 3 parameters but we will try and see what happens if we use the numbers from the baryons. We find

$$\pi^+ - \pi^0 = 4.2 \pm 0.4 \quad (4.6 \pm 0.07)$$
$$K^0 - K^+ = -0.9 \pm 0.2 \quad (4.2 \pm 0.5).$$

Thus it works for the pion but for the kaon we get a wrong number.

Finally from the transition moments for the bosons we find for the partial width

$$\Gamma_{\omega \to \pi_0 + \gamma} = 1.2\,\text{MeV}$$

assuming the quark moment for Bosons is the same as for Baryons.

This is in excellent agreement with the experimental branching ratio of 11% for this decay. For decays like $\varrho \to \pi + \gamma$ are theoretically only 1/10% well below the experimental limit.

References

Beg, M., e. a. Phys. Rev. Lett. **13**, 514 (1964).

Dolgov, A., e. a. Phys. Lett. **15**, 84 (1965).

REPRINT 13

Reprinted from THE PHYSICAL REVIEW, Vol. 158, No. 5, 1630–1638, 25 June 1967
Printed in U. S. A.

Meson-Baryon Couplings in a Quark Model*

A. N. MITRA
Delhi University, Delhi, India

AND

MARC ROSS†‡
University of Michigan, Ann Arbor, Michigan

(Received 20 January 1967; revised manuscript received 7 March 1967)

The widths for decay of low-lying baryons of negative parity into baryon plus pseudoscalar meson are determined in a quark model and extensively compared with experiment. One conclusion is that $\Xi^*(1816)$ is not in an octet with $N^*(1518)$, $Y_1^*(1660)$. A second prediction is a kinematical factor in s-wave decay enhancing the decay into high-mass mesons (K and η over η), which provides a qualitative reason for η peaks at threshold. Properties of the many missing baryon resonances are discussed. Channels appropriate for the search for some of these are indicated.

I. INTRODUCTION

In this article we calculate the widths for strong decay of low-lying baryons, especially those of negative parity, into pseudoscalar meson plus baryon. Our baryon model is the three-quark system.[1] We first discuss the model and the form of the calculation, then we present the many results[2] and discuss implications of the current data.

Baryon states are assumed to be Gell-Mann–Zweig triplets of quarks governed by nonrelativistic dynamics.[3] It is assumed in conformity with Dalitz's general analysis that the baryons form bases for representations of the group $SU(6)\times O_3$,[4] with the lowest-lying representations being[5]:

(a) (56) even-parity states of $L=0$, corresponding to the well-known $\frac{1}{2}^+$ octet and $\frac{3}{2}^+$ decuplet;

(b) $(70)\times(3)$ odd-parity states of $L=1$ corresponding to two $\frac{1}{2}^-$ octets whose N^* components are known, two $\frac{3}{2}^-$ octets and a $\frac{3}{2}^-$ decuplet with $N^*(T=\frac{1}{2})(1518)$, $Y_1^*(1660?)$, and $\Xi^*(1816)$ known, a $\frac{1}{2}^-$ decuplet whose N^* component is known (?), a $\frac{5}{2}^-$ octet with known N^* and $Y_1^*(1765)$, and the known $\frac{1}{2}^-$ and $\frac{3}{2}^-$ singlets $Y_0^*(1405)$ and $Y_0^*(1520)$, respectively.

These known resonances and the assignments we would like to make on the basis of our results are shown in Table I.

In a previous paper[6] one of us demonstrated that this model can be justified by explicit dynamical calculation to determine the lowest-lying states. The main assumptions in this calculation were parastatistics[7] and operation of s- and p-wave forces in Q-Q pairs.[8] The most attractive states separated into three sets:

(a) and (b), above; and

(c) $(20)\times(3)$ even-parity states of $L=1$ corresponding to $\frac{1}{2}^+$, $\frac{3}{2}^+$, $\frac{5}{2}^+$ singlets. Possible candidates[9] for this multiplet are $\frac{1}{2}^+$ $T=\frac{1}{2}$ $N^*(1450)$ (or Roper resonance), and $\Xi^*(1705)$ of unknown J^P. There are also Y^* possibilities. We will not present an extensive discussion of couplings to $(20)\times(3)$ states.

We will show below that, in contrast to the mass spectrum, the baryon partial widths are essentially independent of the choice of quark statistics. The results as presented here, where certain spatial integrals are treated as parameters rather than being evaluated in detail, are the same for Fermi statistics and parastatistics and depend only on the *assignments* of the baryon states.

II. THE MODEL

Within each set (a), (b), (c), the states are degenerate in the presence of the spin- and unitary-spin-independent forces. The actual mass splittings are not of interest to us here: We assume that the wave functions are not influenced by the splitting.

---

* This is a substantially expanded and revised version of a Rutherford High Energy Laboratory Report (August, 1966).

† Supported in part by the U. S. Atomic Energy Commission.

‡ Visiting Professor, Summer School of Theoretical Physics, Department of Physics, Delhi University, during May–June, 1966. Visitor, Rutherford High Energy Laboratory, Summer, 1966.

[1] M. Gell-Mann, Phys. Letters **8**, 214 (1963); G. Zweig, CERN (1964) (unpublished).

[2] Related recent calculations of meson-baryon couplings are R. J. Rivers, Phys. Letters **22**, 514 (1966); J. J. Coyne, S. Meshkov, and G. B. Yodh, Phys. Rev. Letters **17**, 666 (1966). Very closely related results have been obtained by R. Capps (private communication).

[3] G. Morpurgo, Physics **2**, 95 (1965); Y. Nambu, in *Symmetry Principles at High Energy*, edited by B. Kurşunoglu, A. Perlmutter, and I. A. Sakmar (W. H. Freeman and Company, San Francisco, 1965); R. H. Dalitz, in *Proceedings of the Oxford International Conference on Elementary Particles, 1965* (Rutherford High Energy Laboratory, Harwell, England, 1966); A. N. Tavkhelidze, *Seminar on High Energy Physics and Elementary Particles* (International Atomic Energy Agency Vienna, 1965), p. 753.

[4] K. T. Mahanthappa and E. C. G. Sudarshan, Phys. Rev. Letters **14**, 153 (1965).

[5] In most cases our data are taken from A. H. Rosenfeld *et al.*, Rev. Mod. Phys. **37**, 633 (1965). For recently discovered N^*'s we have referred mainly to R. H. Dalitz (Ref. 3) and to P. Bareyre *et al.*, Phys. Letters **18**, 342 (1965), obtaining widths by our own analysis.

[6] A. N. Mitra, Phys. Rev. **151**, 1168 (1966).

[7] O. W. Greenberg, Phys. Rev. Letters **13**, 598 (1964).

[8] A. N. Mitra, Phys. Rev. **142**, (4), 1119 (1966).

[9] See Ref. 5; A. B. Clegg, Nucl. Phys. **76**, 545 (1966); G. Smith, *Second Topical Conference on Resonant Particles*, edited by B. Munir (Ohio University Press, Athens, Ohio, 1965).

TABLE I. Negative-partiy (70,3) baryon resonances. The notation in the left-hand column is $^{2S+1}(SU(3)\text{ dimensionality})_J$, where S is the total quark intrinsic spin. Each dash indicates an unobserved resonance needed in the corresponding $SU(3)$ multiplet.

$(1)_{1/2}$		$Y_0^*(1405)$			
$(1)_{3/2}$		$Y_0^*(1520)$			
$^2(8)_{1/2}$	$N^*(1700)$	···			
$^4(8)_{1/2}$	$N^*(1540)$	$Y_0^*(1670)$	···	···	
$^2(8)_{3/2}$	$N^*(1518)$	···	$Y_1^*(1660)$	···	
$^4(8)_{3/2}$	···	···	···	···	
$(8)_{5/2}$	$N^*(1690)$	···	$Y_1^*(1765)$	···	
$(10)_{1/2}$	$N^*(1680)$	···	···	···	···
$(10)_{3/2}$	···	···	···	$\Xi^*(1816)$	···

The wave functions are sums of products of spatial functions $\psi(\mathbf{p}_1,\mathbf{p}_2,\mathbf{p}_3)$, intrinsic spin functions $\chi(1,2,3)$, and $SU(3)$ functions $\phi(1,2,3)$. We distinguish different functions by their permutation symmetries.[10] There are four permutation symmetries for functions of three variables: symmetric under any permutation (labeled, e.g., ψ^s), antisymmetric under any odd permutation (labeled, e.g., ψ^a), of mixed symmetry but symmetric with respect to, say, thc 2,3 pair of coordinates (labeled e.g., ψ''), and of mixed symmetry but antisymmetric with respect to the 2,3 pair (labeled, e.g., ψ'). The rules for constructing products of these functions with definite permutation symmetry are well known. With particles of intrinsic spin $\frac{1}{2}$ only states χ^s (total spin $\frac{3}{2}$), and χ' and χ'' (each with total spin $\frac{1}{2}$) can be formed. The $SU(3)$ states ϕ^s, ϕ'', ϕ', ϕ^a correspond to $SU(3)$ representations (10), (8), (8), (1), respectively.

Consider first the case of parastatistics where among the three quarks Bose statistics are obeyed. The (56) is characterized by a symmetric spatial wave function ψ^s with total angular momentum $L=0$. The over-all symmetric states which can be constructed are

$$(8):\quad \Psi=\psi^s(\chi'\phi'+\chi''\phi''),$$

$$(10):\quad \Psi=\psi^s\chi^s\phi^s.$$

For the (70,3) the spatial function is of mixed symmetry with $L=1$. Thus Ψ contains terms

$$(\textstyle\sum_{M_S M_L}\langle LM_L SM_S|JM\rangle\psi_{L,M_L}{}^{\alpha}\chi_{S,M_S}{}^{\beta})\phi^{\alpha}$$

which we abbreviate

$$[\psi^{\alpha}\chi^{\beta}]_J\phi^{\gamma},$$

where α, β, γ are the superscripts indicating the permutation symmetry. The over-all symmetric states which can be constructed are [the notation is $(SU(3)$ multiplicity$)_J$]:

$$(1)_{1/2,3/2}:\quad \Psi=([\psi''\chi']_{1/2,3/2}-[\psi'\chi'']_{1/2,3/2})\phi^a,$$

$$(8)_{5/2}\quad :\quad \Psi=[\psi'\chi^s]_{5/2}\phi'+[\psi''\chi^s]_{5/2}\phi'',$$

$$\begin{aligned}(8)_{1/2,3/2}:\quad \Psi=a\{&([\psi''\chi']_{1/2,3/2}+[\psi'\chi'']_{1/2,3/2})\phi'\\&+([\psi'\chi']_{1/2,3/2}-[\psi''\chi'']_{1/2,3/2})\phi''\}\\&+b([\psi'\chi^s]_{1/2,3/2}\phi'+[\psi''\chi^s]_{1/2,3/2}\phi''),\end{aligned}$$

$$(10)_{1/2,3/2}:\quad \Psi=([\psi'\chi']_{1/2,3/2}+[\psi''\chi'']_{1/2,3/2})\phi^s.$$

As there are two $\frac{1}{2}^-$ and two $\frac{3}{2}^-$ octets, their wave functions are only determined to within one parameter.

We evaluate the Yukawa coupling of the baryons to the pseudoscalar meson octet, symbolically $B'\to B+\Pi$ (where Π stands for a member of the pseudoscalar octet), by assuming the basic interaction

$$Q'\to Q+\Pi. \tag{1}$$

On the basis of $SU(3)$ invariance and Galilean invariance, the interaction must have the form

$$\boldsymbol{\sigma}\cdot\left(\mathbf{q}-\frac{\omega}{M_Q}\mathbf{p}\right)F_i\Pi_i, \tag{2}$$

where $i=1,\cdots,8$ runs over the SU_3 generators,[11] $\mathbf{q}$ and $\mathbf{p}$ are the respective meson and quark momenta, $\boldsymbol{\sigma}$ is the quark spin operator, ω is the meson relativistic mass, and M_Q is the quark mass.

The $Q'\to Q+\Pi_i$ amplitude can be calculated as an operation on quark 1:

$$(\Psi(\mathbf{p}_1-\tfrac{2}{3}\mathbf{q}),\sigma_i(\mathbf{q}-\omega\mathbf{p}_1/M_Q)F_i{}^{(1)}\Psi'(\mathbf{p}_1)).$$

This matrix element can be factored into a spatial part times a spin-$SU(3)$ part. Consider, for example, decays from the (70×3) into the (56). The matrix element has the form

$$\sum_{M_L}\int d\mathbf{p}_1 d\mathbf{p}_{23}\psi^S{}_{L=0}(\mathbf{p}_1-\tfrac{2}{3}\mathbf{q},\,\mathbf{p}_{23})^*[\mathbf{q}-\omega\mathbf{p}_1/M_Q]\psi''{}_{L=1,M_L}(\mathbf{p}_1,\mathbf{p}_{23})\cdot\mathbf{S}_{M_L}, \tag{3}$$

where $\mathbf{S}$ is the spin-$SU(3)$ matrix element. This spatial integral which occurs here has two distinct forms corresponding to s- and d-wave decays. Meanwhile, for all p wave decays within the (56) and within the (70×3) the spatial integral involving the direct term q (which presumably dominates in this case) is just the normalization integral for the spatial wave function and can be done. The s, p, and d wave decays thus correspond to three distinct types of transitions. Within each type of transition the ratios of the coupling constants, or partial widths are meaningful. We do *not* need to calculate the spatial integrals. In (56) → (56)+Π, where the standard $SU(6)$ coupling results apply,[3] and $(70,3)^-$

[10] See, e.g., M. Verde, in *Handbuch der Physik*, edited by S. Flügge (Springer-Verlag, Berlin, 1957), Vol. 39, p. 170. For a similar construction of states of higher angular momenta ($L=1$ and 2), see A. N. Mitra, Phys. Rev. **151**, 1168 (1966) and (to be published).

[11] See, e.g., M. Gell-Mann, in *The Eight-Fold Way* edited by M. Gell-Mann and Y. Ne'eman (W. A. Benjamin and Company, Inc., New York, 1964), p. 11.

TABLE II. Order of magnitude of direct and recoil terms for $(70\times3)\to(56)$ transitions.

Decay	Direct	Recoil
s wave	Rq^2	$(1/R)\omega/M_Q$
d wave	Rq^2	$Rq^2\omega/M_Q$

$\to(70,3)^-+\Pi$, with p-wave mesons, we set the scale for all from, e.g.,

$$\Gamma(N^*(1238)\to N+\pi)=120\text{ MeV}.$$

For the s- and d-wave decays, the same spatial integrals occur for all transitions within each type, so within each type one of the partial widths Γ_i can be chosen as input.

The spatial integrals are energy-dependent. It is only here, and in the phase space, that we take into account the actual symmetry-violating masses of the baryons and mesons. The partial widths Γ_i are thus proportional to the square of a Yukawa coupling constant g, where this is the spin-$SU(3)$ matrix element, times an energy dependence which would arise from the spatial integration. The g's are algebraic quantities which could be readily calculated using appropriate group theory. The energy dependence is, however, intimately associated with the quark model and contains a surprise. We must examine both the direct and recoil contributions in the spatial integral in the $(70)\times(3)\to(56)$ matrix element [see Eq. (3)]. For the quark mass we can assume only that $\omega/M_Q\lesssim1$, since some believe that the effective mass in a bound system is as low as $M_N/3$. Meanwhile we can assume that $(qR)^2\ll1$, where R^{-1} is the typical expectation value of a quark momentum operator. The order of magnitude of the direct and recoil terms for s- and d-wave decays is given in terms of these parameters in Table II.[12] It thus seems reasonable that the recoil term dominates the s-wave decay and the direct term dominates the d-wave decay. This is what we assume. The partial widths are then taken to have the forms:

$$s\text{ wave:}\quad \Gamma=c_s g^2 q\omega^2, \tag{4a}$$

$$p\text{ wave:}\quad \Gamma=c_p g^2 q^3/(1+\alpha q^2), \tag{4b}$$

$$d\text{ wave:}\quad \Gamma=c_d g^2 q^5/(1+\alpha q^2)^2. \tag{4c}$$

Here $\alpha=(600\text{ MeV})^{-2}$ introduces the finite range of the angular momentum barrier.[13] In fact, the direct and recoil terms are very different for the s wave case, and experiment is quite inconsistent with the q^5 dependence associated with the former. We have the surprising prediction of a factor ω^2 which is very sensitive to the mass of the emitted meson for a low-Q decay. In the d-wave case the difference between direct and recoil contributions is not large. One could not discriminate between these dependences by current experiment alone.

To complete the description of the calculation note that for all but the $(8)\times(8)\to(8)$ transitions, the quantity g_i is given by the Wigner-Eckart theorem for $SU(3)$, which expresses it as a "reduced width" (independent of I, Y), times the appropriate isoscalar factor,[14] viz.,

$$g_i=X_i(\Pi B|B'). \tag{5}$$

For the $(8)\times(8)\to(8)$ transition, on the other hand, g_i depends on two reduced widths, X_1 and X_2, according to the formula

$$g_i=X_{i1}(88|8_1)+X_{i2}(88|8_2). \tag{6}$$

Let us digress to see that the partial widths will be the same whether we use Fermi statistics or Bose statistics in constructing the baryon wave functions. The over-all antisymmetric wave functions are, for the (56) (where the spatial state has $L=0$ and is antisymmetric):

$$(8):\quad \Psi=\psi^a(\chi'\phi'+\chi''\phi''),$$
$$(10):\quad \Psi=\psi^a\chi^s\phi^s.$$

Meanwhile for the (70,3) (where the spatial states have $L=1$ and mixed symmetry) we have essentially

$$(1):\quad \Psi=([\psi'\chi']+[\psi''\chi''])\phi^a,$$
$$(8):\quad \Psi=a\{([\psi'\chi']-[\psi''\chi''])\phi' -([\psi''\chi']+[\psi'\chi''])\phi''\} +b([\psi''\chi^s]\phi'-[\psi'\chi^s]\phi''),$$
$$(10):\quad \Psi=([\psi''\chi']-[\psi'\chi''])\phi^s.$$

Consider, for example, the transition from a (1) in the (70,3) to an (8) in the (56). The factorization of the matrix elements into spatial$\times$spin-$SU(3)$ part has the form

$$\text{Bose:}\quad (\psi^s,\mathbf{O}_R\psi'')\cdot(\chi'\phi',\mathbf{O}_S\chi'\phi^a),$$
$$\text{Fermi:}\quad (\psi^a,\mathbf{O}_R\psi')\cdot(\chi'\phi',\mathbf{O}_S\chi'\phi^a).$$

Here the operator has been factored into space and spin-$SU(3)$ parts using the notation $\mathbf{O}_R\cdot\mathbf{O}_S$. We see that the spin-$SU(3)$ matrix elements are identical. This result holds for all cases. Indeed if we denote the spatial function of various symmetries by A, S, M', M'', in obvious notation, the only modifications that the spatial integrals would suffer in going from parastatistics to Fermi statistics are $S\to A$, $A\to S$, $M'\to M''$, $M''\to M'$ Within a given type of transition the spatial integral is the same for the transitions. The only difference between Bose and Fermi statistics is then that these spatial factors are formally different. Since we treat a given spatial integral as proportional to a free parameter (except in Sec. VI, below), our results are independent of the choice of statistics.

[12] These estimates do not take into account the degree of overlap on the spatial integral. This will depend on the dynamics and could easily give rise to results at variance with Table II. In particular, in the d-wave case the quark dynamics of Ref. 6 suggest that the overlap may be much greater in the recoil than direct term.

[13] The choice of α effectively determines the scale for the $Y_0^*(1520)$ decays. The results are not, in fact, very sensitive to α, considering the experimental errors.

[14] J. J. de Swart, Rev. Mod. Phys. 35, 916 (1963).

TABLE III. Partial widths for decay of low-lying baryons. There are three major types of decay: The top group is d-wave decays. The second group is s-wave decays. The bottom group is p-wave decays. Masses are chosen to check the assignment of known particles. The plus superscript indicates a mass arbitrarily introduced for illustrative purposes in the case of an undiscovered particle. Other notations are explained in the text.

$SU(3)$ transition $B' \to B$	Reduced width X, for $(8)\times(8)=(8)$: (X_1,X_2)	Transition	g_i^2 For $\frac{3}{2}^-$, $\frac{1}{2}^-$ octets $^2(8)$	$^4(8)$	Γ_i (MeV) Theory $^2(8)$	$^4(8)$	Experiment Γ_i (MeV)
		$N^*(1690) \to N+\pi$	1/6		17		≈ 60
		$Y_1^*(1765) \to \Sigma+\pi$	$-1/9$		6		$\lesssim 2$
		$\Lambda+\pi$	$-1/6$		12 input		12
		$N+\bar{K}$	4/9		29		45
$(8)_{5/2}^- \to (8)_{1/2}^+$	$(-\sqrt{\frac{5}{6}}, -\sqrt{\frac{1}{6}})$	$Y_0^*(?) \to N+\bar{K}$	0			0	not observed
		$\Sigma+\pi$	1/2			$\cdots$	not observed
		$\Xi^*(1930)^+ \to \Lambda+\bar{K}$	1/6		11		not observed
		$\Xi+\pi$	$-2/3$		27		not observed
		$\Sigma+\bar{K}$	1/6		11		not observed
		$Y_1^*(1765) \to Y_1^*(1385)+\pi$	7/18		5		7
$(8)_{5/2}^- \to (10)_{3/2}^+$	$\sqrt{(35/12)}$	$Y_0^*(?) \to Y_1^*(1385)+\pi$	7/4			$\cdots$	$\cdots$
		$\Xi^*(1930)^+ \to \Xi^*(1530)+\pi$	7/12			$\cdots$	$\cdots$
$(1)_{3/2}^- \to (8)_{1/2}^+$	$\sqrt{5}$	$Y_0^*(1520) \to N+E$	$-5/4$		5		5
		$\Sigma+\pi$	15/8		10		9
		$N_3^*(1585)^+ \to N+\pi$	5/36		9		$\cdots$
	$-\sqrt{(5/18)}$	$Y_1^*(1660) \to N+\bar{K}$	5/108		1		see below
		$\Sigma+\pi$	5/108		1		see below
		$\Lambda+\pi$	5/72		3		see below
$(10)_{3/2}^- \to (8)_{1/2}^+$		$\Xi^*(1816) \to \Lambda+\bar{K}$	5/72		2		see below
		$\Xi+\pi$	5/72		2		see below
		$\Sigma+\bar{K}$	5/72		0.4		see below
		$\Omega(1990)^+ \to \Xi+\bar{K}$	5/18		6		$\cdots$
		$N^*(1518) \to N+\pi$	10/9	$-1/36$	52	1	≈ 50
		$\Lambda+K$	$-5/8$	0	$\cdots$	$\cdots$	$\cdots$
		$Y_1^*(1660) \to N+\bar{K}$	$-5/108$	$-2/27$	1.4	2	7
	$-\sqrt{(\frac{5}{2})}1/6\frac{1}{(a^2+b^2)^{1/2}}$	$\Sigma+\pi$	125/108	1/54	29	0.5	13
$(8)_{3/2}^- \to (8)_{1/2}^+$		$\Lambda+\pi$	$-5/72$	1/36	3	1	2
	$(\sqrt{5}a-\sqrt{2}b,$ $-5a-\sqrt{(\frac{2}{5})}b)$	$Y_0^*(1660)^+ \to N+\bar{K}$	5/4	0	37	0	not observed
		$\Sigma+\pi$	5/24	$-1/12$	5	2	not observed
		$\Xi^*(1816) \to \Lambda+\bar{K}$	$-5/18$	$-1/36$	8	1	10
		$\Xi+\pi$	5/72	1/9	2	4	1
		$\Sigma+\bar{K}$	10/9	$-1/36$	7	0.2	< 1
$(10)_{3/2}^- \to (10)_{3/2}^+$	4/9				0(1 MeV)		
$(8)_{3/2}^- \to (10)_{3/2}^+$	$\sqrt{(35/6)}\frac{1}{(a^2+b^2)^{1/2}}$ $1/3(\sqrt{(\frac{5}{2})}a+2b)$				0(1 MeV)		
		$Y_0^*(1405) \to N+\bar{K}$	1/9		$\cdots$	$\cdots$	$\cdots$
$(1)_{1/2}^- \to (8)_{1/2}^+$	$-2/3$	$\Sigma+\pi$	$-1/6$		21 input		35
		$\Lambda+\eta$	1/18		$\cdots$		$\cdots$
		$N_3^*(1680) \to N+\pi$	$-1/81$		48		≈ 50
		$\Sigma+K$	1/81		$0.06q$		$\cdots$
		$Y_1^*(1750)^+ \to N+K$	1/243		19		not observed
		$\Sigma+\pi$	$-1/243$		8		not observed
		$\Lambda+\pi$	$-1/162$		17		not observed
		$\Sigma+\eta$	1/162		$0.038q$		not observed
$(10)_{1/2}^- \to (8)_{1/2}^+$	$-\sqrt{2}/9$	$\Xi+K$	$-1/243$		$\cdots$		not observed
		$\Xi^*(1820)^+ \to \Lambda+\bar{K}$	$-1/162$		26		not observed
		$\Xi+\pi$	$-1/162$		13		not observed
		$\Sigma+\bar{K}$	$-1/162$		19		not observed
		$\Xi+\eta$	1/162		$0.038q$		not observed
		$\Omega(?) \to \Xi+K$	2/81				not observed
		$N^*(1540) \to N+\pi$	8/81	$-2/81$	240	60	≈ 70[a]
		$N+\eta$	$-2/81$	$-2/81$	$0.17q$	$0.17q$	$\approx 0.3q$[a]
		$\Lambda+K$	1/18	0	$0.27q$	0	$\cdots$

TABLE III. (*continued*)

$SU(3)$ transition $B' \to B$	Reduced width X for $(8)\times(8)=(8)$: (X_1,X_2)	Transition	g_i^2 For $\frac{3}{2}^-$, $\frac{1}{2}^-$ octets $^2(8)$; $^4(8)$	Γ_i (MeV) Theory $^2(8)$; $^4(8)$	Γ_i (MeV) Experiment
		$N^*(1700) \to N+\pi$	as above	410 ; 100	≈ 200
		$N+\eta$	as above	90 ; 90	...
		$\Lambda+K$	as above	80 ; 0	...
		$\Sigma+K$	1/162; 8/81	$0.03q$; $0.48q$	
		$Y_1^*(1750)^+ \to N+\bar{K}$	−1/243; −16/243	19 ; 300	not observed
	$\frac{1}{9\sqrt{2}}\frac{1}{(a^2+b^2)^{1/2}}$	$\Sigma+\pi$	5/243; 4/243	42 ; 34	
		$\Lambda+\pi$	−1/162; 2/81	17 ; 68	
$(8)_{1/2}^- \to (8)_{1/2}^+$		$\Sigma+\eta$	−1/162; 2/81	$0.038q$; $.15q$	
		$\Xi+K$	32/243 −8/243	... ...	
	$(-\sqrt{5}a+2\sqrt{5}b,\ 5a+2b)$	$Y_0^*(1670) \to N+\bar{K}$	1/9 ; 0	370 ; 0	$\Gamma_t \approx 18$[b]
		$\Sigma+\pi$	3/162; −6/81	25 ; 100	$\Gamma_{\bar{K}N}\Gamma_{\eta\Lambda} \approx$
		$\Lambda+\eta$	1/162; −2/81	$0.038q$; $0.15q$	$0.2q$ (MeV)[a]
		$\Xi+K$	4/81 ; 4/81	... ...	...
		$\Xi^*(1880)^+ \to \Lambda+K$	−2/81 ; −2/81	102 ; 102	
		$\Xi+\pi$	1/162; 8/81	13 ; 210	not observed
		$\Sigma+\bar{K}$	8/81 ; −2/81	300 ; 75	
		$\Xi+\eta$	1/18 ; 0	$0.34q$; 0	
		$N_3^*(1585)^+ \to N^*(1238)+\pi$	10/81	70	...
$(10)_{3/2}^- \to (10)_{3/2}^+$	4/9	$Y_1^*(1660) \to Y_1^*(1385)+\pi$	16/243	19	...
		$N^*(1238)+K$	16/243	...	...
		$\Xi^*(1816) \to \Xi^*(1530)+\pi$	2/81	8	...
		$\Omega(?) \to \Xi^*(1530)+K$	8/81	$0.5q$	...
$(8)_{3/2}^- \to (10)_{3/2}^+$	$\frac{1}{(a^2+b^2)^{1/2}}\frac{\sqrt{10}}{9}$	$N^*(1518) \to N^*(1238)+\pi$	8/81 ; −20/81	30 ; 74	≈ 50
	$\times(-a+\sqrt{(\frac{5}{2})}b)$	$Y_1^*(1660) \to Y_1^*(1385)+\pi$	−4/243; 10/243	5 ; 12	$\lesssim 8$
		$\to N^*(1238)+K$	16/243; −40/243	$0.3q$; $0.8q$	...
		$Y_0^*(1660)^+ \to Y_1^*(1385)+\pi$	2/27 ; −5/27	22 ; 54	...
		$\Xi^*(1816) \to \Xi^*(1530)+\pi$	−2/81 ; 5/81	8 ; 21	4
		$\to Y_1^*(1385)+K$	2/81 ; −5/81	$0.1q$; $0.3q$	...
$(10)_{3/2}^+ \to (8)_{1/2}^+$	$-\frac{4}{3\sqrt{3}}$	$N^*(1238) \to N+\pi$	8/27	120 input	120
$(8)_{5/2}^- \to (1)_{3/2}^-$	$-\frac{\sqrt{2}}{3\sqrt{3}}$	$Y_1^*(1765) \to Y_0^*(1520)+\pi$	−2/27	16	≈ 8
$(8)_{3/2}^- \to (1)_{3/2}^-$	$\sqrt{(\frac{5}{3})}2/9\frac{1}{(a^2+b^2)^{1/2}} \times(a+\sqrt{(2/5)}b)$	$Y_1^*(1660) \to Y_0^*(1520)+\pi$	20/243; 8/243	...	...
$(8)_{3/2}^- \to (1)_{1/2}^-$	$\frac{\sqrt{3}}{27}\frac{1}{(a^2+b^2)^{1/2}} \times(-4a+\sqrt{10}b)$	$Y_1^*(1660) \to Y_0^*(1405)+\pi$	−16/243; 10/243	16 ; 9	$\lesssim 16$

[a] See C. Michael, Phys. Letters **21**, 93 (1966); A. W. Hendry and R. G. Moorhouse, *ibid.* **18**, 171 (1965); A. T. Davies (private communication).
[b] This guess is based on data of D. Berley *et al.*, Phys. Rev. Letters **15**, 641 (1965).

III. RESULTS

The results of the calculations of partial widths Γ_i are given in Table III. For $(8)_{3/2}^-$ and $(8)_{1/2}^-$ states [the notation is: $(SU(3)\text{ multiplicity})_{J^P}$], the predictions are given for the doublet and quartet quark intrinsic spin (S) states. These octets are labeled $^2(8)$ and $^4(8)$, respectively. The reduced widths are given in terms of the doublet and quartet amplitudes, a and b, i.e., the wave function is

$$\Psi = a\Psi(S=\tfrac{1}{2}) + b\Psi(S=\tfrac{3}{2}), \qquad (7)$$

where the Ψ's are normalized. The threshold production of K's and η's is given in the form: partial width $\Gamma = cq$, where q and Γ are both in MeV. The sign of g is entered before the values of g^2. This column can be used to evaluate rates in case of mixtures.[15]

First some general remarks about the results: (1) The recoil factor ω^2 in the $(70,3) \to (56)$ s-wave rate strongly enhances K and η relative to π for low-Q decays. This means that the K and η partial widths will be much larger than indicated by $SU(3)$ and phase space, which

[15] Relative values of these signs can also be observed directly. See, e.g., A. Kernan and W. M. Smart. Phys. Rev. Letters **17**, 832, 1125 (1966). We note that our results disagree with theirs for the phase $\bar{K}N \to \Lambda\pi$ in $Y_1^*(1660)$, $Y_1^*(1765)$.

can explain the prominence of the $N+\eta$ and $\Lambda+\eta$ peaks near threshold.

(2) At present the sensitivity of experiments is such that many of the resonances will be unobserved. Many states have very small width and/or high inelasticity or are very broad such that they may not be observed for some time. It would be a mistake to assume that lack of observation of a resonance necessarily implies higher mass.

One final remark before detailed discussion of the results. There are three negative-parity Y_0^*'s, Y_1^*, and Ξ^*'s both for spin $\frac{3}{2}$ and spin $\frac{1}{2}$. Some of these probably overlap. For this reason presently quoted experimental partial widths for Y_1^*'s at 1660 and 1766 (as well as those for the N^*'s recently discovered in partial wave analyses) must be regarded as preliminary. For purposes of discussion we will, however, take the present numbers quite seriously.

A. Detailed Discussion of Table III

1. *Decays of* $\frac{5}{2}^-$ *Baryons*

The $(8)_{5/2^-}$ decays are in reasonable agreement with the 6 experimental numbers (including p-wave decay at bottom of Table III). The d-wave decay of $(8)_{5/2^-}$ baryons (into $(8)_{1/2^+}$ and $(10)_{3/2^+}$ plus pseudoscalar mesons) are the same as given by Coyne *et al.*[2] in their study of the (1134) representation of $SU(6)$. We determine the scale factor for d-wave decays [c_d of Eq. (4)] from the input width $Y_1^*(1765)\rightarrow\Lambda\pi$. Two members of the $(8)_{5/2^-}$, Y_0^* and Ξ^*, have not been observed. They are discussed below. [The decay of the $(1)_{3/2^-}$, the $Y_0^*(1520)$, is not the same as in the (1134) as given by Coyne *et al.*, but this fact is of little significance because of the factor α [see Eq. (4)], which can be adjusted to give the correct relation between the low-Q $Y_0^*(1520)$ decays and the high-Q $Y_1^*(1765)$ decays.] The agreement with current data for $Y_1^*(1765)$ and $N^*(1690)$ is satisfactory.

2. *Decays of* $\frac{3}{2}^-$ *baryons*

All other (70,3) states except the N^* decuplets have 2- or 3-fold degeneracy. Assuming $SU(3)$ is good and that the octet states divide into $^2(8)$ and $^4(8)$ we have to choose which of the assignments *most* suits experiment. For known $\frac{3}{2}^-$ baryons we have one of our most interesting results: they are not in the same octet.[16] The $N^*(1518)$, $Y^*(1660)$ (assumed $\frac{3}{2}^-$), and $\Xi^*(1816)$ are fitted semiquantitatively by placing N^* and Y_1^* in the $^2(8)$ and Ξ^* in the (10). An excellent fit to data in the latter case can be obtained with 10% $^2(8)$ mixing. The state $(9/10)^{1/2}(10)+(1/10)^{1/2}\,{}^2(8)$ yields satisfactory widths: $\Gamma_{\Lambda\bar{K}}$, $\Gamma_{\Xi\pi}$, $\Gamma_{\Sigma\bar{K}}$, $\Gamma_{\Xi^*\pi}=5$, 1, 0.0, 4 MeV respectively. Small admixture to a dominant $^2(8)$ state does not work if we believe that $\Xi^*(1816)\rightarrow\Sigma+\bar{K}$ is very small. For the $Y_1^*(1660)$ small admixture of $^4(8)$ to the dominant $^2(8)$ yields good agreement with current experiment. The many unobserved $\frac{3}{2}^-$ states are discussed below.

3. *Decays of* $\frac{1}{2}^-$ *baryons*

Among $\frac{1}{2}^-$ baryons the $Y_0^*(1405)$ $\frac{1}{2}^-$ observed decay width is relatively large. It would be convenient for the model if the actual width were about $\frac{1}{2}$ the quoted 35 MeV or if the theoretical widths were slightly damped compared with the expression (4a) for higher-Q decays. The only other observed $\frac{1}{2}^-$ states are N^*(nominal 1540) and $Y_0^*(1670)$ associated with η decays, which should be placed in the $^4(8)$, the probable $T=\frac{3}{2}N^*(1680)$ in the (10), and the very wide $N^*(1700)$ which should be placed in the $^2(8)$. Only fair agreement is achieved. Possible mixing which could remedy the disagreements is exemplified by the $Y_0^*(1670)$, whose observed narrowness is a serious difficulty. One needs to *adjust* the mixture *sensitively*. Just as an example,

$$(\sqrt{(17/20)})\,{}^4(8)-(1/\sqrt{10})(10)+(1/\sqrt{20})\,{}^2(8)$$

yields $\Gamma_{\bar{K}N}-3$, $\Gamma_{\pi\Sigma}=12$, $\Gamma_{\eta\Lambda}=0.25q$. One of the most interesting results is that the $^2(8)_{1/2^-}$ lies above $^4(8)_{1/2^-}$. Several other $\frac{1}{2}^-$ states are indicated to have reasonable widths so that they should be observable in spite of the low statistical weight. These are discussed in Sec. V below.

We do not present here any model of QQ forces which would lead to the mixtures mentioned above.

The properties of the missing resonances in the (70,3) are summarized in Table IV. In this table "input width" refers to the formation channel of the resonance relevant in most experiments. The three resonances which should be most visible are not inconsistent with observation. There is a possible Y_0^* around 1700 MeV.[17] There is a $\Xi^*(1930)$ quite consistent with the 1870 state indicated in the table. Masses in the Ξ^* around 2040 MeV are not well explored.

IV. MISSING $\frac{3}{2}^-$ AND $\frac{5}{2}^-$ STATES

Now consider the as yet unobserved resonances in the (70,3) of spin $\frac{3}{2}$ and $\frac{5}{2}$. All reference below is to the $\frac{3}{2}^-$ states except when explicitly stated. Very crude mass guesses are indicated for these particles in Table IV.

N^*: There are a (10) and a $^4(8)$ with $I=\frac{3}{2},\frac{1}{2}$, respectively. These N^*'s are relatively narrow and inelastic. The $I=\frac{3}{2}\,N^*$, in particular, should have low mass if our assignment to $\Xi^*(1816)$ is correct and is so narrow that it would likely be missed in the current mesh of accurate experiments.

Y_1^*: There are (10) and $^4(8)$ Y_1^*'s. They have very similar characteristics. They will be very difficult to observe, being highly inelastic. Perhaps indirect production, such as a missing-mass experiment, would reveal

[16] Compare, for example, S. L. Glashow and A. H. Rosenfeld, Phys. Rev. Letters 10, 192 (1963).

[17] J. D. Davies *et al.*, Phys. Rev. Letters 18, 62 (1967).

TABLE IV. Properties of missing resonances in the (70,3). The assumed masses are crude guesses made in order to be definite. They are not generally the same masses considered in Table III. Those without (*) were chosen according to the rules: For octets $M=M_c+175Y+A(1-Y^2)(I-1/4)$ MeV with A determined empirically in each multiplet, for decuplets $M=M_c+175Y$. [There is considerable reason to believe, however, that the Gell-Mann–Okubo mass formula will not hold in the (70,3).[a]] Those masses marked (*) had to be selected quite arbitrarily because of insufficient information. The total widths quoted are based only on the channels shown in Table III. Under remarks we note that the visibility of Y_1^*'s in $^4(8)_{3/2}$ and $(10)_{3/2}$ is sensitive to mixing which may affect the small input width $\Gamma_{\bar{K}N}$. The $^4(8)_{1/2}\Xi^*$ may be effectively highly inelastic.

Y_I	$^{2S+1}(SU(3))_J$	Assumed mass (MeV)	Γ (MeV)	Input widths (MeV)	Readily visible	Remarks
$N_{1/2}^*$	$^4(8)_{3/2}$	1518*	75	$\Gamma_{\pi N}=1$	No	Highly inelastic
$N_{3/2}^*$	$(10)_{3/2}$	1465	25	$\Gamma_{\pi N}=4$	Perhaps	Narrow and inelastic
Y_0^*	$^2(8)_{1/2}$	1875*	800	$\Gamma_{\bar{K}N}=750$	No	Too wide
Y_0^*	$^2(8)_{3/2}$	1705	90	$\Gamma_{\bar{K}N}=45$	Yes	$\bar{K}N$ decay dominant
Y_0^*	$^4(8)_{3/2}$	1660*	55	$\Gamma_{\bar{K}N}=0$	No	Highly inelastic
Y_0^*	$(8)_{5/2}$	1900	110	$\Gamma_{\bar{K}N}=0$	No	Highly inelastic
Y_1^*	$^2(8)_{1/2}$	1875*	450	$\Gamma_{\bar{K}N}=30$	Perhaps	Large width mainly ΞK
Y_1^*	$^4(8)_{1/2}$	1800*	550	$\Gamma_{\bar{K}N}=400$	No	Too wide
Y_1^*	$(10)_{1/2}$	1855	85	$\Gamma_{\bar{K}N}=30$	Perhaps	Low statistical weight
Y_1^*	$^4(8)_{3/2}$	1660*	30	$\Gamma_{\bar{K}N}=2$	Perhaps }	May be highly inelastic
Y_1^*	$(10)_{3/2}$	1640	20	$\Gamma_{\bar{K}N}=1$	Perhaps }	
$\Xi_{1/2}^*$	$^2(8)_{1/2}$	2050	1000		No	Too wide
$\Xi_{1/2}^*$	$^4(8)_{1/2}$	1890	400		No	Too wide
$\Xi_{1/2}^*$	$(10)_{1/2}$	2030	125		Perhaps	Low statistical weight
$\Xi_{1/2}^*$	$^2(8)_{3/2}$	1870	50		Yes	$Y\bar{K}$ decay dominant
$\Xi_{1/2}^*$	$^4(8)_{3/2}$	1816*	25		Perhaps	Very small $Y\bar{K}$ coupling
$\Xi_{1/2}^*$	$(8)_{5/2}$	2040	125		Yes	Large $\Xi\pi$ width
Ω^-	$(10)_{1/2}$	2205	160		No	Too wide
Ω^-	$(10)_{3/2}$	1990	10		Perhaps	Sensitive to Ξ^*K threshold

[a] G. Kane, Phys. Rev. Letters 17, 719 (1966).

them. The $\Lambda\pi$ channel is also weak.[18] A possible experiment is $K^-n\rightarrow Y_1^*\pi$.

Y_0^*: There are $^2(8)$ and $^4(8)$ and also the member of the $\frac{5}{2}^-$ octet. The $^2(8)$ is mainly $\bar{K}N$ and should be seen in total cross sections and in elastic scattering.[17] In a heavy liquid one could look at $K^-p\rightarrow Y_0^*\pi^0$ which is characteristic of $I=0$ (the $\Sigma\pi$ coupling is small). The $^4(8)$ presents no obvious method of detection. The $(8)_{5/2}$ has very small $\bar{K}N$ coupling. It should be looked at in indirect production through the large $\Sigma\pi$ and $Y_1^*\pi$ modes.

Ξ^*: There are, as for Y_0^*, $^2(8)$, $^4(8)$, and $(8)_{5/2}^-$. The $^2(8)$ is characterized by the large $\Sigma\bar{K}$ (and $\Lambda\bar{K}$) mode (unless the mass is too low), while $\Xi\pi$ is small. The $^4(8)$ is dominated by $\Xi^*\pi$, and $\Xi\pi$ is significant. The $(8)_{5/2}^-$ is mainly $\Xi\pi$ and perhaps can be identified with the structure that has been observed[5] at 1930 MeV.

V. DISCUSSION OF ENHANCED HEAVY MESON DECAY

The ω^2 recoil factor more than overcomes the suppression due to phase space of the s-wave decays into K or η compared to π, once one is a few MeV above the relevant threshold. Let us examine whether this effect is confirmed by experiment. We will say an inelastic cross section has a "threshold peak" when in crossing the threshold (e.g., with increasing energy across the threshold in $\pi N\rightarrow\eta N$) the cross section rises (with infinite derivative as it must) to a large value and then drops down shortly above (say <100 MeV) threshold. The following conditions lead to a threshold peak: (1) The resonance mass is appropriately placed in the vicinity of the threshold. (2) The resonance is not too wide in other than the threshold channel. (3) The branching ratio into threshold channel is large (and not too small into input channel). Let us review the predictions of our model to see when conditions (2) and (3) are met [with some comments on (1)]. We first discuss $\frac{1}{2}^-$ to $\frac{1}{2}^+$ decay.

N^*'s: The relevant thresholds are $N\eta(1488)$, $\Lambda K(1611)$, and $\Sigma K(1689)$. The prediction for $^4(8)_{1/2}$ satisfies the conditions for (2) and (3) for $N\eta$. The ΛK branching ratio is very small. ***The $N\eta$ threshold peak is observed.*** The $(10)_{1/2}$ and $^2(8)_{1/2}$ are probably near the ΣK threshold, but $^2(8)$ is too wide and both have small ΣK branching ratio. A very accurate experiment could show a ΣK threshold peak due to the (10).

Y_1^*'s: The relevant thresholds are $\Sigma\eta(1742)$ and $\Xi K(1814)$. The $^4(8)$ is too wide for a threshold peak. The $^2(8)$ is narrow except for the possible ΞK channel, and the $\Sigma\eta$ branching ratio is significant. There could be an observable $\Sigma\eta$ threshold peak. If the mass is not too far below threshold ***a large ΞK peak should be seen.*** Experimental work to check this possibility would be of great interest. The (10) is narrow, and $\Sigma\eta$ branching ratio is large. There should be a $\Sigma\eta$ threshold peak if the mass is

[18] A possible new Y_1^* at 1680 produced indirectly at high energy has been observed by M. Derrick *et al.* (private communication). Since the enhancement is strong in the $\Lambda\pi$ channel and appears rather wide, there is some doubt that this Y_1^* could be associated with either state under discussion here.

right. *A* Σ_η *threshold peak is observed.*[19] It could be either (10) or $^2(8)$.

Y_0^*'s: The relevant thresholds are $\Lambda\eta(1664)$ and $\Xi K(1814)$. The $^4(8)$ satisfies the conditions for a $\Lambda\eta$ threshold peak *which is observed.* (A little mixing is needed to fit the observation.) The $^2(8)$ is too wide.

Ξ^*'s: The relevant thresholds are $\Lambda\bar{K}(1611)$, $\Sigma\bar{K}(1689)$, and $\Xi\eta(1867)$. The $^4(8)$ is rather wide but is strong in $\Sigma\bar{K}$. The $^2(8)$ is narrow except for $\Sigma\bar{K}$ and $\Xi\eta$, which are quite strong; $\Lambda\bar{K}$ is significant. The (10) is narrow and relatively strong in these channels. *Threshold peaks in one or more of these channels should be seen,* depending on mass. Threshold peaks will be difficult to see, however, for $Y=-2$.

One can also consider the *s* wave decays: $\frac{3}{2}^- \to \frac{3}{2}^+$. The $N^* \to Y_1^*+K$ or $N^*+\eta$ thresholds are probably too high in mass. The decay $Y_1^* \to N^*+\bar{K}$ (threshold ≈ 1730) is predicted to be large if any of the $^2(8)_{3/2}$ or $^4(8)_{3/2}$ or $(10)_{3/2}$ has high enough mass. Presumably, according to results discussed above, the $^2(8)$ and (10) have too low a mass. Similarly, $\Xi^* \to Y_1^*+K$ would be large if any state overlaps the threshold.

We conclude that all threshold peaks seen are contained in the model. Further cases are predicted. We feel the evidence for the heavy meson enhancement is very good.

We should also discuss the theoretical justification of this recoil correction. The justification lies in the validity of the nonrelativistic quark model as opposed simply to the quark model. If quark model dynamics are taken seriously, the determining factor is the detailed form of the interaction. Roughly speaking, very strong QQ forces at the origin lead to large relativistic effects, making our Galilean invariance argument unreliable. If, on the other hand, the forces are not singular, most of the quark wave function will involve low momenta, and the Galilean invariance argument is good.

VI. DISCUSSION

It is seen that we obtain a semiquantitative agreement with baryon-decay rates, especially the *d*-wave decays, which is quite encouraging at the present time. The quark model specific kinematical effect of a factor (meson energy)^2 in the *s*-wave rates is helpful in obtaining agreement with data. Further experiments are needed to obtain definitive widths, and theoretical work[20] is needed to remove the degeneracies in order to properly test the model.

This discussion would be incomplete without reference to the possibly low-lying $\frac{1}{2}^+$ singlet Y_0^* in the (20,3). Its mass depends on problematical symmetry-breaking effects. One estimate[6] places it very low: $1280<M<1350$ MeV. If $M<1330$ it will decay into $\Lambda+\gamma$. If $M>1395$ it would decay predominantly into $\Lambda\pi\pi$. The coupling of (70,3) baryons to this Y_0^* involve several different radial integrals depending on dynamical details. We just remark that since coupling $(56,1)^+ \to (20,3)^+ + \Pi$ is small (it vanishes in our model), it is probably via decay of negative parity Y^*'s produced in $\bar{K}N$ reactions that the easiest experimental search could be made.

One of the interesting results is in the absolute rates. From our fit we already have $\alpha^{-1/2}=0.6$ BeV. Presumably the baryon radius is $R=O(\alpha^{1/2})$. Quoting q, ω, Γ in BeV in the following, the empirically fitted rates in Table III obey

$$s \text{ wave:} \quad \Gamma=20g^2q\omega^2, \tag{8a}$$

$$p \text{ wave:} \quad \Gamma=42g^2q^3/(1+\alpha q^2), \tag{9a}$$

$$d \text{ wave:} \quad \Gamma=6g^2q^5/(1+\alpha q^2)^2. \tag{10a}$$

The coefficients of g^2 on the right-hand side are proportional to the squares of radial integrals:

$$s \text{ wave:} \quad \frac{\omega}{M_Q}\int \psi^S \mathbf{p}_1\cdot \psi''d\tau \propto O\left(\frac{\omega Y_0(\hat{q})}{RM_Q}\right), \tag{8b}$$

$$p \text{ wave:} \quad q_z\int |\psi^S|^2 d\tau \propto qY_1^0(\hat{q})/[3(1+\alpha q^2)]^{1/2}, \tag{9b}$$

d wave:

$$\int \psi^S[\tfrac{3}{2}q_z\psi_z''-\tfrac{1}{2}\mathbf{q}\cdot\psi'']d\tau=O\left(\frac{Rq^2Y_2^0(\hat{q})}{1+\alpha q^2}\right), \tag{10b}$$

where $\mathbf{p}_1$ is the momentum of quark 1, and ψ^s and ψ'' are spatial wave functions symmetric and of mixed symmetry (symmetric in quarks 2, 3), respectively, normalized:

$$\int |\psi^S|^2 d\tau = \int \psi''\cdot\psi''d\tau=1.$$

The relations (8b) and (10b) are *exceedingly crude*, but are chosen optimistically to obtain large $1/R$ and M_Q. Comparing right-hand sides of Eqs. (8) and (9) we have $O(M_QR)=(42\times 3/20)^{1/2}$, and comparing (9) and (10) we have $O(1/R)=(42\times 3/6)^{1/2}$. Thus

$$M_Q=O(10 \text{ BeV}), \tag{11}$$
$$1/R=O(5 \text{ BeV}).$$

These should be regarded as upper limits. If the overlap in both (8) and (10) is, say, 1/5 we would obtain $1/R=1$ BeV, $M_Q=0.5$ BeV. The significance of these results is not obvious and we will not discuss it.

Finally, let us review the problem of quark statistics. To distinguish between the two forms of statistics one

[19] There is recent evidence for a $\Sigma\eta$ enhancement near threshold consistent with the total width of roughly MeV predicted for (10) or $^2(8)$ by the model. See D. Cline and J. Robinson, Phys. Letters **23**, 509 (1966). Note that the model predicts that this Y_1^* is not in the same multiplet with the resonances found from their $N\eta$ and $\Lambda\eta$ decays.

[20] In addition to R. Capps (Ref. 2), O. W. Greenberg and M. Resnikoff (private communication) are considering mass splitting and mixing in the (70,3).

must resort to more specific dynamical considerations. In particular the symmetry-breaking mass differences and mixing of wave functions, and the structure of the radial function (form factors) must be considered.

For example, the role of the $\mathbf{L}\cdot\mathbf{S}$ coupling is very different for the two. Clearly, a p-wave spin-orbit force, which one might expect to play the dominant role in bringing about the splitting among the various members of the (70,3) super multiplet, has the $SU(3)$-spin dependence P_u^- for parastatistics and P_u^+ for Fermi statistics, where $P_u^\pm$ are respectively the projection operators for the (6) and (3*) states of a Q-Q system. Since, on the other hand, P_u^- is a null operator for (10) states and likewise P_u^+ for (1) states, one would expect a p-wave spin-orbit force to split the (1) states but not (10) under parastatistics and vice versa under Fermi statistics. This would immediately explain the splitting between the $Y_0^*(1405)$ and $Y_0^*(1520)$ states under parastatistics, but not under Fermi statistics.

Our results also indicate that the $(10)_{3/2}$ and $(10)_{1/2}$ states are strongly split. In parastatistics this splitting might come about through $SU(3)$ violating terms, say of the form $\lambda_8^{(i)}\lambda_8^{(j)}$, in the Q-Q potential. The near degeneracy among several $SU(3)$ multiplets makes this hypothesis rather attractive. We have not yet worked out the detailed consequences of such a hypothesis. The splitting of (8) states by an $\mathbf{L}\cdot\mathbf{S}$ force is comparable under both forms of statistics.

A more interesting piece of evidence favoring parastatistics against Fermi statistics comes from the role of the positive parity states other than the (56). Dynamically A functions of $L^P=1^+$ have strongly attractive kernels under p wave interaction. These functions give a total of (20,3) states of $SU(6)\times O_3$ under parastatistics and (56,3) under Fermi statistics. The spin-orbit force splits these states into various $SU(3)$ multiplets, the lowest ones having $J^P=\frac{1}{2}^+$. This leaves for the states $J^P=\frac{1}{2}^+$ of lowest energies, a singlet and an octet under parastatistics, and a decuplet and an octet under Fermi statistics. Experimentally, it is tempting to identify the 1450-MeV Roper resonance with the $Y=1$, $I_3=\frac{1}{2}$ member of the above octet. Parastatistics therefore give a (more economical) prediction of a mere extra singlet, while Fermi statistics require a whole extra decuplet of low energy.

A third feature bearing on statistics concerns the shape of baryon form factors in relation to the kind of spatial symmetry (S or A) assumed.[21] Thus an A function predicts nodal behavior for the form factor at $q^2\approx 20$ F^{-2}, in complete disharmony with experiment. An S function, on the other hand, predicts a smooth monotonic fall, which is at least consistent with experiment. This again favors parastatistics to Fermi statistics, as long as the (56) representation for baryons is not questioned.

ACKNOWLEDGMENTS

This work was initiated at the Delhi University Summer School of Theoretical Physics (1966) at Udaipur. The authors would like to thank Professor R. C. Majumdar, Director of the Summer School, for his interest and encouragement. One of us (M. R.) would like to thank the Rutherford High Energy Laboratory for a summer appointment and for its hospitality, and Professor R. H. Dalitz and Dr. P. Coulter and Dr. A. W. Hendry for discussions.

[21] A. N. Mitra and Rabi Majumdar, Phys. Rev. **150**, 1194 (1966).

JETP LETTERS VOL 2, NO 3 1 AUGUST 1965

THE QUARK HYPOTHESIS AND RELATIONS BETWEEN CROSS SECTIONS AT HIGH ENERGIES

E. M. Levin and L. L. Frankfurt
A. F. Ioffe Physico-technical Institute, USSR Academy of Sciences
Submitted 2 June 1965

Numerous attempts are now under way to apply higher symmetries to the process of particle interaction. In spite of some success [1], the physical meaning of the operations performed remains unclear. We propose here a physically lucid approach to the account of symmetry in particle interaction at high energies. It is assumed that the particles are made up of quarks [2] and that the wave function of the free particles transforms in accordance with SU(6) symmetry [3] in the particle rest frame. It is assumed that fast-particle collision process consists principally of single scattering of a quark of one particle by a quark of the other.

The validity of such an approximation can be explained by means of the following model. Let us assume that the heavy quarks are on the bottom of a deep vector well of rectangular form [4]. In this case we can assume that the quark wave function is equal to zero outside the well and that the quarks inside the well are nonrelativistic if the well is sufficiently broad. If we assume that the wells do not change appreciably during the course of the collision of the relativistic particles and that the interaction radius of the bound quark with a quark (antiquark) decreases with increasing energy, then the main contribution is made by single scattering of the quark (antiquark) of one particle by the quark of the other, provided the momentum of the colliding particles is much larger than the momentum of the quark inside the well. According to estimates obtained in this model, the interaction radius of a bound quark with a quark (antiquark), determined from the total cross section, is smaller by a factor 2 - 3 than the interaction radius of the nucleons at high energies, thus favoring this approximation. We note that the physical meaning of our approximation is entirely different from the case of the deuteron, since the quarks collide inside the well. The amplitude for relativistic quark-quark (antiquark) scattering in a broad rectangular well can be written in the c.m.s. as follows:

$$\begin{aligned} M_{ij} = a + b(\sigma_i, \sigma_j) + c(\sigma_i + \sigma_j, \nu) + d(\sigma_i K)(\sigma_j K) + \\ + e(\sigma_i N)(\sigma_j N) + (F_i F_j)[a_F + b_F(\sigma_i \sigma_j) + c_F(\sigma_i + \sigma_j, \nu) + \\ + d_F(\sigma_i K)(\sigma_j K) + e_F(\sigma_i N)(\sigma_j N)] \end{aligned} \tag{1}$$

where σ are Pauli matrices, $\nu = [n \times n']/|n \times n'|$, $\underset{\sim}{N} = (n - n')/|n - n'|$, $\underset{\sim}{K} = (n + n')/|n + n'|$, $\underset{\sim}{n}$ and $\underset{\sim}{n}'$ are unit vectors in the directions of the quark momenta before and after scattering in the c.m.s., and F_i and F_j are Gell-Mann's 8 operators for the quarks.

Knowing the form of the "quark" amplitude, we can express the particle scattering amplitude in terms of M_{ij}; averaging over the coordinate wave function of the quark inside the particle is easy if the momentum of the colliding particles is much larger than the momentum of the quark inside the well. Assuming that the free nucleons belong to the representation $\underline{56}$ and the mesons to representation of the 35 group of SU(6), we can express all the amplitudes in terms of M_{ij}.

Using the optical theorem, we obtain the following relations between the total cross sections:

$$\sigma_{pn} - \sigma_{p\Sigma^+} = \sigma_{p\Sigma^-} - \sigma_{p\Xi^0} = 0 \tag{2}$$

$$\sigma_{p\lambda} = 2\sigma_{pn} - \sigma_{pp} = (1/2)(\sigma_{p\Sigma^+} + \sigma_{p\Sigma^-}) = (1/3)(2\sigma_{p\Xi^-} + \sigma_{pp}) \tag{3}$$

$$(1/2)(\sigma_{K^+p} - \sigma_{K^-p}) = \sigma_{K^0p} - \sigma_{\bar{K}^0p} = \sigma_{\pi^+p} - \sigma_{\pi^-p} \tag{4}$$

$$\sigma_{K^+p} + \sigma_{K^-p} = (1/2)(\sigma_{K^0p} + \sigma_{\bar{K}^0p} + \sigma_{\pi^-p} + \sigma_{\pi^+p}) \tag{5}$$

These relations can be obtained from the pure SU(3) symmetry, confining ourselves in the t-channel to the representations $\underline{1}$ and $\underline{8}_F$ for the baryon-antibaryon vertex and to $\underline{1}$, $\underline{8}_F$, and 8_D for the meson-meson vertex. Relations (2 - 3) cannot be verified experimentally, and (4) is the Jonson-Treiman relation [1]. The left side of (5) is equal to 40 mb at a momentum P = 18 BeV/c, while the right side is equal to 44 mb. If we assume that the "quark" amplitudes are the same for meson-nucleon and nucleon-nucleon interactions, then we can assume the additional relations

$$\sigma_{pp} - \sigma_{pn} = \sigma_{K^-p} - \sigma_{K^-n} \tag{6}$$

$$\sigma_{pp} - \sigma_{pn} = (1/2)[\sigma_{\pi^+p} - \sigma_{K^-n}] \tag{7}$$

$$\sigma_{pp} - \sigma_{pn} = \sigma_{\pi^-p} - \sigma_{K^-p} \tag{8}$$

$$\sigma_{\overline{pp}} - \sigma_{\overline{pn}} + \sigma_{pp} - \sigma_{pn} = \sigma_{\pi^-p} - \sigma_{\pi^+p} \tag{9}$$

$$2(\sigma_{pp} + \sigma_{\overline{pn}}) - (\sigma_{pn} + \sigma_{\overline{pp}}) = 3\sigma_{\pi^+p} \tag{10}$$

$$2\sigma_{pn} - \sigma_{pp} + 5\sigma_{\overline{pn}} - 4\sigma_{\overline{pp}} = 3\sigma_{K^+n} \tag{11}$$

To judge whether relations (6 - 11) are satisfied, it is reasonable to compare them with experiment at maximal energies, when the cross sections are almost constant. This comparison was made in accordance with the data of [5]. The left sides of (6 - 8) are equal to 0.6 mb at P = 18 BeV/c. The right side of (6) is equal to 1.3 mb, whereas that of (7) is approximately zero, and that of (8) is 4 mb. Relation (9) is satisfied in almost the same manner as (6). In the case of (10) at 18 BeV/c, the right and left sides are 72 and 88 mb, respectively. For (11) the corresponding values are 54 and 88 mb. We see thus that relations (10 - 11) are strongly violated. This can be attributed, for example, either to the breaking of the SU(3) symmetry or to the insufficient energy.

In addition, we can obtain relations for the cross sections averaged over the multiplet, which are conserved when SU(3) is broken:

$$\langle \sigma_{NN} \rangle + \langle \sigma_{N\bar{N}} \rangle = 3\langle \sigma_{\pi N} \rangle \tag{12}$$

$$[\langle \sigma_{NN} \rangle + \langle \sigma_{N\bar{N}} \rangle]\langle \sigma_{\pi\pi} \rangle = 2[\langle \sigma_{\pi N} \rangle]^2 \tag{13}$$

where $\langle \sigma \rangle$ is the cross section averaged over the multiplet. If we assume that in the limit of Pomeranchuk's theorem the cross section σ_{pp} tends to 39 mb while $\sigma_{\pi p}$ tends to 25 mb, then (12) is fairly well satisfied; an exact check is difficult, since $\langle \sigma_{NN} \rangle$ and $\langle \sigma_{N\bar{N}} \rangle$ are unknown. Equation (13) recalls the relation from reference [6]. In addition to relations (6 - 13) for the cross sections, we can obtain relations for the inelastic cross sections and for the cross sections for small-angle scattering with charge exchange:

$$(3/4)[\sigma_{\pi^- p \to \Delta^0 \pi^0} + (2/3)\sigma_{\pi^+ p \to \Delta^{++}\pi^0}] =$$

$$= \sigma_{K^- p \to \pi_0 \lambda} + \sigma_{\pi^+ n \to \lambda K^+} - (3/2)[\sigma_{K^- p \to \Sigma^+ \pi^-} + \sigma_{\pi^+ p \to K^+ \Sigma^+}] \tag{14}$$

$$\sigma_{K^- p \to \pi_0 \lambda} - (3/4)\sigma_{K^- p \to \Sigma^+ \pi^-} = (3/4)\sigma_{K^- p \to \Sigma_\delta^+ \pi^-} \tag{15}$$

$$\sigma^{el}_{K^+ p} - \sigma^{el}_{K^- p} = [\sigma^{el}_{\pi^+ p} - \sigma^{el}_{\pi^- p} + \sigma^{el}_{K^0 p} - \sigma^{el}_{\bar{K}^0 p}] \tag{16}$$

An important feature of the proposed model is that the Gell-Mann operators enter the matrix elements in the first power, so that the transitions of p into Σ^-, Ξ, Σ_δ^-, and Ξ_δ are forbidden, in correspondence with octet dominance according to SU(3). In addition, the suppression of the production of particles of representation 10 in πN collisions can be related with the fact that this process is governed by the spin-flip amplitude. We note that these hindrances hold true also in the case when SU(3) is broken in the usual manner, and are in fair agreement with experiment [7]. If further experimental verification confirms the derived relations, this can be regarded as an argument in favor of the existence of quarks.

In conclusion, the authors thank V. N. Gribov for suggesting the topic and continuous interest in the work, V. V. Anisovich and I. M. Shmushkevich for useful advice and discussions, and G. S. Danilov and V. M. Shekhter for a discussion of the results.

[1] K. Jonson and S. B. Treiman, Phys. Rev. Lett. 14, 189 (1965); R. Good and Nguyen-huu Xuong, Phys. Rev. Lett. 14, 191 (1965).

[2] M. Gell-Mann, Phys. Lett. 8, 214 (1964); L. Zweig, CERN Preprint 8419/TH, 412, 1964.

[3] F. Gursey and L. Radicatti, Phys. Rev. Lett. 13, 173 (1964); A. Pais, Phys. Rev. Lett. 13, 175 (1964).

[4] Bogolyubov, Struminskii, and Tavkhelidze, JINR Preprint D-1968, 1965.

[5] S. L. Lindenbaum, Paper at 1964 Dubna High-energy Physics Conference.

[6] Gribov, Ioffe, Pomeranchuk, and Rudik, JETP 42, 1419 (1962), Soviet Phys. JETP 15, 984 (1962).

[7] H. Harari and H. Y. Lipkin, Phys. Rev. Lett. 13, 208 (1964); Meshkov, Snow, and Yodh, Phys. Rev. Lett. 13, 212 (1964).

REPRINT 15

VOLUME 16, NUMBER 2 PHYSICAL REVIEW LETTERS 10 JANUARY 1966

QUARK MODEL FOR FORWARD SCATTERING AMPLITUDES

H. J. Lipkin and F. Scheck*

Department of Physics, Weizmann Institute of Science, Rehovoth, Israel

(Received 29 November 1965)

We should like to point out some remarkable relations which follow from an extremely simple quark-model[1] assumption. These include (a) relations between meson-baryon and baryon-baryon forward-scattering amplitudes which are in good agreement with experiment and which are not obviously obtainable in any other way, and (b) relations for meson-baryon scattering which are also obtainable from higher symmetries. Our basic assumption is that the forward-scattering amplitude for any reaction is simply the sum of all possible contributing two-body quark-quark or quark-antiquark scattering amplitudes.

Consider, for example, π^+P scattering. We denote the proton and neutron by P and N, respectively, and the basic triplet of quarks by p, n, λ, where p, n constitute an isodoublet of strangeness zero and λ is an isosinglet of strangeness -1. The quark constitution of π^+ is $(p\bar{n})$, of P is (ppn). The π^+P forward-scattering amplitude is then given by[2]

$$\begin{aligned}\langle\pi^+P\,|\,\pi^+P\rangle &= \langle(p\bar{n})(ppn)\,|\,(p\bar{n})(ppn)\rangle \\ &= 2\langle pp\,|\,pp\rangle + \langle pn\,|\,pn\rangle + 2\langle\bar{n}p\,|\,\bar{n}p\rangle + \langle\bar{n}n\,|\,\bar{n}n\rangle. \qquad (1)\end{aligned}$$

We offer no dynamical justification for this assumption at this point.

The following relations follow directly from this assumption, and the additional assumption that the individual quark-quark and quark-antiquark scattering amplitudes satisfy SU(3) symmetry. We use the notation (AB) for the forward-scattering amplitude $\langle AB|AB\rangle$. By the optical theorem these relations hold also for the total AB cross section.

$$(PP)-(NP)=(K^+P)-(K^+N), \tag{2a}$$

$$(PP)+(\bar{P}P)=\tfrac{3}{2}[(\pi^+P)+(\pi^-P)]+\tfrac{1}{2}[(K^+P)+(K^-P)]-\tfrac{1}{2}[(K^+N)+(K^-N)], \tag{2b}$$

$$(PP)+(\bar{P}P)=2[(\pi^+P)+(\pi^-P)]-\tfrac{1}{2}[(K^+P)+(K^-P)], \tag{2c}$$

$$(\bar{P}P)-(\bar{P}N)=(K^-P)-(K^-N), \tag{2d}$$

$$(\Lambda P)-(PP)=(K^-N)-(\pi^+P), \tag{2e}$$

$$(K^+P)-(K^-P)=(\pi^+P)-(\pi^-P)+(K^+N)-(K^-N), \tag{3a}$$

$$\tfrac{1}{2}[(K^+P)-(K^-P)]=(\pi^+P)-(\pi^-P)=(K^+N)-(K^-N), \tag{3b}$$

$$(K^+P)+(K^-P)=\tfrac{1}{2}[(\pi^+P)+(\pi^-P)+(K^+N)+(K^-N)]. \tag{3c}$$

The relations between meson-baryon and baryon-baryon reactions have no obvious interpretation other than that of the quark model. Comparison with experiment must cope with finding the proper values of energy and momentum at which reactions involving particles with different masses should be compared. At high energies this difficulty is avoided as the variation of cross sections with energy is small. However, at very high energies, relations (2a) and (2d) are trivially $0=0$. Relations (2b) and (2c) provide nontrivial tests even at asymptotically high energies, since there is no other reason why these should be expected to hold.

The relations (2a) and (2b) follow from the quark model without the additional assumption of SU(3) symmetry. Relation (2c) is obtained from (2b) by using SU(3) to eliminate reactions with neutron targets.

The comparison of relations (2b) and (2c) with experiment is shown in Fig. 1. The points for all reactions are taken at the same energy in the center-of-mass system, and the agreement is reasonably good. Although relation (2b) does not depend upon SU(3) symmetry, while relation (2c) does, there is no evidence for SU(3) symmetry breaking. On the contrary, the relation (2c) is perhaps slightly in better agreement than (2b).

Relations (2a) and (2d) are difficult to test, as the differences between the cross sections are of the order of the experimental errors. The differences in (2a) have the correct sign.[3] For the case of (2d) the sign of the difference between the two nucleon-antinucleon cross sections is not established.[3]

Relation (2e) would provide an interesting test if better data on ΛP scattering were available. Presently available data are in rough agreement,[4] but the errors are large and the energy is low.

The meson-baryon scattering relations (3) are all obtainable without the quark model, if additional symmetry is assumed. For example, the relations (3b) are just the Johnson-Treiman relations,[5] which have been obtained previously under the assumption of SU(6) symmetry. The quark model thus leads to these

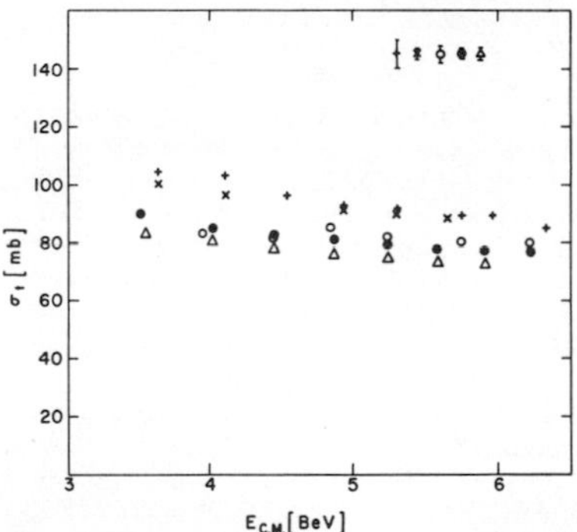

FIG. 1. Comparison of relations (2b) and (2c) with experiment. × and +, $\sigma_t(PP)+\sigma_t(\bar{P}P)$ [× from Ref. 3, + from S. J. Lindenbaum, W. A. Love, J. A. Niederer, S. Ozaki, J. J. Russell, and L. C. L. Yuan, Phys. Rev. Letters 7, 185 (1961)]. ○ and ●, $2[\sigma_t(\pi^+P)+\sigma_t(\pi^-P)]-\frac{1}{2}[\sigma_t(K^+P)+\sigma_t(K^-P)]$ [○ from G. von Dardel, D. Dekkers, R. Mermod, M. Vivargent, G. Weber, and K. Winter, Phys. Rev. Letters 8, 173 (1962); W. F. Baker, R. L. Cool, E. W. Jenkins, T. F. Kycia, R. H. Phillips, and A. L. Read, Phys. Rev. 129, 2285 (1963), ● from Ref. 3]. Δ, $\frac{3}{2}[\sigma_t(\pi^+P)+\sigma_t(\pi^-P)]+\frac{1}{2}[\sigma_t(K^+P)+\sigma_t(K^-P)]-\frac{1}{2}[\sigma_t(K^+N)+\sigma_t(K^-N)]$ (see Ref. 3). On top are given the average experimental errors.

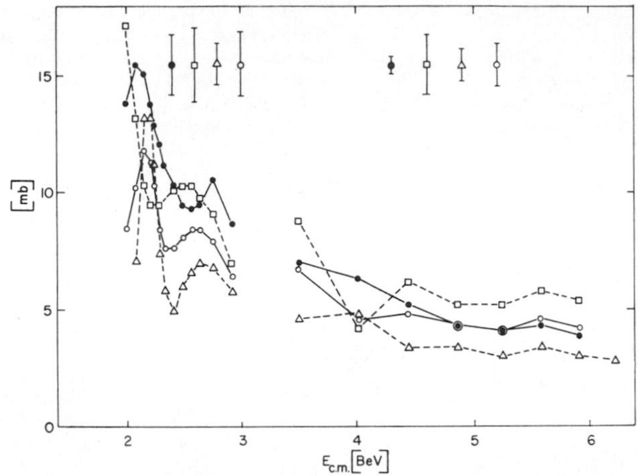

FIG. 2. Comparison of the antisymmetric sum rule (3a) and the Johnson-Treiman relations (3b) with experiment. ●, $A=\sigma_t(K^-P)-\sigma_t(K^+P)$; □, $B=2[\sigma_t(K^-N)-\sigma_t(K^+N)]$; Δ, $C=2[\sigma_t(\pi^-P)-\sigma_t(\pi^+P)]$; ○, $D=\sigma_t(\pi^-P)-\sigma_t(\pi^+P)+\sigma_t(K^-N)-\sigma_t(K^+N)$. On top are the average experimental errors. The data below 3 GeV are taken from A. N. Diddens, E. W. Jenkins, T. F. Kycia, and K. F. Riley, Phys. Rev. Letters 10, 262 (1963) and Ref. 12, those beyond 3 GeV from Ref. 3. The antisymmetric sum rule requires the two solid lines to coincide.

relations with weaker symmetry assumptions than are required otherwise. Since it is not clear which if any of these derivations correctly describes strong interactions, we summarize the minimum sets of assumptions required to obtain each relation for the following three cases: (a) SU(3) symmetry without the quark model, (b) SU(6) symmetry without the quark model, and (c) the quark model.

The "antisymmetric sum rule" (3a) is a weaker relation than the Johnson-Treiman relations (3b). It can be obtained either from (a) SU(3) symmetry with octet dominance[6] in the t channel (no 10 or 10*), (b) SU(6) symmetry with no additional assumption, or (c) quark model only for mesons, no model for nucleons. No higher symmetry is assumed, except isospin.

The Johnson-Treiman relations (3b) are obtained either from (a) SU(3) symmetry with octet dominance[7] in the t channel and a pure F coupling for the baryons, (b) SU(6) symmetry with no additional assumptions, or (c) quark model only for nucleons, no model for mesons, and SU(3) symmetry.

The symmetric sum rule (3c) is completely unrelated to the Johnson-Treiman relations. It can be obtained either from (a) SU(3) symmetry with singlet and octet dominance in the t channel (no 27) and a pure F coupling for the octet baryon vertex, (b) SU(6) symmetry with singlet and 35 dominance in the t channel (no 405), or (c) quark model only for nucleons, no model for mesons, and SU(3) symmetry.

Comparison of these relations with experiment is illustrated in Figs. 2 and 3. The results show a reasonable agreement, comparable to that already demonstrated for the Johnson-Treiman relations.[8] The antisymmetric sum rule seems to be better than the other relations, particularly at higher energies. This is simply explained in the quark model, as the antisymmetric sum rule is the only relation obtained without SU(3) and is not affected by SU(3) symmetry breaking.

Many of these relations become trivial in the high-energy limit, where the Pomeranchuk theorem is valid and any given inelastic channel can be neglected in comparison with the elastic channels. Relations (3a) and (3b) are trivial by the Pomeranchuk theorem. Isospin symmetry and neglect of charge exchange make (2a) and (2d) trivial. SU(3) symmetry and ne-

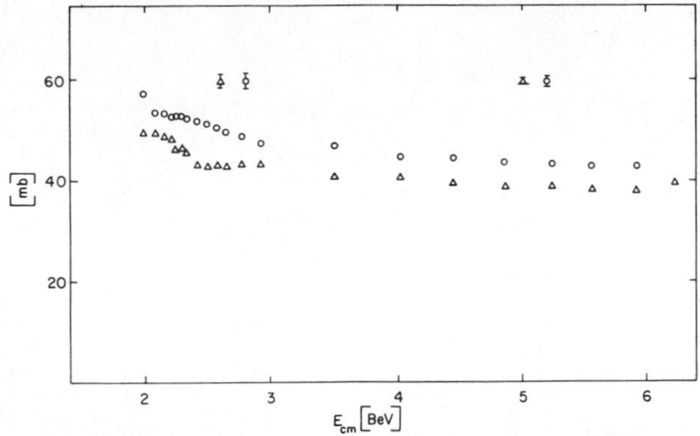

FIG. 3. Comparison of the symmetric sum rule (3c) with experiment (references as in Fig. 2). Δ, $\sigma_t(K^+P)+\sigma_t(K^-P)$; $\bigcirc$, $\frac{1}{2}[\sigma_t(K^+N)+\sigma_t(K^-N)+\sigma_t(\pi^+P)+\sigma_t(\pi^-P)]$.

glect of charge exchange make (2a) and (2d) trivial. SU(3) symmetry and neglect of charge and strangeness exchange make (3c) trivial.[9] The only nontrivial relations are (2b) and (2c) which both become[10]

$$(PP)=(\bar{P}P)=\tfrac{3}{2}(\pi^+P)=\tfrac{3}{2}(\pi^-P). \qquad (4)$$

This simply states that in the limit where quarks and antiquarks have the same scattering, baryon and meson cross sections are proportional to the number of constitutent quarks and antiquarks, thus giving the ratio $\frac{3}{2}$.

The predictions (2) and (3) follow directly from the quark model and the assumption of additivity of the two-body quark scattering amplitudes, with no further dynamical assumptions other than SU(3) symmetry for some cases. One may ask what kind of dynamical picture might lead to this additivity of amplitudes. The simplest picture is a "nonrelativistic quark model"[11] for the particles and the impulse approximation for the scattering process (the particle velocities, being relativistic, are greater than the velocities of the internal quark motion). Such a picture might be expected to hold for processes of a peripheral nature, and would certainly break down if there are strong resonances in the s channel which imply quark-antiquark annihilation. The additivity assumption would be best for forward scattering processes, with zero momentum transfer. For processes with finite momentum transfer, a characteristic form factor would be needed, analogous to the "Debye-Waller factor" in x-ray scattering and the Mössbauer effect.[12] Such a factor might explain the sharp decrease of all high-energy cross sections with increasing momentum transfer.[13] It could also provide a reason why those predictions of the higher symmetries which agree with experiment relate processes which do not require corrections for large mass differences between particles in the same multiplets.[14] The presence of mass differences makes difficult the comparison of reactions at the same momentum transfer, and a form factor very sensitive to momentum transfer would destroy any manifestations of the symmetry in comparison at different momentum transfers. If this picture is correct, the analysis of high-energy scattering data would provide information on the "structure of the mesons and baryons," analogous to the investigations of atomic and crystal structure by "high-energy x-ray scattering."

We wish to thank G. Alexander, G. Goldhaber, S. Goldhaber, A. Shapira, and G. Yekutieli for fruitful discussions of the experimental situation.

---

*On leave of absence from the University of Freiburg, Germany, on a Fellowship of the Volkswagenwerk Foundation.

[1]M. Gell-Mann, Phys. Letters 8, 214 (1964). G. Zweig, unpublished.

[2]For simplicity we consider the single-triplet model,

in which quarks have third-integral electric charges. The results obtained in this paper can be extended to many of the models with several triplets, possibly with integral charges. Let the members of any triplet in such a model be denoted by p_i, n_i, λ_i, where p,n and λ denote the SU(3) quantum numbers and the index i labels the particular triplet. Then if the quark structure of mesons and baryons is such that Eq. (1) is modified only by putting indices on all the quark labels and adding summations in some places, the results presented here should be valid provided that appropriate assumptions are made regarding SU(3) symmetry.

[3]W. Galbraith, E. W. Jenkins, F. F. Kycia, B. A. Leontić, R. H. Phillips, A. L. Read, and R. Rubenstein, Phys. Rev. 138, B913 (1965).

[4]G. Alexander, private communication.

[5]K. Johnson and S. B. Treiman, Phys. Rev. Letters 14, 189 (1965). For a derivation based on the collinear $SU(6)_W$ group, see J. C. Carter, J. J. Coyne, S. Meshkov, D. Horn, M. Kugler, and H. J. Lipkin, Phys. Rev. Letters 15, 373 (1965). From the table of $SU(6)_W$ amplitudes, it is clear that the symmetric sum rule (3c) does not follow from $SU(6)_W$ without additional assumptions.

[6]The antisymmetric sum rule and its SU(3) derivation are well known, particularly in the crossed channel of $\bar{p}p$ annihilation. See, for example, K. Tanaka, Phys. Rev. 135, B1186 (1964), and V. Barger and M. H. Rubin, Phys. Rev. 140, B1365 (1965).

[7]R. F. Sawyer, Phys. Rev. Letters 14, 471 (1965).

[8]R. Good and N.-h. Xuong, Phys. Rev. Letters 14, 191 (1965).

[9]P. G. O. Freund, H. Ruegg, D. Speiser, and A. Morales, Nuovo Cimento 25, 307 (1962).

[10]This $\frac{3}{2}$ ratio and its rough agreement with experiment was quoted by L. B. Okun' in discussions at the Seminar on High-Energy Physics and Elementary Particles, International Atomic Energy Agency, Trieste, Italy, 1965 (unpublished). The exact source of this observation is not known to the authors. After this paper was submitted for publication we received a preprint from P. G. O. Freund [Phys. Rev. Letters 15, 929 (1965)], who has also obtained this result independently from other considerations. We are grateful to Dr. Freund for calling this point to our attention. Other results in Freund's paper are different from ours and the relation between the two approaches is not clear.

[11]Y. Nambu, in Proceedings of the Second Coral Gables Conference on Symmetry Principles at High Energies, University of Miami, January 1965, edited by B. Kurşunoğlu, A. Perlmutter, and I. Sakmar (W. H. Freeman & Company, San Francisco, California, 1965). G. Morpurgo, Physics 2, 95 (1965); R. H. Dalitz, Oxford International Conference on Elementary Particles, Oxford, 1965 (unpublished).

[12]H. Frauenfelder, The Mössbauer Effect (W. A. Benjamin, Inc., New York, 1962). For a general discussion of the application of the concept of the Debye-Waller factor in high-energy physics, see H. J. Lipkin, Argonne National Laboratory Report No. ANL-6873, 1964 (unpublished).

[13]N. Byers and C. N. Yang, to be published.

[14]This has been pointed out by H. Harari, Lectures at the Symposium on High Energy Physics, Boulder, Colorado, 1965 (unpublished).

J. J. J. KOKKEDEE, *et al.*
1° Aprile 1966
Il Nuovo Cimento
Serie X, Vol. 42 pag. 711-716

Quark Model and High-Energy Scattering.

J. J. J. KOKKEDEE and L. VAN HOVE
CERN - Geneva

(ricevuto il 26 Febbraio 1966)

As was shown recently [1], some successful predictions concerning meson and baryon scattering cross-sections can be derived from the quark model [2], using a very simple assumption of additivity for the two-body quark amplitudes. We derive hereunder further consequences of this assumption which we also formulate more explicitly than was done by previous authors. Some of the new consequences are remarkably analogous to predictions of an entirely different dynamical model, namely the Regge-pole model for high-energy scattering.

1. – The additivity assumption for elastic scattering can be formulated as follows. The S-matrix element for elastic scattering of hadrons A and B is approximated by a sum of terms describing the scattering of individual quarks and antiquarks treated as « quasi-free » particles. One writes in the c.m. system of the A+B collision

$$(1)\qquad \langle A, p'_{\text{A}}; B, p'_{\text{B}}|S|A, p_{\text{A}}; B, p_{\text{B}}\rangle = \sum_{ij}\int \mathrm{d}^4x\int \mathrm{d}^4y\; \tau_{ij}[s_{ij}, (x-y)^2]\cdot \\ \cdot\langle A, p'_{\text{A}}|\overline{q}_i(x)\, q_i(x)|A, p_{\text{A}}\rangle\langle B, p'_{\text{B}}|\overline{q}_j(y)\, q_j(y)|B, p_{\text{B}}\rangle\,,$$

q_i runs over all quarks and antiquarks composing A, $q_i(x)$ being the field operator associated with q_i, and the q_j have a similar meaning for B. The four-momenta p_{A}, p_{B} and p'_{A}, p'_{B} refer respectively to the initial and final states of A and B, and $|Ap_{\text{A}}\rangle$ for example represents the plane wave $\exp[i(p_{\text{A}}x_{\text{A}})]$. All spins are neglected throughout. The scalar function τ_{ij} is so defined that the operator

$$(2)\qquad \int \mathrm{d}^4x\int \mathrm{d}^4y\; \overline{q}_i(x)\, q_i(x)\, \overline{q}_j(y)\, q_j(y)\, \tau_{ij}[s_{ij}, (x-y)^2]$$

(1) E. M. LEVIN and L. L. FRANKFURT: *Žurn. Ėksp. Teor. Fiz. Pis'ma Redak.*, **2**, 105 (1965) [English translation *Sov. Phys. JETP Lett.*, **2**, 65 (1965)]; H. J. LIPKIN and F. SCHECK: *Phys. Rev. Lett.*, **16**, 71 (1966).
(2) M. GELL-MANN: *Phys. Lett.*, **8**, 214 (1964); G. ZWEIG: CERN Preprints TH 401 and TH 402 (1964), unpublished.

gives, in the A+B c.m. system, the correct S-matrix elements for elastic scattering of a quasi-free q_i with a quasi-free q_j for a value $s_{ij}^{\frac{1}{2}}$ of the c.m. energy of the $q_i + q_j$ system. For given c.m. energy $s^{\frac{1}{2}}$ of the A+B collision, s_{ij} must be chosen so as to simulate as well as possible the kinematical conditions of the $q_i + q_j$ system in the A+B collision. At high values of s, it seems reasonable to estimate s_{ij} by attributing to the quasi-free q_i, q_j in the initial state four-momenta $p_i \simeq c_i^{\rm A} p_{\rm A}$, $p_j \simeq c_j^{\rm B} p_{\rm B}$, where the coefficients $c_i^{\rm A}$, $c_j^{\rm B}$ depend only on the structure of A and B respectively. This makes sense if the *effective* mass of the quasi-free quarks in the hadrons is not too high. We then have

$$s_{ij} \simeq -2(p_i p_j) \simeq -2c_i^{\rm A} c_j^{\rm B}(p_{\rm A} p_{\rm B}) \simeq c_i^{\rm A} c_j^{\rm B} s\,. \tag{3}$$

For the elastic scattering amplitudes $T_{\rm AB}$ defined by

$$\langle A, p_{\rm A}'; B, p_{\rm B}' | S | A, p_{\rm A}; B, p_{\rm B}\rangle = i\delta_4(p_{\rm A}'+p_{\rm B}'-p_{\rm A}-p_{\rm B})\, T_{\rm AB}(s,t), \quad t=(p_{\rm A}-p_{\rm A}')^2, \tag{4}$$

we obtain from eq. (1)

$$T_{\rm AB}(s,t) = \sum_{ij} f_i^{\rm A}(t) f_j^{\rm B}(t)\, T_{ij}(s_{ij}, t)\,, \tag{5}$$

where we have defined

$$T_{ij}(s, \Delta p^2) = -(2\pi)^4 i \int {\rm d}^4x \exp[ix\,\Delta p]\,\tau_{ij}(s, x^2)\,, \tag{6}$$

$$\langle A, p_{\rm A}' | \bar{q}_i(x) q_i(x) | A, p_{\rm A}\rangle = \exp[i(p_{\rm A}'-p_{\rm A})x] f_i^{\rm A}(t)\,, \tag{7}$$

and similarly for $f_j^{\rm B}(t)$. The $f(t)$ have the significance of form factors. T_{ij} is the scattering amplitude of quasi-free quarks, defined from (2) in the same normalization (4) as for hadrons. (Note that this normalization is such that s-independence of the amplitude implies, for high energy, s-independence of total and differential cross-sections.) Equations analogous to (5) hold for $T_{\rm AA}$ and $T_{\rm BB}$, for example

$$T_{\rm AA}(s,t) = \sum_{ii'} f_i^{\rm A}(t) f_{i'}^{\rm A}\, T_{ii'}(s_{ii}\,, t)\,. \tag{8}$$

2. – Assume now that all $T_{ij}(s,t)$ have at very high energy a common value independent of s

$$T_{ij}(s,t) = ig(t)\,. \tag{9}$$

Equation (5) then factorizes to

$$T_{\rm AB}(s,t) = ig(t)\Big[\sum_i f_i^{\rm A}(t)\Big]\Big[\sum_j f_j^{\rm B}(t)\Big]\,. \tag{10}$$

Similarly,

$$T_{\rm AA}(s,t) = ig(t)\Big[\sum_i f_i^{\rm A}(t)\Big]^2, \qquad T_{\rm BB}(s,t) = ig(t)\Big[\sum_j f_j^{\rm B}(t)\Big]^2. \tag{11}$$

These equations imply

$$[T_{\rm AB}(s,t)]^2 = T_{\rm AA}(s,t)\, T_{\rm BB}(s,t)\,, \tag{12}$$

which is the *factorization property* predicted by the Regge-pole model [3] under neglect of spin effects and for such high energies that the only important contribution to the amplitude comes from the Pomeranchuk trajectory. We here derived this property from quite different assumptions.

The validity of (9) at high energy holds under the following natural conditions:

i) The diffraction picture for quark-quark and antiquark-quark scattering which with our definition of amplitudes means

$$T_{ij}(s,t) = ig_{ij}(t)\,, \qquad g_{ij}\ \text{real}. \tag{13}$$

It implies total and differential cross-sections independent of energy. Furthermore, one has from the generalized Pomeranchuk theorem [4]

$$g_{ij}(t) = g_{i'j}(t) = g_{ij'}(t) \tag{14}$$

if $q_{i'}$ is the antiparticle of q_i and $q_{j'}$ the one of q_j;

ii) The neglect of charge-exchange quark-quark scattering implying that relation (14) holds if q_i, $q_{i'}$ belong to the same multiplet of an assumed strong-interaction symmetry (isospin or SU_3) and similarly for q_j $q_{j'}$.

If condition ii) is assumed for isospin symmetry alone, we obtain factorization for those hadrons which are composed of $I=\frac{1}{2}$ quarks and antiquarks, like pions, nucleons and antinucleons. If ii) is taken assuming exact SU_3 symmetry, the factorization will follow for all hadrons.

One should perhaps remark that (9) is not the most general condition under which the factorization (12) holds. It is for example clear that (12) would also follow from a factorization property

$$T_{ij}(s,t) = i\gamma_i(t)\,\gamma_j(t)\,,$$

for the quark amplitudes themselves.

3. – Equation (5), *i.e.*, the additivity assumption for quark amplitudes, has also more general implications. If T_{AB} is analysed in terms of SU_3 quantum numbers in the t-channel, eq. (5) combined with SU_3 symmetry implies that these quantum numbers are restricted to *octets and singlets, with even and odd signature.* Furthermore the s-dependence is contained in the quark amplitudes T_{ij}. Under validity of (3) one would therefore have the same powers of s or $\log s$ in the asymptotic expansion of nucleon-nucleon and meson-nucleon scattering amplitudes. It is interesting that once again these features coincide with predictions of the Regge-pole model.

4. – Returning to the asymptotic form (10) for high-energy amplitudes one can wonder about the fact that all diffraction peaks appear experimentally to have about the same slope at very high energy. Rather than attributing this effect to some uni-

---

[3] M. GELL-MANN: *Phys. Rev. Lett.*, **8**, 263 (1962); V. N. GRIBOV and I. YA. POMERANCHUK: *Phys. Rev. Lett.*, **8**, 343 (1962).

[4] L. VAN HOVE: *Phys. Lett.*, **5**, 252 (1963).

versality of slope of all form factors $f(t)$, we tend to believe that it may be due more simply to the fact that $g(t)$ would be a much steeper function of t than the $f(t)$. This could be easily understood. The steep slope of g would be due to the effect of multiple meson production on shadow scattering, as has been discussed in some detail for the nucleon-nucleon system (5-7). The broader shape of the form factors, on the contrary, would be controlled by the rather compact structure of hadrons as bound states of quarks.

With the above assumption that at very high energy $g(t)$ has about the same slope as the observed diffraction peaks of hadrons, the fact that the quark-quark total cross-section is, from additivity, about one ninth of the proton-proton total cross-section means that quark-quark collisions have surprisingly great transparency. It is tempting to speculate that this transparency could provide the main reason for the empirical success encountered by the additivity assumption.

5. – The additivity assumption supplemented by assumptions i) and ii) above enables one to express all asymptotic total cross-sections for reactions involving mesons and baryons as linear combinations of g_0, g_1 and g_2, where ig_n is the common value of all the forward quark amplitudes $ig_{ij}(0)$ for which there are in total n quarks or antiquarks with $I=0$ in the initial state. If we take condition ii) above for isospin symmetry alone, g_0, g_1 and g_2 can be different, as is in fact suggested by the large experimental difference of πp and Kp cross-sections at high energy (8). By elimination of the g_n one obtains *relations between the asymptotic total cross-sections*. For instance,

(15-*a*) $$\sigma_{pp} = \tfrac{3}{2}\sigma_{\pi p}\,, \qquad \sigma_{\pi\pi}\sigma_{pp} = \sigma_{\pi p}^2\,,$$

(15-*b*) $$\sigma_{\Sigma p} = \sigma_{\Lambda p} = \tfrac{1}{2}\sigma_{\pi p} + \sigma_{Kp}\,, \qquad \sigma_{\Xi p} = 2\sigma_{Kp} - \tfrac{1}{2}\sigma_{\pi p}\,,$$

(15-*c*) $$\sigma_{\Lambda\Lambda} - \sigma_{KK} = \tfrac{2}{3}\sigma_{Kp} + \tfrac{1}{6}\sigma_{\pi p}\,, \qquad \sigma_{\pi K} = \tfrac{2}{3}\sigma_{Kp}\,.$$

The first relation (15-*a*), first mentioned by OKUN, is also quoted in ref. (1). The second relation (15-*b*) is of course identical to the factorization property (12) at $t=0$. The right-hand sides of relations (15-*b*-*c*) can be calculated from the extrapolated asymptotic values $\sigma_{\pi p} \simeq 22$ mb and $\sigma_{Kp} \simeq 17.5$ mb, giving, for instance, $\sigma_{\Sigma p} = \sigma_{\Lambda p} \simeq$ $\simeq 28.5$ mb and $\sigma_{\Xi p} \simeq 24$ mb.

6. – Let us consider the *real parts* of the elastic-scattering amplitudes. From the additivity assumption, and neglecting spins as before, one derives for the forward amplitudes

(16-*a*) $$\mathrm{Re}\, T_{\bar{p}p} = \mathrm{Re}(2T_{\pi^-p} + T_{\pi^+p} - T_{np})\,,$$

(16-*b*) $$\mathrm{Re}\, T_{\bar{p}n} = \mathrm{Re}(T_{\pi^-p} + 2T_{\pi^+p} - T_{pp})\,.$$

These equations, as well as those given in the next Section, are derived from (5) by neglecting the differences between the various values of s_{ij} (this was also done in

(5) L. VAN HOVE: *Nuovo Cimento*, **28**, 798 (1963); *Rev. Mod. Phys.*, **36**, 655 (1964).

(6) A. BIAŁAS: *Nuovo Cimento*, **33**, 972 (1964).

(7) J. J. J. KOKKEDEE: CERN Preprint TH 621 (1965), to be published in *Nuovo Cimento*.

(8) W. GALBRAITH, E. W. JENKINS, T. F. KYCIA, B. A. LEONTIC, R. H. PHILLIPS and A. L. READ: *Phys. Rev.*, **138**, B 913 (1965).

previous papers [1]). Inclusion of these differences can be made roughly by putting $c_i \simeq \frac{1}{3}$ for nucleons and $c_i \simeq \frac{1}{2}$ for mesons. It would amount to changes of no more than 30% in our predictions.

For the forward direction the real parts on the right-hand sides of these relations have been measured for certain energies, although the experimental uncertainties are large. From the data around 10 GeV/c [9] one obtains by means of (16)

$$X_{\bar{p}p} \simeq 0.0 \pm 0.20\,, \qquad X_{\bar{p}n} \simeq 0.0 \pm 0.14\,, \tag{17}$$

with the notation $X = (\mathrm{Re}\, T/\mathrm{Im} T)_{t=0}$. This is in agreement with theoretical predictions based on analyticity in s [10]. In fact, it has been shown to be possible to reproduce the experimental data concerning cross-sections and small-angle elastic scattering of $\bar{p}p$ scattering above 4 GeV/c with a purely imaginary amplitude [7].

7. – On *charge exchange reactions*, the following relations follow from the additivity assumption:

$$T(K^- p \to \bar{K}^0 n) = T(\bar{p}p \to \bar{n}n)\,, \qquad T(K^+ n \to K^0 p) = T(np \to pn)\,, \tag{18-a}$$

$$\sqrt{2}\, T(\pi^- p \to \pi^0 n) = T(K^+ n \to K^0 p) - T(K^- p \to \bar{K}^0 n)\,, \tag{18-b}$$

where T now denotes the forward amplitude for the reaction within brackets. The Regge-pole analysis of existing scattering data predicts that the forward amplitudes for the reactions $K^- p \to \bar{K}^0 n$ and $\bar{p}p \to \bar{n}n$ are dominantly imaginary, whereas those for the processes $K^+ n \to K^0 p$ and $np \to pn$ are dominantly real [11]. Recent experimental results on the reactions $np \to pn$ [12] and $K^- p \to \bar{K}^0 n$ [13] seem to support this prediction. The relations (18-*a*) agree with it in that they equate the two mainly imaginary amplitudes and the two mainly real ones.

Accepting this prediction and neglecting the real part of $T(K^- p \to \bar{K}^0 n)$ as well as the imaginary part of $T(K^+ n \to K^0 p)$, we obtain from (18-*b*) the relation

$$2[\mathrm{d}\sigma(\pi^- p \to \pi^0 n)/\mathrm{d}t]_{t=0} = [\mathrm{d}\sigma(K^+ n \to K^0 p)/\mathrm{d}t]_{t=0} + [\mathrm{d}\sigma(K^- p \to \bar{K}^0 n)/\mathrm{d}t]_{t=0}\,. \tag{19}$$

From the data for $\pi^- p \to \pi^0 n$ [14] and $K^- p \to \bar{K}^0 n$ [13] around 10 GeV/c, one finds by

---

(9) K. J. Foley, R. S. Gilmore, R. S. Jones, S. J. Lindenbaum, W. A. Love, S. Ozaki, E. H. Willen, R. Yamada and L. C. L. Yuan: *Phys. Rev. Lett.*, **14**, 862 (1965); K. Chernev, N. Dalkhazhav, P. Devinski, M. Kachaturian, L. Khristov, L. Kirrillova, Z. Korbel, P. Markov, V. Nikitin, A. Nomofilov, V. Pantuev, L. Rob, M. Shafranova, I. Sitnik, L. Slepetz, L. Strunov, V. Sviridov, D. Tuvdendorzh, Z. Zlatanov and L. Zolin: Dubna preprint E 2413 (October 1965).

(10) P. Söding: *Phys. Lett.*, **8**, 285 (1964); A. Białas and E. Białas: *Nuovo Cimento*, **37**, 1686 (1965).

(11) E. Leader: *Rev. Mod. Phys.* (to be published).

(12) J. L. Friedes, H. Palevsky, R. L. Stearns and R. J. Sutter: *Phys. Rev. Lett.*, **15**, 38 (1965); G. Manning, A. G. Parham, J. D. Jafar, H. B. van der Raay, D. H. Reading, D. G. Ryan, B. D. Jones, J. Malos and N. H. Lipman: *Nuovo Cimento*, **41**, 167 (1966).

(13) P. Astbury, G. Finocchiaro, A. Michelini, C. Verkerk, D. Websdale, C.H. West, W. Beusch, B. Gobbi, M. Pepin, M. A. Pouchon and E. Polgar: *Phys. Lett.*, **16**, 328 (1965).

(14) I. Mannelli, A. Bigi, R. Carrara, M. Wahlig and L. Sodickson: *Phys. Rev. Lett.*, **14**, 408 (1965); A. V. Stirling, P. Sonderegger, J. Kirz, P. Falk-Vairant, O. Guisan, C. Bruneton and P. Borgeaud: *Phys. Rev. Lett.*, **14**, 763 (1965).

means of (19)

$$[d\sigma(K^+n \to K^0p)/dt]_{t=0} \simeq (240 \pm 60)\ \mu b/(GeV/c)^2 ,$$

which is in reasonably good agreement with the theoretical prediction of about 300 μb/(GeV/c)^2 obtained from the Regge-pole model ([15])

8. – We have derived from the additivity assumption for quark amplitudes a number of consequences which we think to be of some interest. We are fully aware, however, of the questionable nature of this assumption, and we are as ignorant as previous authors of its possible justification. We want nevertheless to stress that, as far as we can see, strong binding is not necessarily an argument against additivity. Despite the strong binding forces, quarks inside hadrons might behave for small momentum transfers as quasi-free particles, with properties which could be quite different from those of truly free quarks. This could be the case for the scattering operator (2), and also for the effective mass of the quasi-free quarks which might be rather low, as is strongly suggested by the electromagnetic properties of hadrons ([16]).

([15]) R. J. N. PHILLIPS and W. RARITA: *Phys. Rev.*, **139**, B 1336 (1965).

([16]) W. THIRRING: *Phys. Lett.*, **16**, 335 (1965); C. BECCHI and G. MORPURGO: *Phys. Rev.*, **140**, B 687 (1965).

VOLUME 16, NUMBER 22 PHYSICAL REVIEW LETTERS 30 MAY 1966

QUARK MODELS AND HIGH-ENERGY SCATTERING

H. J. Lipkin
Department of Physics, Weizmann Institute of Science, Rehovoth, Israel
(Received 20 April 1966)

The large amount of precise experimental data now available on total cross sections for meson-nucleon scattering presents a challenge to the theorist.[1] Symmetries[2,3] and quark models[4] have had a certain degree of success in obtaining relations between these cross sections which are in agreement with experiment. However, some predictions from SU(3) symmetry seem to be in disagreement with experiment.[1,5] Furthermore, the most striking regularity of the data has not been predicted by any of these symmetries or quark models, namely the equality of the K^+p and K^+n total cross sections over a wide energy range.[1,6] Many models and theories predict that all meson-baryon cross sections become equal at sufficiently high energy.[4,7] However, experimental data show that some of these are more equal than others, as indicated in Fig. 1. This feature has not been predicted by any of the higher symmetries which include SU(3).

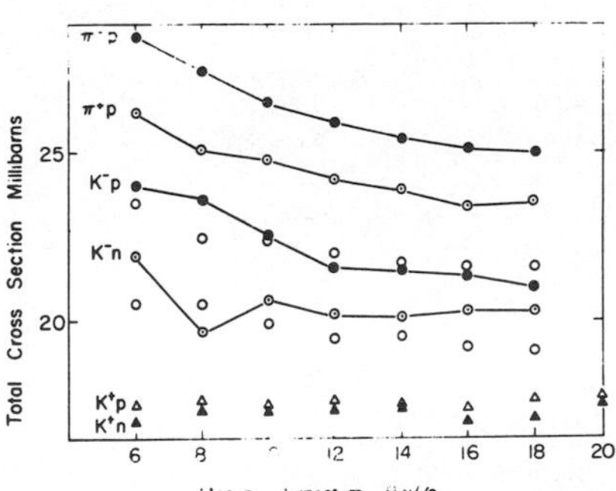

FIG. 1. Meson-baryon cross sections and relations (3a), (5a), and (5b). ○ left- and right-hand sides of Eq. (3a), ● left- and right-hand sides of Eq. (5a), ⊙ left- and right-hand sides of Eq. (5b).

We should like to show that good agreement with experiment is obtained by a slight extension of the quark model[4] along the lines suggested by Kokkedee and Van Hove.[8] In addition to the additivity assumption for the two-body quark scattering amplitudes assumed in the previous treatments,[4] we have certain simplifying assumptions about the two-body quark-quark and quark-antiquark scattering amplitudes. The basic physical idea is that scattering of 6- to 20-BeV/c mesons is sufficiently close to the asymptotic region so that the two-body scattering amplitudes exhibit some, but not all of the asymptotic features. In particular, it is assumed that the quark-quark amplitudes exhibit these asymptotic features, while they are not yet present in the quark-antiquark amplitudes, possibly because of the presence of the annihilation channel in the latter.[8] We consider several different combinations of these assumptions, both with and without SU(3) symmetry.

In order to enable a fair comparison with experiment of different treatments, we express all predicted relations between meson-baryon total cross sections in the following standard form: The expressions on both sides of the equality involve only sums, no differences. They are normalized so that in the limit where all meson-baryon cross sections are equal, the expressions on two sides are just equal to the common meson-baryon cross section. We first list relations which have been previously obtained. We consider only total cross sections, which are related to the forward scattering amplitude by the optical theorem.

The antisymmetric sum rule[4] follows directly from the basic additivity assumption of the quark model, without any symmetry assumptions. In our standard form this becomes

$$\tfrac{1}{3}[\sigma(K^-p)+\sigma(\pi^+p)+\sigma(K^0p)] = \tfrac{1}{3}[\sigma(K^+p)+\sigma(\pi^-p)+\sigma(\bar{K}^0p)]. \quad (1)$$

H519 1-5

The additional assumption of SU(3) symmetry for the basic two-body amplitudes[4] leads to the Johnson-Treiman relations[2]

$$\tfrac{1}{3}[\sigma(K^-p)+2\sigma(\pi^+p)]=\tfrac{1}{3}[\sigma(K^+p)+2\sigma(\pi^-p)], \quad (2a)$$

$$\tfrac{1}{3}[\sigma(K^-p)+2\sigma(K^+n)]=\tfrac{1}{3}[\sigma(K^+p)+2\sigma(K^-n)], \quad (2b)$$

and also the symmetric sum rule

$$\tfrac{1}{4}[\sigma(\pi^+p)+\sigma(\pi^-p)+\sigma(K^-n)+\sigma(K^+n)]$$
$$=\tfrac{1}{2}[\sigma(K^-p)+\sigma(K^+p)]. \quad (3a)$$

Equations (2a) and (3a) can be combined to give the more convenient form

$$\tfrac{1}{2}[\sigma(\pi^+p)+\sigma(K^-n)]=\tfrac{1}{2}[\sigma(\pi^-p)+\sigma(K^+n)]$$
$$=\tfrac{1}{2}[\sigma(K^-p)+\sigma(K^+p)]. \quad (3b)$$

In our standard form, relations always appear as equalities between weighted means of different meson-baryon cross sections. A consistent measure of the relative agreement with experiment of different relations is given by the absolute value of the discrepancy in millibarns or by the percent deviation.

We now consider the consequences of the following new set of assumptions:

(1) The basic additivity assumptions of Ref. 4, without SU(3) symmetry. This leads immediately to the sum rule (1).

(2) Neglect of the imaginary part of the charge-exchange amplitude for nonstrange quark-quark scattering. This would follow from the physical assumption that the nonstrange quark-quark scattering is already in the asymptotic region, while other amplitudes are not. If the notation $\mathcal{P}\mathcal{N}\lambda$ is used for the three quarks, then this assumption together with isospin implies that $\mathcal{P}\mathcal{P}$, $\mathcal{P}\mathcal{N}$, $\mathcal{N}\mathcal{P}$, and $\mathcal{N}\mathcal{N}$ two-body contributions to the total cross sections are all equal. This leads to one new relation in addition to (1),

$$\sigma(K^+p)=\sigma(K^+n). \quad (4a)$$

Substitution of (4a) into (1) gives the simpler sum rule

$$\tfrac{1}{2}[\sigma(K^-p)+\sigma(\pi^+p)]=\tfrac{1}{2}[\sigma(K^-n)+\sigma(\pi^-p)]. \quad (4b)$$

The result (4a) is just the equality of the K^+p and K^+n cross sections mentioned above as a hitherto unexplained feature of the experimental data.

If the assumption of SU(3) symmetry is added to the two assumptions above, relations (2) and (3) are obtained. These can be simplified by substituting the relation (4a) to give

$$\sigma(\pi^-p)=\sigma(K^-p), \quad (5a)$$

$$\sigma(\pi^+p)=\sigma(K^-n), \quad (5b)$$

$$\sigma(K^-n)=\tfrac{1}{2}[\sigma(K^+p)+\sigma(K^-p)]. \quad (5c)$$

However, we wish to avoid the assumption of SU(3) symmetry at this stage. Instead we consider the addition of the following assumption to the two assumptions leading to the relations (4a) and (4b), without assuming SU(3).

(3) The Pomeranchuk theorem applies to the $(\mathcal{P}\mathcal{N})$ and $(\lambda\mathcal{N})$ quark amplitudes. This, together with isospin and the assumptions above, leads to the following equalities between quark-quark and quark-antiquark amplitudes:

$$(\mathcal{P}\mathcal{N})=(\mathcal{N}\mathcal{P})=(\bar{\mathcal{P}}\mathcal{N})=(\bar{\mathcal{N}}\mathcal{P})=(\mathcal{P}\mathcal{P})=(\mathcal{N}\mathcal{N})\equiv P, \quad (6a)$$

$$(\lambda\mathcal{P})=(\lambda\mathcal{N})=(\bar{\lambda}\mathcal{P})=(\bar{\lambda}\mathcal{N})\equiv P-S, \quad (6b)$$

where P defined by Eq. (6a) denotes the common amplitude for the nonstrange quarks and antiquarks, and S, defined by Eq. (6b), represents the contribution of SU(3) symmetry breaking in the strange-quark scattering. The omission of the $(\bar{\mathcal{P}}\mathcal{P})$ and $(\bar{\mathcal{N}}\mathcal{N})$ amplitudes from this assumption corresponds to the physical picture in which an isosinglet annihilation channel still gives significant contribution and breaks the Pomeranchuk theorem for all amplitudes which can have an isosinglet component. By analogy with the definitions of P and S, we can define the "annihilation contribution" A by the relation

$$(\bar{\mathcal{P}}\mathcal{P})=(\bar{\mathcal{N}}\mathcal{N})\equiv P+A. \quad (6c)$$

The assumptions (6) lead to the Johnson-Treiman relations (2), obtained now without SU(3). However, the symmetric sum rule (3a) is not obtained. Thus we obtain the relations (4) and (2).

A simple physical picture of these results is obtained by writing all the meson-baryon amplitudes in terms of the quantities P, S, and A:

$$(K^+p)=(K^+n)=6P-3S, \quad (7a)$$

$$(K^-n)=6P-3S+A, \quad (7b)$$

$$(\pi^+p)=6P+A, \quad (7c)$$

$$(K^-p)=6P-3S+2A, \quad (7d)$$

$$(\pi^-p)=6P+2A. \quad (7e)$$

The Johnson-Treiman relations thus arise in this picture as a result of the annihilation

Table I. Meson-baryon cross sections.[a]

Momentum (BeV/c)	$\sigma_t(K^+p)$ (mb)	$\sigma_t(K^+n)$ (mb)	$\sigma_t(K^-p)$ (mb)	$\sigma_t(K^-n)$ (mb)	$\sigma_t(\pi^+p)$ (mb)	$\sigma_t(\pi^-p)$ (mb)
6	17.0 ± 0.1	17.5 ± 0.4	24.0 ± 0.3	21.9 ± 0.4	26.2 ± 0.2	28.5 ± 0.3
8	17.3 ± 0.1	17.6 ± 0.4	23.6 ± 0.2	19.7 ± 0.4	25.1 ± 0.2	27.5 ± 0.3
10	17.3 ± 0.1	17.5 ± 0.4	22.5 ± 0.2	20.6 ± 0.4	24.8 ± 0.2	26.5 ± 0.3
12	17.3 ± 0.1	17.6 ± 0.4	21.6 ± 0.2	20.2 ± 0.4	24.2 ± 0.2	25.9 ± 0.3
14	17.4 ± 0.1	17.5 ± 0.4	21.5 ± 0.2	20.1 ± 0.4	23.9 ± 0.2	25.4 ± 0.3
16	17.0 ± 0.1	17.4 ± 0.4	21.3 ± 0.4	20.3 ± 0.6	23.4 ± 0.2	25.1 ± 0.3
18	17.1 ± 0.1	17.6 ± 0.4	21.0 ± 0.8	20.3 ± 1.1	23.5 ± 0.2	25.0 ± 0.3
20	17.5 ± 0.1	17.7 ± 0.4	22.4 ± 4.6	...	23.4 ± 0.2	24.8 ± 0.3

[a]See Ref. 6.

contribution A and are obtained simply by counting the number of quarks in the target proton which are the same as the antiquark in the meson and which can therefore give isosinglet annihilation. The SU(3) symmetry breaking does not affect these relations as the symmetry-breaking term S simply gives a constant difference between pion-nucleon and kaon-nucleon amplitudes which cancels out in the Johnson-Treiman relations.

Let us now compare these various sets of predictions with experiment. The relevant experimental data are given in Table I and plotted in Figs. 1 and 2.

Relations (4a) and (4b) are in excellent agreement with experiment. In both cases the discrepancies are within the experimental errors. However, one can argue that a discrepancy of about 0.3 mb is present in Eq. (4a) by averaging the data over all energies. The next best relations are the Johnson-Treiman relations.[2] The discrepancy there is of the order of $\frac{1}{2}$ mb. The "symmetric sum rule" (3a) has a discrepancy of about $2\frac{1}{2}$ mb, while the relations (5a) and (5b) have discrepancies of about 4 mb.

The worst disagreements are thus of the order of 15-20% and are found in relations (5a) and (5b) whose derivation always involves SU(3). On the other hand, the best agreements are found in relations (4a) and (4b) where the discrepancy is two percent or less. These relations are obtained without assuming SU(3). The two Johnson-Treiman relations give discrepancies of 2-3% while the symmetric sum rule has a 12% discrepancy.

The good agreement with experiment of relations (1), (2a), (2b), and (4a) is graphically shown in Fig. 2, which plots the eight quantities appearing on the left- and right-hand sides of these relations. Since these are all normalized weighted means of different meson-baryon cross sections, they can all be expected a priori to be equal in some asymptotic limit. Figure 2 shows that they are far from equal and divide into four well-separated pairs of nearly equal quantities, namely just those pairs which satisfy the relations. The poorer relations (3a), (5a), and (5b) whose derivation requires SU(3) are indicated on Fig. 1 and can be compared with the difference between the K^+p and K^+n cross sections. That these are qualitatively worse than those of Fig. 2 is immediately evident.

These results are very reasonable in view of the derivations. A discrepancy of 10-20% is not unexpected for reaction predictions which completely neglect SU(3)-symmetry breaking. The best prediction is the antisymmetric sum

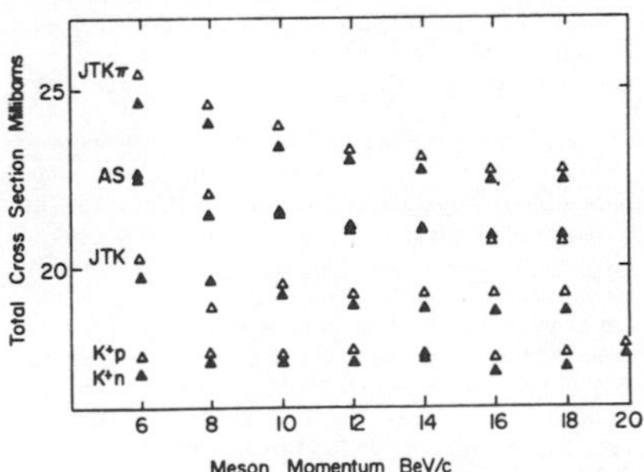

FIG. 2. Experimental tests of relations (1), (2a), (2b), and (4a). Δ left-hand side, ▲ right-hand side. JTπK, Johnson-Treiman relation (2a); JTK, Johnson-Treiman relation (2b); AS, antisymmetric sum rule (1).

rule reported previously[2,4] which is obtained only from the quark-model additivity assumption. The next best, still in the 2% range, is obtained by neglecting the charge exchange in nonstrange quark-quark scattering. The two Johnson-Treiman relations require the additional assumption of the Pomeranchuk relation.[6] This is evidently a 2-3% approximation.

The assumption (6) can also be applied to baryon-baryon total cross sections. These give the results

$$\sigma(pp)=\sigma(pn)=9P, \quad (8a)$$

$$\sigma(\bar{p}p)=9P+5A, \quad (8b)$$

$$\sigma(\bar{n}p)=9P+4A. \quad (8c)$$

Combining Eqs. (8) and (7) leads to relations between meson-baryon and baryon-baryon scattering, which turn out to be identical to those obtained by Freund,[2]

$$\sigma(\bar{p}p)-\sigma(pp)=5/4[\sigma(\bar{n}p)-\sigma(np)]$$
$$=5[\sigma(\pi^-p)-\sigma(\pi^+p)]. \quad (9)$$

The agreement of these relations with experiment has been discussed,[2] and is quite good in view of the larger experimental errors. However, quark-model relations between meson-baryon and baryon-baryon scattering have been shown[4] to be good only to about 10%, in contrast to the relations for meson-baryon scattering, even without the additional assumption (6). This may be due to breakdown of the basic additivity assumption for the baryon case, or to the effects of binding on the effective quark-quark scattering amplitude[8]; e.g., the "effective mass" of a bound quark may have different values in a baryon and in a meson.

It is not clear whether the success of the relations obtained here should be considered as convincing evidence for the validity of the assumptions used, or whether relations (7) and (8) simply constitute a successful parametrization of the experimental data. In particular, the relation between quark-model derivations without higher symmetries and other symmetry derivations[9] possibly together with universality[2] should be investigated. However, whatever the interpretation, it appears significant that three independent relations can be derived, without the use of SU(3) symmetry, which show an agreement with experiment roughly an order of magnitude better than normally obtained for SU(3) relations between transition amplitudes.

Other derivations[2,4] of the Johnson-Treiman relations which use SU(3) have the difficulty of explaining why they are so good relative to other SU(3) predictions.[5] Note also that the relations (5a) and (5b), which are reasonable SU(3) predictions (20%), do not appear in other derivations. The particular choice of the reactions appearing in (5a) and (5b) seems to be significant. One might just as well expect similar relations involving the charge conjugate mesons; i.e., π^+p and K^+p instead of (5a), or π^-p and K^+n instead of (5b). These are not predicted in this model and are in strong disagreement with experiment; the characteristic discrepancies are about 9 mb or 40-50%.

The author would like to acknowledge stimulating discussions with J. J. J. Kokkedee, H. R. Rubinstein, F. Scheck, and L. Van Hove, and to thank H. Harari for important critical comments on the manuscript.

[1]S. J. Lindenbaum, in Proceedings of the Oxford International Conference on Elementary Particles, Oxford, England, 1965 (Rutherford High Energy Laboratory, Chilton, Berkshire, England, 1966).

[2]K. Johnson and S. B. Treiman, Phys. Rev. Letters 14, 189 (1965); P. G. O. Freund, Phys. Rev. Letters 15, 929 (1965); V. Barger and M. H. Rubin, Phys. Rev. 140, B1366 (1965).

[3]H. J. Lipkin and S. Meshkov, Phys. Rev. Letters 14, 670 (1965).

[4]E. M. Levin and L. L. Frankfurt, Zh. Eksperim. i Teor. Fiz.—Pis'ma Redakt. 2, 105 (1965) [translation: JETP Letters 2, 65 (1965)]; H. J. Lipkin and F. Scheck, Phys. Rev. Letters 16, 71 (1966).

[5]H. Harari, in Proceedings of the Seminar on High-Energy Physics and Elementary Particles (International Atomic Energy Agency, Vienna, 1965), p. 353.

[6]W. Galbraith, E. W. Jenkins, F. F. Kycia, B. A. Leontić, R. H. Phillips, A. L. Read, and R. Rubinstein, Phys. Rev. 138, B913 (1965).

[7]P. G. O. Freund, H. Ruegg, D. Speiser, and A. Morales, Nuovo Cimento 25, 307 (1962).

[8]J. J. J. Kokkedee and L. Van Hove, CERN Report No. 66/248/5-TH. 642, 1966 (unpublished). In particular, these authors point out that the energy dependence of pp and $\bar{p}p$ total cross sections indicate that quark-quark scattering reaches the asymptotic limit before quark-antiquark scattering.

[9]It is tempting to try to link these results with a higher symmetry or the algebra of currents, particularly in view of the recent formulations using states at infinite momentum. See R. F. Dashen and M. Gell-Mann, in Proceedings of the Coral Gables Conference, 1966 (to be published). The high-energy scattering states considered here have $v\sim c$ in the center-of-mass system and could be considered to be near the infinite-momentum limit. The equality of $\sigma(K^+p)$ and $\sigma(K^+n)$ is obtainable from the assumption of invariance of the S matrix under a peculiar SU(2)⊗SU(2) group,

where the two SU(2) groups are the isospins of (1) quarks with $p=+\infty$ and antiquarks with $p=-\infty$; (2) quarks with $p=-\infty$ and antiquarks with $p=+\infty$. Unfortunately this group is not a subgroup of the U(12) group generated by the conventional current algebras. The corresponding SU(2)⊗SU(2) subgroup of U(12) does not give the momentum reversal for quarks and antiquarks and simply gives the trivial result that all forward two-body inelastic processes are negligible in comparison with elastic scattering in the high energy limit. The author is grateful to H. Harari for an elucidation of this point.

Volume 22, number 3 PHYSICS LETTERS 15 August 1966

THE ALGEBRA OF SCALAR AND VECTOR VERTEX STRENGTHS IN REGGE RESIDUES

N. CABIBBO
CERN, Geneva

L. HORWITZ *
Institut de Physique Théorique, Université de Genève

and

Y. NE'EMAN **
Tel Aviv University
Institut de Physique Théorique, Université de Genève and
CERN, Geneva

Received 4 July 1966

An algebra of "strong" scalar and vector currents coupled to Regge residues accounts for the composite model predictions in high-energy elastic scattering. Some new relations are given; $\sigma(K^+N) = \sigma(K^+P)$ is accounted for in a simple way.

We shall present an approach based upon the identification of an algebra of scalar and vector currents in the structure of the residue functions associated with Regge trajectories, somewhat in analogy to the way in which the weak and electromagnetic transitions of the hadrons define the system of vector and axial-vector currents. Applying the theory directly to high-energy scattering, we find we can predict some hitherto unexplained features. In so doing, we also produce a theoretical interpretation of a number of good results [1-5] whose derivation has generally been considered to imply a composite-particle structure for the hadrons.

Physical intuition based upon somewhat unrealistic models has twice before within recent years opened up new extensions of unitary symmetry; in both cases [6, 7] - non-relativistic SU(6) and too-relativistic SU(6, 6) - excellent results have been obscured at times by difficulties and dilemmas in the theoretical foundations [8]. Much clarification, a new understanding and a series of new results were each time provided by the definition of an algebraic methodology [9, 10] which was gradually improved and made consistent with relativistic quantum theory [11]. It is our contention that the present use of a "naive" quark model, - leading to a new subparticle physics with methods emulating those used in nuclear structure and the many-body problem - should be regarded in the same light as the previous suggestive break-ins.

It is with this motivation in mind - an algebraic foundation for the high-energy results - that we make our suggestions. We deal with the simple case of forward scattering, though it is probable that the treatment can be extended to other situations. Our formulation should be regarded as a first rough definition, to be further refined extensively.

The description of high-energy baryon-baryon and baryon-meson phenomena in terms of Regge trajectories has been highly [12] successful and supplies the most appropriate framework for our treatment. In a series of recent studies [13], one finds a useful and consistent parametrization of the data, based upon the residue functions $\beta(t)$ and the pole trajectories $\alpha(t)$, where t is the square of the momentum transfer and the energy dependence is explicit. The real part of the trajectory is effectively described by its intercept $\alpha(0)$ and its slope at that point.

The factorization theorem [14] allows us to re-

* Supported in part by the Swiss National Fund.
** Sponsored in part by the Air Force Office of Scientific Research under Grant AF EOAR 66-39 through the European Office of Aerospace Research (OAR) United States Air Forces.

place $\beta(t)$ by a product of two *vertex strength* functions $\gamma_C^{AB}(t)$, which are analogous to form factors in quantum electrodynamics; γ_C^{AB} stands for example for an upper vertex where the trajectory C occurs as an intermediate state in the t channel scattering of incoming particles A and B and as an exchanged system (Regge pole) in the s channel scattering of A into B.

Actual high-energy phenomenology has achieved a general fit of known processes in terms of vertex strength functions coupled to two even intrinsic-parity trajectories with opposite signature, dominated by two meson unitary nonets with $j = 1^-$ and 2^+. Some differences exist between the workers in the field, mainly with respect to the number of 2^+ unitary singlet-dominated trajectories. We shall here adopt the view that one is faced with an octet-singlet set for each signature, including the Pomeranchuk trajectory.

Observations indicate that apart from the latter (whose intercept $\alpha_{s^0}(0) = 1$, where s^i denotes an even-signature trajectory corresponding to the ith unitary index, counting from 0 to 8), all trajectories s^i and v^i (v denotes odd signature) have $\alpha(0) \sim 0.5$. Deviations from the Pomeranchuk limit $\sigma^{AB} = \sigma^{\bar{A}B}$ should thus tend to disappear with increasing energy at some general common rate. Variegation in the "law of force" picture seems to result in the main from differences between residues.

We assume that the vertex strengths $\gamma_C^{AB}(0)$ in the limit of forward scattering are given by matrix elements of algebraic operators belonging to a U(12) algebra. We introduce a system of nine *strengths* S^i with scalar densities; when adjoined to a second nonet of strengths V^i with the same algebraic properties as the unitary spin generators, they close on a U(3) × U(3) sub-algebra completely isomorphic to the $[U(3) \times U(3)]_\beta$ contained in the $[U(6) \times U(6)]_\beta$ "good" *rest* symmetry * defined by Dashen and Gell-Mann.

The matrix elements of the system of S^i and V^i strengths are to be identified with the $\gamma_{s^i}^{AB}(0)$ and $\gamma_{v^i}^{AB}(0)$ respectively as

$$\delta^3(p_A - p_B)\gamma_{s^i}^{AB}(0) = \langle A | \int \mathcal{D}(\beta\sigma^0\lambda^i;\ x,\ 0)\, d^3x\, | B \rangle \tag{1}$$

$$\delta^3(p_A - p_B)\gamma_{v^i}^{AB}(0) = \langle A | \int \mathcal{D}(\sigma^0\lambda^i;\ x, 0)\, d^3x\, | B \rangle \tag{2}$$

where the integrals are carried out *in the rest frame* of the incident particle **. Note that to account for spin flip we would use an entire set of U(6) × U(6) generators. In the following we shall deal with elastic scattering only, thus using in fact σ^0 with $i = 0,\ 3,\ 8$ only. The S^i and V^i would be written in a quark representation as

$$S^i = \tfrac{1}{2} \int d^3x\, q^+ \beta \lambda^i q \tag{3}$$

$$V^i = \tfrac{1}{2} \int d^3x\, q^+ \lambda^i q\ . \tag{4}$$

We note that

$$[S^i, S^j] = i f^{ij}{}_k V^k \tag{5}$$

$$[V^i, S^j] = i f^{ij}{}_k S^k\ . \tag{6}$$

The effect of β in the U(12) algebra can be represented in terms of constituent (1,0,0) representations - mathematical quarks [15] - as additive (positively) in quark and antiquark unitary charges. S^0, for example, has eigenvalues proportional to the number of "quark charges" plus "antiquark charges" (in opposition to V^0 which is proportional to baryon charge, i.e., to the number of "quark charges" minus "antiquark charges"). S^i adds up λ^i contributions of quarks plus $\lambda^{i\sim}$ contributions of antiquarks (V^i picks out the differences, since $-\lambda^{i\sim}$ is the unitary spin representation of the antiquarks). It is for the above reason that using S^i densities reproduces the results of "quark-additivity" and "quark counting" applied in composite models. As a simplest example, consider this crude derivation of the $\sigma_{\pi^+p}/\sigma_{pp}$ ratio. Fig. 1 shows the t channel exchange of a Pomeranchuk trajectory. Assuming this to be dominant ‡ at the highest energies, we derive for the total cross sections the Levin-Frankfurt ratio [1].

$$\frac{\sigma_{\pi P}}{\sigma_{PP}} = \frac{\gamma_{s^0}^{\pi\pi}(0)\, \gamma_{s^0}^{PP}(0)}{\gamma_{s^0}^{PP}(0)\, \gamma_{s^0}^{PP}(0)} \approx \frac{2}{3} \tag{7}$$

since $\gamma_{s^0}(0)$ is, according to its definition, just the eigenvalue n_{s^0} of the generator S^0. We have used, of course, the $[U(6) \times U(6)]_\beta$ assignments

* It is not clear that our strengths are really to be identified with the space integrals of the currents associated directly with weak transitions. For instance, we may be dealing with a class of source currents of strong transitions, consistently definable in terms of the Regge formalism. The complete U(12) algebra of strengths would contain pseudoscalar and axial-vector operators (corresponding to trajectories with 0^- and 1^+ exchange). These additional operators cannot represent rest symmetries.

** The densities will supply form factors; however we deal with $t \neq 0$ elsewhere.

‡ Similar considerations with both S^0 and S^8 contributing predict $\sigma_{\pi P} > \sigma_{KP}$ as can be seen from the table below. We are indebted to Dr. J.J.J. Kokkedee for this remark.

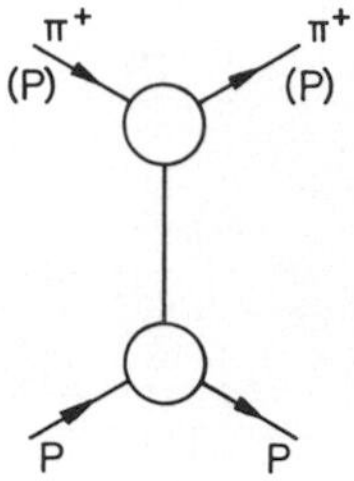

Fig. 1.

of $(56,1)^+$ and $(6,6^*)^-$ for baryons and mesons respectively. In this connection we wish to emphasize an approximation, implicit in our adoption of the Regge formalism, in which we have defined the vertex strengths at each vertex independently. It may be that a complete theory would require us to treat both vertices simultaneously and that the same classification of states in upper and lower vertices cannot be maintained as far as the S^i part of $[U(3)\times U(3)]_\beta$ goes. The possibility of an alteration in F/D ratio at one vertex should therefore be taken into account for the S^i matrix elements (this is the only allowed alteration); we discuss this later in connection with the comparison of our ideas with experiment. However, in cases such as eq. (7), where the ratio of cross sections with the same baryon-scalar vertices is computed, this possible effect cancels out completely and no approximation is involved.

Note that the commutation relations fix the relative scales of γ_{si} and γ_{vi} by imposing a quadratic relation.

We assume that the elastic scattering amplitude is given by ‡ (γ^A now stands for γ^{AA}, etc.)

$$T_{AB}(\nu,t) = -\sum_{i=0,3,8}\Big\{\gamma^A_{si}(t)\,\gamma^B_{si}(t)\,g(\alpha^s_i)\times \times\frac{1+\exp(-i\pi\alpha^s_i)}{\sin\pi\alpha^s_i}\,\frac{\Gamma(\alpha^s_i+\frac{3}{2})}{\Gamma(\alpha^s_i+1)}\Big(\frac{\nu}{\nu_s}\Big)^{\alpha^s_i(t)} + +\gamma^A_{vi}(t)\,\gamma^B_{vi}(t)\,\frac{1-\exp(-i\pi\alpha^v_i)}{\sin\pi\alpha^v_i}\,\frac{\Gamma(\alpha^v_i+\frac{3}{2})}{\Gamma(\alpha^v_i+1)}\Big(\frac{\nu}{\nu_v}\Big)^{\alpha^v_i(t)}\Big\} \quad (8)$$

where

$$\nu = (\text{total energy in c.m.})^2 + \tfrac{1}{2}t - m_A^2 - m_B^2 \,. \quad (9)$$

$g(\alpha^s_i)$ is a ghost-killing factor which we have to separate explicitly in order to cancel out the pole at $\alpha^s_i = 0$. We shall assume that in the neighbourhood of $t = 0$, $g(\alpha^s_i) \approx 1$. Since these trajectories

Table 1
Total cross sections

$\bar{P}N$	=	$6t^s_0$	$+\ 3t^s_8$	$-\ t^s_3$	$+\ 6t^v_0$	$+\ 3t^v_8$	$-\ t^v_3$
PN	=	$6t^s_0$	$+\ 3t^s_8$	$-\ t^s_3$	$-\ 6t^v_0$	$-\ 3t^v_8$	$+\ t^v_3$
PP	=	$6t^s_0$	$+\ 3t^s_8$	$+\ t^s_3$	$-\ 6t^v_0$	$-\ 3t^v_8$	$-\ t^v_3$
$\bar{P}P$	=	$6t^s_0$	$+\ 3t^s_8$	$+\ t^s_3$	$+\ 6t^v_0$	$+\ 3t^v_8$	$+\ t^v_3$
π^+P	=	$4t^s_0$	$+\ 2t^s_8$				$-\ 2t^v_3$
π^-P	=	$4t^s_0$	$+\ 2t^s_8$				$+\ 2t^v_3$
K^+P	=	$4t^s_0$	$-\ t^s_8$	$+\ t^s_3$		$-\ 3t^v_8$	$-\ t^v_3$
K^-P	=	$4t^s_0$	$-\ t^s_8$	$+\ t^s_3$		$+\ 3t^v_8$	$+\ t^v_3$
K^+N	=	$4t^s_0$	$-\ t^s_8$	$-\ t^s_3$		$-\ 3t^v_8$	$+\ t^v_3$
K^-N	=	$4t^s_0$	$-\ t^s_8$	$-\ t^s_3$		$+\ 3t^v_8$	$-\ t^v_3$

describe the exchange of 2^+ and 1^- particles respectively, the absolute signs of their contributions are determined by the requirement that they give rise to forces between equal particles which are respectively attractive and repulsive. We assume no ambivalence is introduced by the t dependence.

The $j = 1^-$ trajectory may couple to the 1^- particles in the usual way. As to the $j = 2^+$ mesons, they cannot couple directly with scalar quantities, but our prescription is appropriate for the coupling of their trajectory at $\alpha = 0$. The problem of coupling to Regge recurrences is not special to the scalar, but occurs also for the other trajectories.

The contribution of each pole to the total cross section is equal to the product of vertex strengths defined according to eqs. (1) and (2), a factor (t^v_i or t^s_i) depending upon energy and the position of the pole, and a sign determined by the signature in eq. (8) (negative for the vector contribution). Our basic result is given in table 1, where a normalization corresponding to tr $\lambda^2_i = 2$ is used to avoid fractional coefficients.

The coefficients actually correspond to overall F coupling for the vector trajectories and for the mesons and baryons D and F coupling, respectively, to the scalar trajectories. SU(3) symmetry would imply the equality $t^s_3 = t^s_8$ and $t^v_3 = t^v_8$; U(3) among the vector contributions would imply $t^v_0 = t^v_3 = t^v_8$ and $[SU(3)\times SU(3)]_\beta$ (excluding

‡ We neglect ω-φ mixing since we consider the case in which their trajectories are essentially degenerate. Our identification of s^0 with the Pomeranchuk trajectory requires no $s^0 - s^8$ mixing at $\alpha = 0$.

t_0^s) would finally imply ($t_3^v = t_3^s$) that all * but the Pomeranchuk coefficients are equal. We note here that $t_3^s = t_3^v$ alone immediately implies that [5]

$$K^+P = K^+N \, . \tag{10}$$

This relation is well satisfied between 6 and 20 GeV/c and may be interpreted in our theory as a close degeneracy between the s_3 and v_3 intercepts (both contributions become small, however at higher energies).

The parameter t_0^s is positive; it follows from our basic picture that all t_i^s and t_i^v are positive numbers and we derive the following inequalities, valid without any other restriction:

$$\begin{aligned} K^-P &> K^-N \\ \pi^-P &> \pi^+P \\ K^-P &> K^+P \\ K^-P &> K^+N \\ K^-P - K^-N &> |K^+P - K^+N| \\ K^+P + K^-P &> K^+N + K^-N \end{aligned} \tag{11}$$

The relations (11) are strikingly verified. For baryon-baryon scattering we obtain

$$\begin{aligned} \bar{P}P &> PP \\ \bar{P}P &> PN \\ \bar{P}P &> \bar{P}N \\ \bar{P}P - PP &> \bar{P}N - PN \\ \bar{P}P + PP &> \bar{P}N + PN \end{aligned} \tag{12}$$

Four identities also follow since there are 10 relations and only 6 parameters:

$$\begin{aligned} K^+P - K^+N &= PP - NP \; [5] \\ K^-P - K^-N &= \bar{P}P - \bar{P}N \; [5] \\ 3(\pi^+P + \pi^-P) &= \bar{P}N + PN + PP + \bar{P}P \; [2,4] \\ K^+P + \pi^-P + K^-N &= K^-P + \pi^+P + K^+N \; [2] \end{aligned} \tag{13}$$

Following the procedure used for table 1 we obtain

$$\Lambda P = 6t_0^s + 6t_0^v \tag{14}$$

and therefore

$$\Lambda P - PP = K^-N - \pi^+P \; [2] \, . \tag{15}$$

The additional "antisymmetric" (t_i^s cancelling) relations follow from SU(3) (the Johnson-Treiman relation [16]) and U(3), for the Freund [3] relation,

$$\bar{P}P - PP = \tfrac{5}{4}(\bar{P}N - PN) = 5(\pi^-P - \pi^+P) \, . \tag{16}$$

As to the other "symmetric" (t_i^v cancelling) relations of Lipkin and Scheck [2]

$$\begin{aligned} PP + \bar{P}P &= 2[\pi^+P + \pi^-P] - \tfrac{1}{2}[K^+P + K^-P] \\ K^+P + K^-P &= \tfrac{1}{2}[\pi^+P + \pi^-P + K^+N + K^-N] \end{aligned} \tag{17}$$

they require SU(3) among the scalar trajectories, which is a stronger condition and seems to be less well satisfied.

Imposing the $[SU(2) \times SU(2)]_\beta$ relation $t_3^s = t_3^v$ [leading immediately to (10)] as well as SU(3) among the vector trajectories ($t_3^v = t_8^v$) we obtain

$$K^-N = \tfrac{1}{2}(K^-P + K^+P) \; [5] \, , \tag{18}$$

which is well satisfied. However, setting also $t_3^s = t_8^s$ (imposing SU(3) among the scalar trajectories) one obtains [5]

$$\begin{aligned} \pi^-P &= K^-P \\ \pi^+P &- K^-N \end{aligned} \tag{19}$$

which are not as good. As mentioned above we should expect some mixing of the (56,1) with other $[U(6) \times U(6)]_\beta$ states, which would generate some D coupling at the scalar trajectory nucleon vertex, affecting mainly t_8^s. Adjoining a small negative admixture of D coupling to this vertex, the experimental meson-nucleon data can be fit to within a millibarn, taking common t_i^v and t_j^s ($j \neq 0$). Alternatively, solving for the coefficients, one notices that t_8^s is rather large.

We would like to thank C.P.Enz, J.Harte, H.Högaasen, J.M.Jauch, J.J.J.Kokkedee, R.Socolow and L.Van Hove for helpful discussions. We are also indebted to A.Martin for an edifying session on ghosts and ghost killing. One of the authors (Y.N.) would like to thank the Convention Intercantonale pour l'Enseignement du 3ème Cycle de la Physique en Suisse Romande for inviting him to deliver the Summer Semester Lectures on Particle Physics. He would also like to thank CERN for its hospitality.

* A rest symmetry in the t channel and degeneracy of the trajectories implies equality of the scale factors ν_s and ν_v.

References

1. E.M.Levin and L.L.Frankfurt, Zh.Eksp. i Teor. Fiz. Pisma v Redak. 2 (1965) 105; JETP Letters 2 (1965) 65.
2. H.J.Lipkin and F.Scheck, Phys.Rev.Letters 16 (1966) 71.
3. P.G.O.Freund, Phys.Rev.Letters 15 (1965) 929.
4. J.J.J.Kokkedee and L.Van Hove, Nuovo Cimento 42 (1966) 711.

5. H.J.Lipkin, Phys.Rev.Letters 16 (1966) 1015.
6. F.Gürsey and L.A.Radicati, Phys.Rev.Letters 13 (1964) 173;
G.Zweig, Symmetries in elementary particle physics (1964 International School of Physics, Ettore Majorana), ed. A.Zichichi (Academic Press, N.Y. 1965).
7. A.Salam, R.Delbourgo and J.Strathdee, Proc.Roy. Soc. (London) A284 (1965) 146;
M.A.B.Bég and A.Pais; Phys.Rev.Letters 14 (1965) 267;
B.Sakita and K.C.Wali, Phys.Rev.139 (1965) B1355.
8. S.Coleman, Phys.Rev.138 (1965) B1262;
M.A.B.Bég and A.Pais, Phys.Rev.Letters 14 (1965) 509, 577.
9. R.P.Feynman, M.Gell-Mann and G.Zweig, Phys. Rev.Letters 13 (1964) 678.
10. R.F.Dashen and M.Gell-Mann, Phys.Rev.Letters 17 (1965) 142. We use the notation and definitions of this reference in the present work.
11. S.Coleman, Physics Letters 19 (1965) 144.
12. R.J.N.Phillips and W.Rarita, Phys.Rev.139 (1965) B1336.
13. V.Barger and M.Olsson, Phys.Rev.Letters 15 (1965) 930, for example.
14. M.Gell-Mann, Phys.Rev.Letters 8 (1962) 263;
V.N.Gribov and I.Ya.Pomeranchuk, Phys.Rev. Letters 8 (1962) 343.
15. H.Goldberg and Y.Ne'eman, Nuovo Cimento 27 (1963) 1.
16. K.Johnson and S.B.Treiman, Phys.Rev.Letters 14 (1965) 189.

* * * * *

Author's additional remarks to the paper:

A detailed fit to the high energy total cross-section data has been made on the basis of this model [N. Cabibbo, J.J.J. Kokkedee, L. Horwitz, and Y. Néeman, Nuovo Cimento 45, 275 (1966)]. In order not to have total cross sections increasing with energy it is necessary here to assume the intercept of the Pomeranchuk trajectory to be slightly less than one. Also an admixture of D-type coupling in the baryon scalar vertex strengths is needed to fit nucleon-antinucleon data.

REPRINT 19

8.A.4 Nuclear Physics B1 (1967) 169-179. North-Holland Publ. Comp., Amsterdam

QUARK MODEL AND ANNIHILATION AT HIGH ENERGY

J. J. J. KOKKEDEE and L. VAN HOVE
CERN, Geneva

Received 25 January 1967

Abstract. Baryon-antibaryon annihilation contributions to high energy total cross-sections are discussed in the quark model. It is argued that they cannot be included in the additivity assumption for quark amplitudes. In this modified form, additivity with isospin and charge conjugation invariance predicts four relations, two of which are in very good agreement with the data while the other two are at present inconclusive because of the large experimental uncertainties. Regarding annihilation cross-sections, an alternative assumption of multiplicative type is proposed: it cannot be tested with present data. The paper ends with a few final remarks.

1. INTRODUCTION

Among the various relations between high energy cross-sections recently derived from the quark model [1-8], a distinction should be made between those which assume only the additivity property for quark amplitudes and those which require additional, "ad hoc" assumptions. If we restrict ourselves to spin-averaged total cross-sections, the most familiar relations of the former type are (P = proton, N = neutron)

$$S^{+}(\mathrm{PP}) + S^{+}(\mathrm{PN}) = 3S^{+}(\pi^{+}\mathrm{P}) \,, \tag{1}$$

$$S^{-}(\mathrm{K^{+}P}) - S^{-}(\mathrm{K^{+}N}) = S^{-}(\pi^{+}\mathrm{P}) \,, \tag{2}$$

$$S^{-}(\mathrm{PP}) - S^{-}(\mathrm{PN}) = S^{-}(\pi^{+}\mathrm{P}) \,, \tag{3}$$

with the notation

$$S^{\pm}(\mathrm{AB}) = \sigma_{\mathrm{T}}(\bar{\mathrm{A}}\mathrm{B}) \pm \sigma_{\mathrm{T}}(\mathrm{AB}) \,. \tag{4}$$

As to the second type, one has mainly the Freund relations [6,7,9]

$$S^{-}(\mathrm{PP}) = 5S^{-}(\pi^{+}\mathrm{P}) \,, \tag{5}$$

$$S^{-}(\mathrm{PN}) = 4S^{-}(\pi^{+}\mathrm{P}) \,, \tag{6}$$

and the Levinson-Wall-Lipkin relations [8]

$$S^-(PP) = 2S^-(K^+P) + S^-(K^+N) \,, \tag{7}$$

$$S^-(PN) = S^-(K^+P) + 2S^-(K^+N) \,. \tag{8}$$

Relations (5) and (6) are equivalent if one has (3); similarly (7) and (8) are equivalent on the basis of (2) and (3). The "ad hoc" assumption required to obtain (5) and (6) is that the quark-quark and antiquark-quark "total cross-sections" satisfy

$$S^-(pn) = 0 \,, \tag{9}$$

(we denote the three quarks by p, n, λ). To obtain (7) and (8) one needs the "ad hoc" assumption

$$S^-(\lambda p) = 0 \,. \tag{10}$$

Neither of these assumptions is particularly natural in the framework of the quark model with additive amplitudes. Both should be regarded as expressing within the model the empirical facts that (5) - (6) are rather well and (7) - (8) very well satisfied by the data. We note that in the momentum range where they have been tested ($6 \leqslant p_L \leqslant 18$ GeV/c), the left-hand sides of relations (5) - (8) are overwhelmingly determined by the annihilation parts $\sigma_A(\bar{P}P)$, $\sigma_A(\bar{P}N)$ of the antinucleon-nucleon total cross-sections $\sigma_T(\bar{P}P)$ and $\sigma_T(\bar{P}N)$. Thus, any theoretical argument leading to a derivation of any of the relations (5) - (10) would relate antinucleon-nucleon annihilation cross-sections σ_A to non-annihilation effects.

We also note that the σ_A do not play such a dominant role in relations (1) - (3). They are absent in the very successful relation (2) and largely compensate each other in (3). In (1) they have a negligible effect at very high energy where $\sigma_A/\sigma_T \to 0$. At lower energies their contribution seems to be the main source of the imperfect agreement of (1) with experiment [5]. Indeed, the relation

$$2\sigma_T(PP) + 2\sigma_T(PN) = 3S^+(\pi^+P) \,, \tag{11}$$

is in much better agreement with the data than (1), from which it differs by the quantity

$$S^-(PP) + S^-(PN) \simeq \sigma_A(\bar{P}P) + \sigma_A(\bar{P}N) \,. \tag{12}$$

At $p_L \approx 14$ GeV/c, (12) is about 26 mb compared to ≈ 160 mb for both sides of (11). This situation remains qualitatively unchanged if in (1) and (11) the left-hand and right-hand cross-sections are taken at laboratory momenta in the ratio $\frac{3}{2}$, as is needed to obtain approximately the same effective energy for the quark-quark collisions [3, 5].

The preceding discussion implies that the additivity assumption of quark amplitudes has not been tested so far for the annihilation parts σ_A of the antibaryon-baryon cross-sections, and the excellent agreement of (11) as opposed to (1) with experiment suggests that additivity does not hold for σ_A.

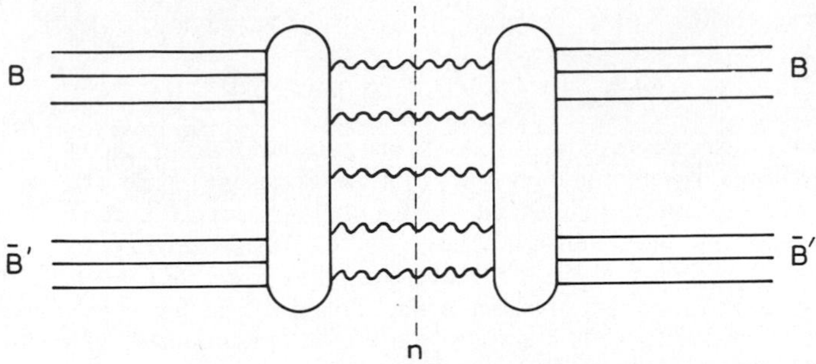

Fig. 1. Diagram representing antibaryon-baryon annihilation contributions to the sum in (13).

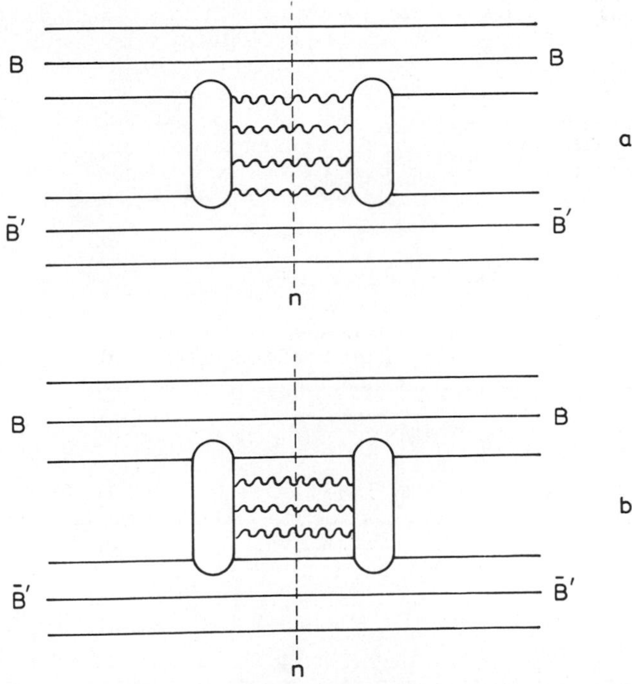

Fig. 2. Diagrams describing, for antibaryon-baryon scattering, the sum in (13) under the additivity assumption for quark amplitudes, with (diagram a) and without (diagram b) quark-antiquark annihilation. Similar diagrams can be drawn for baryon-baryon and meson-baryon scattering.

It is interesting that purely theoretical arguments point to the same conclusion. This is seen by using the unitarity condition in the form

$$2\sigma_T(AB) = \sum_n \langle AB | T^\dagger | n \rangle \langle n | T | AB \rangle \; , \tag{13}$$

where the sum extends over all elastic and inelastic final states of the A + B collision (with energy momentum conservation taken into account), and where T is the properly normalized scattering operator. For $A = \overline{B}'$ = antibaryon, B = baryon, the annihilation part $2\sigma_A$ of (13) is represented by diagrams of the type shown in fig. 1, where the solid lines represent quarks and antiquarks and the wavy lines mesons. These diagrams have to be contrasted with those of figs. 2a and 2b which must approximately describe the total sum (13) if the additivity assumption for quark amplitudes is valid. It is indeed unnatural to expect the contributions of figs. 2 to provide good approximations to the annihilation process of fig. 1. The reason is that the right-hand half of fig. 1, representing $\langle \text{mesons} | T | \overline{B}'B \rangle$, contains exchange of a baryon, i.e., of three quarks, an effect not included in figs. 2. A similar but less important limitation affects meson-nucleon scattering because it has in (13) a contribution from backward collisions corresponding to baryon exchange; this contribution is quantitatively very small, however. Finally, for all hadrons A, B, we expect that only the diagrams of the type depicted in fig. 2b and not those of fig. 2a can provide a good approximation to the non-annihilation part of the sum (13). The reason is that the right-hand half of fig. 2a contains quark-antiquark annihilation, i.e., a one-quark exchange process which experimentally has never been found to occur among the observed inelastic collisions $\langle n | T | AB \rangle$. [See note added in proof.]

2. ADDITIVITY WITHOUT ANNIHILATION

As suggested by the above discussion, we now apply additivity of the quark amplitudes to quantities $\tilde{S}^{\pm}(AB)$ defined as identical to $S^{\pm}(AB)$ when A = meson and B = baryon, and as

$$\tilde{S}^{\pm}(AB) = S^{\pm}(AB) - \sigma_A(\bar{A}B) \; , \tag{14}$$

when both A and B are baryons. The existing data concern the following cases $A = \pi^+$, K^+, P; B = P, N. We define analogous quantities $\tilde{S}^{\pm}(qq')$ for quarks q, q', thereby excluding the antiquark-quark annihilation contribution of the type depicted in fig. 2a. Additivity gives

$$\begin{aligned}
\tilde{S}^+(\pi^+P) &= \tilde{S}^+(\pi^+N) = 3\tilde{S}^+(pp) + 3\tilde{S}^+(pn) \; , \\
\tilde{S}^-(\pi^+P) &= -\tilde{S}^-(\pi^+N) = \tilde{S}^-(pp) - \tilde{S}^-(pn) \; , \\
\tilde{S}^{\pm}(K^+P) &= 2\tilde{S}^{\pm}(pp) + \tilde{S}^{\pm}(pn) \pm 3\tilde{S}^{\pm}(\lambda p) \; , \\
\tilde{S}^{\pm}(K^+N) &= \tilde{S}^{\pm}(pp) + 2\tilde{S}^{\pm}(pn) \pm 3\tilde{S}^{\pm}(\lambda p) \; ,
\end{aligned} \tag{15a}$$

$$\tilde{S}^{\pm}(PP) = 5\tilde{S}^{\pm}(pp) + 4\tilde{S}^{\pm}(pn) ,$$
$$\tilde{S}^{\pm}(PN) = 4\tilde{S}^{\pm}(pp) + 5\tilde{S}^{\pm}(pn) , \qquad (15b)$$

where the upper (or lower) signs have to be taken together. In (15) isospin and charge conjugation invariance are used.

By elimination of quark amplitudes one obtains

$$\tilde{S}^{+}(PP) + \tilde{S}^{+}(PN) = 3\tilde{S}^{+}(\pi^{+}P) , \qquad (16)$$

$$\tilde{S}^{+}(PP) - \tilde{S}^{+}(PN) = \tilde{S}^{+}(K^{+}P) - \tilde{S}^{+}(K^{+}N) , \qquad (17)$$

$$\tilde{S}^{-}(PP) - \tilde{S}^{-}(PN) = \tilde{S}^{-}(\pi^{+}P) , \qquad (18)$$

as well as

$$\tilde{S}^{-}(K^{+}P) - \tilde{S}^{-}(K^{+}N) = \tilde{S}^{-}(\pi^{+}P) . \qquad (2')$$

As mentioned above, (16) agrees very well with experiment. The agreement of (17) and (18) with experiment is undecided because of the large uncertainties on the left-hand sides. As to (2'), it is identical to the "good" Johnson-Treiman relation (2) and is in excellent agreement with experiment. Thus, restricting ourselves to spin-averaged total cross-sections with exclusion of the annihilation parts, we find that the additivity assumption (with isospin and C invariance) predicts four relations, two of which are in excellent agreement with the facts while the others are fully compatible with them but have to await better data to be tested in a significant way.

We briefly mention typical values of the quark amplitudes following from measured hadron cross-sections. Equations (15) give at 10 GeV/c laboratory momentum

$$\tilde{S}^{-}(pp) \simeq -\tilde{S}^{-}(np) \simeq 1 \text{ mb} , \quad \tilde{S}^{-}(\lambda p) \simeq -1.5 \text{ mb} ,$$
$$\tilde{S}^{+}(pp) \simeq 9.5 \text{ mb} , \quad \tilde{S}^{+}(np) \simeq 7.7 \text{ mb} , \quad \tilde{S}^{+}(\lambda p) \simeq 4.4 \text{ mb} . \qquad (19)$$

One obtains for the spin-averaged quark "total cross-sections" $a(qq')$, excluding annihilation contributions

$$a(\bar{p}p) \simeq 5.25 \text{ mb} , \quad a(pp) \simeq a(np) \simeq 4.25 \text{ mb} ,$$
$$a(\bar{n}p) \simeq 3.25 \text{ mb} , \quad a(\lambda p) \simeq 3 \text{ mb} , \quad a(\bar{\lambda}p) \simeq 1.5 \text{ mb} . \qquad (20)$$

The signs of the $\tilde{S}^{-}(qq')$ deserve a comment. One expects that for quarks as for hadrons the sign of $\tilde{S}^{-}(qq')$ is positive if more charge and/or hypercharge exchange channels are open to $\bar{q}+q'$ than to $q+q'$ collisions. This rule applies quite well to hadrons [5]. For quarks and antiquarks it predicts

$$\tilde{S}^-(\mathrm{pp}) > 0\ , \qquad \tilde{S}^-(\mathrm{np}) < 0\ , \qquad \tilde{S}^-(\lambda\mathrm{p}) < 0\ , \tag{21}$$

(remember that only integral charge and hypercharge can be exchanged). Equations (19) agree with these predictions *.

3. QUARKS AND HIGH ENERGY ANNIHILATION

Having abandoned the additivity assumption of quark amplitudes for the annihilation part $\sigma_A(\bar{B}'B)$ of antibaryon-baryon cross-sections, we are faced with the question of how the quark structure of baryons would manifest itself in annihilation at high energy. The quark rearrangement scheme proposed by Rubinstein and Stern for low energy [10, 11] does not seem to give a satisfactory answer to this question. For high energy annihilation, the simplest model we can propose is based on the assumption that the antibaryon-baryon annihilation amplitudes approximately factorize into the product of three antiquark-quark annihilation amplitudes, momentum and energy being approximately conserved in each of the latter. This amounts to approximating fig. 1 by fig. 3. One must suppose that interaction and exchange effects be-

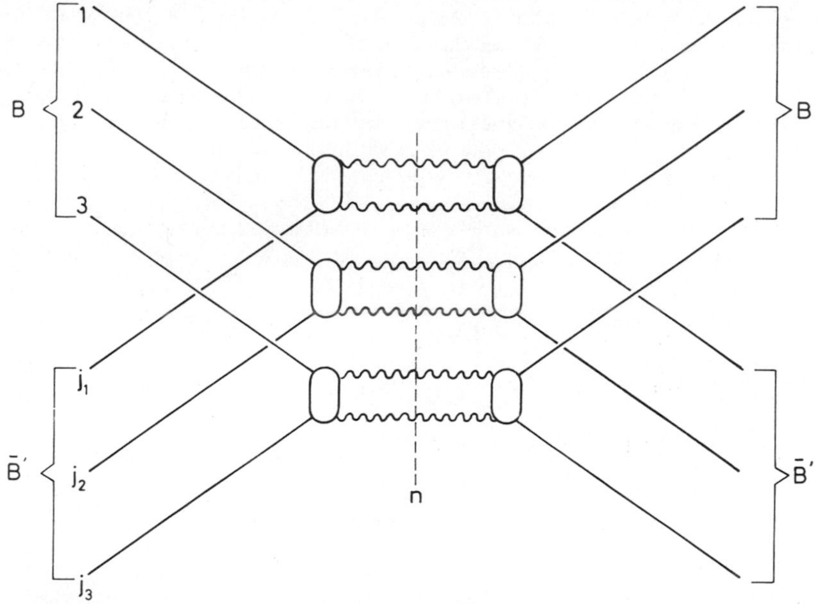

Fig. 3. Diagram showing the factorization of antibaryon-baryon annihilation into three antiquark-quark annihilations.

* One might say that this provides a consistency check for the notion that in (15) only the non-annihilation parts $\tilde{S}^{\pm}(\mathrm{qq}')$ occur, in the sense that if one would have found $\tilde{S}^-(\mathrm{np})$ or $\tilde{S}^-(\lambda\mathrm{p})$ positive this would have been an indication that $S^{\pm}(\mathrm{qq}')$ rather than $\tilde{S}^{\pm}(\mathrm{qq}')$ should have occurred in (15).

tween the mesons produced in annihilation do not impair the approximation too much, at least for a quantity like $\sigma_A(\overline{B}'B)$ which is integrated over all annihilation states. Our assumption is compatible with the fact that the dominant annihilations in flight are found experimentally to be into channels with six or more mesons (counting resonances as single mesons) [12].

The factorization assumption for $\overline{B}'B$ annihilation is mathematically expressed as follows

$$\sigma_A(\overline{B}'B) = \sum_{\{j_1 j_2 j_3\}} \prod_{i=1,2,3} Z(j_i, i) , \tag{22}$$

where j_1, j_2, j_3 run over the permutations of 1, 2, 3 and $Z(j_i, i)$ describes the contribution of all annihilations of antiquark j_i in $\overline{B}'$ with quark i in B (see fig. 3). Z is the product of an antiquark-quark annihilation cross-section and a factor determined by the wave function of the baryon as bound state of three quarks. We assume this factor to be the same for all baryons. Writing

$$Z_1 = Z(\bar{p}p) , \quad Z_2 = Z(\bar{p}n) , \quad Z_3 = Z(\bar{\lambda}p) , \tag{23}$$

and using isospin and chargé conjugation invariance, one then finds

$$\begin{aligned}
\sigma_A(\overline{P}P) &= 2Z_1^3 + 4Z_1 Z_2^2 , \\
\sigma_A(\overline{N}P) &= 2Z_2^3 + 4Z_1^2 Z_2 , \\
\sigma_A(\overline{\Lambda}P) = \sigma_A(\overline{\Sigma}^oP) &= 2Z_1 Z_2 Z_3 + 2Z_1^2 Z_3 + 2Z_2^2 Z_3 , \\
\sigma_A(\overline{\Sigma}^+P) &= 2Z_1^2 Z_3 + 4Z_1 Z_2 Z_3 , \\
\sigma_A(\overline{\Sigma}^-P) &= 2Z_2^2 Z_3 + 4Z_1 Z_2 Z_3 , \\
\sigma_A(\overline{\Xi}^-P) &= 2Z_1 Z_3^2 + 4Z_2 Z_3^2 , \\
\sigma_A(\overline{\Xi}^oP) &= 2Z_2 Z_3^2 + 4Z_1 Z_3^2 , \\
\sigma_A(\overline{\Omega}^-P) &= 6Z_3^3 ,
\end{aligned} \tag{24}$$

and similar equations for the other members $\overline{N}^*$, $\overline{Y}^*$, $\overline{\Xi}^*$ of the antidecuplet. Tests of these relations will only become possible through observation of antihyperon annihilation in flight.

The empirical relations (5) - (8) imply in the present model the following relations between quark annihilation and non-annihilation cross-sections: from (5) and (6)

$$Z_1^3 = Z_2^3 = -\tfrac{3}{2}\tilde{S}^-(np) , \tag{25}$$

and from (7) and (8)

$$Z_1^3 = Z_2^3 = -\tfrac{3}{2}\tilde{S}^-(\lambda p) . \tag{26}$$

Remember that both right-hand sides are positive, see (21). Simultaneous validity of relations (5) - (8) requires

$$\tilde{S}^{-}(\mathrm{np}) = \tilde{S}^{-}(\lambda\mathrm{p}) \ , \tag{27}$$

which is precisely the condition needed to obtain from (15) the "second" Johnson-Treiman relations

$$\tfrac{1}{2}\tilde{S}^{-}(\mathrm{K^+P}) = \tilde{S}^{-}(\pi^+\mathrm{P}) \ . \tag{28}$$

One knows that it is less well satisfied by the data than the "first" relations (2), just as relations (5), (6) are less well satisfied than (7), (8). Finally, introduced in (24), the equality $Z_1{}^3 = Z_2{}^3$ implied by (25) or (26) leads to the result that the annihilation cross-sections $\sigma_A(\overline{\mathrm{B}}\mathrm{P})$ do not depend on the isospin and charge of $\overline{\mathrm{B}}$, but only on its strangeness. Denoting $\sigma_A(\overline{\mathrm{B}}\mathrm{P})$ by $\sigma_A(S)$ for strangeness S of $\overline{\mathrm{B}}$, one finds

$$\frac{\sigma_A(0)}{\sigma_A(1)} = \frac{\sigma_A(1)}{\sigma_A(2)} = \frac{\sigma_A(2)}{\sigma_A(3)} \ . \tag{29}$$

4. CONCLUDING REMARKS

We end with a few remarks on various questions raised by the preceding discussion.

(i) As far as observable predictions are concerned, the main difference between the original version of the additivity assumption for quark amplitudes and the modified model here proposed lies in the fact that in the modified model baryon-antibaryon annihilation processes are kept separate from all other high energy processes. The original model predicts relations between these classes of processes, e.g.,

$$S^{-}(\Omega^{-}\mathrm{P}) = S^{-}(\mathrm{PP}) - 2S^{-}(\mathrm{K^+P}) - S^{-}(\mathrm{K^+N}) \ . \tag{30}$$

The right-hand side of (30) vanishes on the basis of (7). The modified model, on the other hand, keeps $\sigma_A(\overline{\Omega}^{-}\mathrm{P}) = 6Z_3{}^3$ independent from the non-annihilation processes described in terms of the quantities (14). It should be noted, however, that if $Z_1 \simeq Z_2 \simeq Z_3$ (i.e., all $\sigma_A(\overline{\mathrm{B}}'\mathrm{B})$ are equal), the annihilation contributions in relations of type (30) cancel out. As mentioned in the previous section, present data suggest $Z_1 \simeq Z_2$. The further equality $Z_1 \simeq Z_3$ can only be checked by measuring $\sigma_A(\overline{\mathrm{Y}}\mathrm{P})$ at high energy for some hyperon Y.

(ii) Our discussion has dealt only with the imaginary part of the forward scattering amplitudes. For each pair of reactions $\mathrm{B'+B \to B'+B}$ and $\overline{\mathrm{B}}'+\mathrm{B} \to \overline{\mathrm{B}}'+\mathrm{B}$ the real and imaginary parts of the corresponding forward amplitudes T and $\overline{T}$ are related by crossing relations. This implies that, depending on the power α of s in the second term of the asymptotic series [13, 14]

$$T \underset{s\to+\infty}{=} c_1 s + c_2 s^\alpha + \dots , \quad \alpha \text{ real} , \quad c_1 \simeq i|c_1| ,$$

$$\overline{T} \underset{s\to+\infty}{=} - c_1^* s + c_2^* e^{-i\pi\alpha} s^\alpha + \dots ,$$

the exclusion of annihilation processes from the additivity assumption for Im $\overline{T}$ will affect the validity of additivity for T as well as for Re $\overline{T}$. For $\alpha \simeq \frac{1}{2}$ mainly Re T is affected, for $\alpha \simeq 0$ mainly Im T. The latter case would lead to an inconsistency because under our assumption additivity holds for the imaginary part of the whole amplitude T, and this then would imply the same for Im $\overline{T}$ including annihilation contributions. Fortunately, the present data on PP and $\overline{\text{P}}$P scattering at high energy are fully compatible with the value $\alpha = \frac{1}{2}$ [14, 15]. A more precise experimental determination of α will therefore provide an important test of the present considerations. As to the non-forward amplitudes, the simplest presentation of the modified model will again be based on the unitarity condition (13), now taken for non-vanishing momentum transfer, additivity of quark amplitudes being restricted to the non-annihilation contribution to the right-hand side.

(iii) In eqs. (19) and (20) we have given the numerical values of quark "total cross-sections" derived from 10 GeV/c data under the modified additivity model. One immediately notices a few simple empirical relations between them:

$$a(\text{pp}) \simeq a(\text{np}) , \tag{31}$$

$$\tilde{S}^+(\text{pp}) + \tilde{S}^+(\text{np}) \simeq 4\tilde{S}^+(\lambda\text{p}) , \tag{32}$$

$$\tilde{S}^-(\text{pp}) + \tilde{S}^-(\text{np}) \simeq 0 . \tag{33}$$

On the basis of available data, eqs. (31) - (32) hold in the interval $6 \leqslant p_L \leqslant 18$ GeV/c. Equation (31) reflects the well-known approximate equality of $\sigma_T(K^+P)$ and $\sigma_T(K^+N)$; it can be understood in the Regge pole model in terms of Arnold's proposal of exchange degeneracy [16]. Equation (32) is surprisingly well satisfied and corresponds to *

$$3\tilde{S}^+(\pi^+P) = 2\,[\tilde{S}^+(K^+P) + \tilde{S}^+(K^+N)] . \tag{34}$$

Equation (33), which reflects the relation

$$\tilde{S}^-(\text{PP}) + \tilde{S}^-(\text{PN}) \simeq 0 , \tag{35}$$

is only roughly valid because of the uncertainty on annihilation cross-sections. Neither (32) nor (33) have been given simple dynamical interpretations.

* Extrapolating (32) and using the Pomeranchuk theorem for quarks, one gets $\sigma_T(PP) : \sigma_T(\pi P) : \sigma_T(KP) = 6 : 4 : 3$ in the limit $s \to \infty$.

(iv) The next remark is of a more general nature. Our theoretical argument against including annihilation effects in the quark model with additive amplitudes rests on the fact that these effects correspond to baryon exchange. At high energy ($p_L \gtrsim 5$ GeV/c), they are the only baryon exchange processes having a cross section $\gtrsim 1$ mb. All other hadron collision processes of sizable cross-section at high energy are of very different type, corresponding to exchange of vanishing baryon number. It may therefore be that no dynamical model would give a successful unified description of both types of processes, not even of their contribution to the total cross-sections. A similar conjecture is expressed in a recent paper by Białas and Zalewski [17], who direct it in particular against applicability of the Regge pole model to the annihilation part of the baryon-antibaryon total cross-sections. The model presented in sections 2 and 3 of the present paper gives an example of a situation where different mechanisms control the annihilation and non-annihilation parts of the cross-sections. The latter, because of additivity of quark amplitudes, are compatible with quark-antiquark exchange, i.e., with exchange of meson Regge trajectories of singlet and octet character. The annihilation cross-sections on the contrary, if expressed by (24), require in general exchange of higher SU(3) multiplets; this is for example the case if $Z_1 = Z_2 \neq Z_3$, unless one neglects $(Z_3 - Z_1)^2$ compared to $Z_3 - Z_1$; experimentally, a decision on this question can only be reached by measuring antihyperon-proton annihilation cross-sections at high energy.

(v) We end with some comments on approximate SU(3) symmetry and show that the additivity model here advocated avoids the criticisms recently raised by Barger and Durand [18] against additivity in its original form. For the quark amplitudes, SU(3) symmetry implies the two relations

$$\tilde{S}^{\pm}(\mathrm{np}) = \tilde{S}^{\pm}(\lambda\mathrm{p}) . \tag{36}$$

The numerical values (19) show that these relations are seriously violated. Assuming nevertheless their validity, we derive from (15) two additional relations between known cross-sections, one of which is (28) and the other one

$$\tilde{S}^{+}(\mathrm{PP}) = 2\tilde{S}^{+}(\pi^{+}\mathrm{P}) - \tfrac{1}{2}\tilde{S}^{+}(\mathrm{K}^{+}\mathrm{P}) . \tag{37}$$

These relations are in approximate agreement with the data, the discrepancy at 10 GeV/c being of order of 1 mb between the two sides of (28) and of 3 mb between those of (37). The relative discrepancy is of course high in relation (28) since its two sides are very small, $\tilde{S}^{-}(\pi^{+}\mathrm{P}) = 1.7 \pm 0.4$ mb, $\tilde{S}^{-}(\mathrm{K}^{+}\mathrm{P}) = 5.2 \pm 0.3$ mb.

The discrepancy in (37) becomes much larger, of order 10 mb, if $\tilde{S}^{+}(\mathrm{PP})$ is replaced by $S^{+}(\mathrm{PP})$ as would be required in the original additivity model. This fact and the good agreement of (16) with the data show that our modified model is free of the difficulties stressed by Barger and Durand for total cross-sections. The latter authors consider in addition forward differential cross-sections for charge-exchange reactions, in particular the relations [3]

$$\frac{d\sigma}{dt}(\bar{\mathrm{P}}\mathrm{P} \to \bar{\mathrm{N}}\mathrm{N}) = \frac{d\sigma}{dt}(\mathrm{K}^{-}\mathrm{P} \to \bar{\mathrm{K}}^{0}\mathrm{N}) , \qquad \frac{d\sigma}{dt}(\mathrm{PN} \to \mathrm{NP}) = \frac{d\sigma}{dt}(\mathrm{K}^{+}\mathrm{N} \to \mathrm{K}^{0}\mathrm{P}) .$$

It should first be stressed that the relations only hold in the original additivity model if the amplitudes are spin-independent, which is not necessarily true even at $t=0$ for the left-hand side reactions. In our modified model, the relations do not hold even for spin-independent amplitudes. Indeed, the forward PN $\rightarrow$ NP amplitude is dominantly real [19, 20] and is therefore affected by lack of additivity as explained in remark (ii) above, whereas $\bar{P}P \rightarrow \bar{N}N$ is dominantly imaginary [17, 20] and is affected by annihilation effects [17], meaning again lack of additivity. Forward strangeness exchange and η production reactions, the latter also discussed by Barger and Durand, cannot test additivity without additional assumptions.

REFERENCES

[1] E.M. Levin and L.L. Frankfurt, Zh. Eksperim. i Teor. Fiz. Pisma v Redak 2 (1965) 105; English translation: JETP Letters 2 (1965) 65.
[2] H.J. Lipkin and F. Scheck, Phys. Rev. Letters 16 (1966) 71.
[3] J.J.J. Kokkedee and L. Van Hove, Nuovo Cimento 42 (1966) 711.
[4] L. Van Hove, Proceedings of the Stony Brook Conference on High Energy Two-Body Reactions (April 1966).
[5] L. Van Hove, Lectures at 1966 Scottish Universities Summer School, CERN Preprint TH 676 (1966).
[6] H.J. Lipkin, Phys. Rev. Letters 16 (1966) 1015.
[7] J.J.J. Kokkedee, Phys. Letters 22 (1966) 88.
[8] C.A. Levinson, N.S. Wall and H.J. Lipkin, Phys. Rev. Letters 17 (1966) 1122.
[9] P.G.O. Freund, Phys. Rev. Letters 15 (1965) 929.
[10] H.R. Rubinstein and H. Stern, Phys. Letters 21 (1966) 447.
[11] J. Harte, R.H. Socolow, J. Vandermeulen and K. Zalewski, CERN Preprint TH 701 (1966).
[12] K. Böckmann et al., Nuovo Cimento 42A (1966) 954.
[13] L. Van Hove, in: High Energy Physics and Elementary Particles (International Atomic Energy Agency, Vienna, 1965) p. 179.
[14] A. Białas and E. Białas, Nuovo Cimento 37 (1965) 1686.
[15] J.J.J. Kokkedee, Nuovo Cimento 43 (1966) 919.
[16] R.C. Arnold, Phys. Rev. Letters 14 (1965) 657.
[17] A. Białas and K. Zalewski, Nuovo Cimento 46A (1966) 425.
[18] V. Barger and L. Durand III, University of Wisconsin Preprint (1966).
[19] G. Manning et al., Nuovo Cimento 41 (1966) 167.
[20] E. Leader, Rev. Mod. Phys. 38 (1966) 476.

NOTE ADDED IN PROOF

The only annihilation cross-section measured so far at high energy is $\sigma_A(\bar{P}P)$ at $p_L = 5.7$ GeV/c [12]. It verifies

$$\sigma_A(\bar{P}P) = 22.5 \pm 2 \text{ mb} \simeq S^-(PP) = 21.5 \pm 1 \text{ mb}.$$

It seems reasonable to assume that for $p_L \gtrsim 6$ GeV/c one has

$$\sigma_A(\bar{P}P) \simeq S^-(PP), \quad \sigma_A(\bar{P}N) \simeq S^-(PN),$$

with errors of the order of one or two millibarns. This assumption will allow us to compare our further theoretical considerations with experiment.

Index